CW00341076
Ramanas rose
alder buckthorn
plum
field maple
blackthorn
gorse
dogwood
purging buckthorn

New Hedges for the Countryside

A ten-year-old hawthorn hedge at its final 3 m (10 ft) trimmed height at Collins Farm, Frilford.

New Hedges for the Countryside

Murray Maclean

FARMING PRESS

First published 1992

ISBN 0 85236 242 0

A catalogue record for this book is available
from the British Library

Published by Farming Press Books
Wharfedale Road, Ipswich IP1 4LG, United Kingdom

Distributed in North America
by Diamond Farm Enterprises,
Box 537, Alexandria Bay, NY 13607, USA

Line drawings by Valerie Petts
Cover design by Mark Beesley
Typeset by Galleon Photosetting
Printed and bound in Great Britain by Jolly & Barber Ltd

Contents

Acknowledgements viii
Introduction xi

1 **The Hedge in History** 1
The Norman Conquest • The War of the Roses • Civil war • An age of change • War with France • The age of the canal • The impact of the railways • Hedgerow removal • The first census • War in Europe • The 'War Ags' (County War Agricultural Committees) • Airfields • Mechanisation

2 **The Choice of Trees and Shrubs** 16
Species suitable for a hedgerow • Species to be avoided in any hedge • Choice and requirements

3 **Effect of Soil Type and Topography** 43
Soil Surveys

4 **Conservation Considerations** 54
Birds • Mammals • Invertebrates • Field margins

5 **Raising Trees and Shrubs from Seed** 64
Seed treatment • Hedgerow shrubs from seed • Trees from seed • Choice and preparation of a suitable site • Soil sterilisation • Seed sowing • Fertilisers for emerging and growing seedlings • Definition of words used in seedling production

6 From Seedling to Transplant 88

Seedling source ● Ground preparation ● Planting ● Machine planting ● Bed size and plant spacing ● Weed control ● Pest and disease control ● Nutrition ● Irrigation ● Summer operations ● Autumn lifting ● Harvest considerations

7 Preparation and Planting of Hedges 110

Planning – choice and supply of planting material ● Ground preparation ● Planting time and conditions ● Hedge position ● Marking out ● Care of plants prior to planting ● Single row hand planting ● Double row hand planting ● Machine planting ● Spacing ● Regional differences in the choice of species ● Care after planting ● Protective clothing

8 Alternative and Regional Hedges 133

The Devonwade hedgebank ● The Pembroke hedgebank ● Willow osier hedges ● Holly hedges ● The false acacia (or black locust) (Robinea pseudoacacia)

9 The Use of Trees in Hedgerows 150

Suitable trees for use in new hedges ● Trees for wet sites ● Common trees not recommended for hedgerow planting ● Planting spacing

10 Field Margins 168

Creating an arable field margin ● Natural regeneration ● A sown sward ● The timing of mowings ● Encouraging butterflies ● Exclusion of fertiliser and sprays

11 Weed Control 175

Organic mulches ● Polythene sheet mulch ● The use of herbicides

12 Disease and Pest Control 196

13 Hedge Maintenance and Trimming 205
Hedge laying • Hedge trimming • Coppicing

14 Protection and Fencing 223

15 Costings 234
Machine planting of transplants • Hand planting of transplants • Machine planting of seedlings • Hand planting of seedlings • Hedge planting costs

16 Hedges and the Law 247

Appendix 1 British Imperial and Continental Metric Measures 255

Appendix 2 Grant Aid 257

Index 268

A colour section appears between pages 84 and 85

Acknowledgements

As a working grower, one needs to be a jack of all trades yet a master of some, and I cannot claim to be a master of all the trades necessary to complete a book on the subject of hedges. However, I have fortunately been able to draw on the help of friends and the experience of professionals to cover all aspects of hedging as thoroughly as possible. My sincere thanks go to the following for their valued assistance with specific queries or for the provision of information for the chapters, in sequence.

Jane Waite	*Early field patterns*
Ministry of Defence	*Aerial photographs*
Bill King	*Second World War airfields*
Alan Pottinger	*Native trees and shrubs*
Joy Greenall (FWAG)	*Conservation matters*
The Forestry Commission	*Tree and shrub seeds*
Mervyn John (Dyfed County Council)	*Hedgebank design*
Ron Spice	*Hollies*
Dr Helen Smith	*Field margin experiments*
Janet Allen (ADAS)	*Weed and disease control*
Clive Fowkes	*Bomford Turner hedge cutters*
Jim and Jane Antill	*Jafco Tools*
Butterworths Ltd	*Law publishers*
David Gordon (my solicitor)	*Legal information*
Susie Smith (ADAS)	*Advice and grants*
The University of Reading and T. P. Roskrow	*Photographs*

I reserve my deepest gratitude for those who have had to suffer most in helping me. Foremost, to my wife Joey for her patience and ready help at a moment's notice; to my father Gordon Maclean for his time and the rolls of film required to provide most of the photographs; to Valerie Petts for the line drawings; to Judith Fontaine for translating my handwritten pages into the original type; to Michele Bennett for preparing the final draft; and to Yvonne Newman for her help and encouragement.

I would also like to thank Julie Musk, Julanne Arnold and Roger Smith of Farming Press who have prepared and presented the book for you to read.

TO MY LATE GODPARENTS
JOHN AND MARJORIE BUXTON

Berries

I will bring you berries
From the spinneys and the hedges,
From deep in the dark woods,
From the slow streams' edges.

I will bring you berries
From the Chiltern hills,
And from Notley mill-race
Where dark water spills.

I will bring you berries
Dusty with bloom,
And berries like lanterns
To glisten in your room.

I will bring you berries
Of juniper and yew,
Sloes from the blackthorn,
Hips whence roses grew,

And four-cleft spindle
With the orange-red pips
Shown by its cleaving
Into coral lips,

And juicy blackberries
To give a summer taste
When all the autumn
Has run to winter waste.

I will bring you berries
From the spinneys and the hedges,
From deep in the dark woods,
From the slow streams' edges.

JOHN BUXTON, OFLAG VIIB, 10 DECEMBER 1940

This is one of many poems sent home from the confines of a POW camp which show his sorrow at being parted from his wife Marjorie and the English countryside; both he deeply loved.

Introduction

Hedges are not a natural feature of our landscape. They are the visible sign of man's efforts, over many centuries, to bring order to the land. A farmer's need to contain his own stock and protect his crops from his neighbour's wandering animals has resulted in a complex pattern of enclosed fields.

The shape and size of a field may be dictated by an external boundary, a stream or river, a block of woodland, roads or drovers' tracks. All are physical constraints which influence boundary positions. Parish boundaries, changes in soil type and old plough furlongs are further contributions which have combined over the centuries to produce a pattern unique to our landscape.

The changing pattern of farming since the Second World War has already broken down the hedgerow system in those parts of the country where arable cropping has become the dominant use of land, such as the grain-producing areas of East Anglia and up into Norfolk and the Lincolnshire Wolds.

The full value of a hedge is still appreciated in the dairy and stock areas of the West Country, Devon and Cornwall and throughout most of Wales. The stock farmer knows that barbed wire is not versatile enough to contain livestock in every case. The physical barrier of a good hedge prevents cattle from both seeing and getting at fresh grass in the next field; and how much shelter does a barbed wire fence give from the cutting edge of a cold north-east wind? One only has to see cattle and sheep standing with their backs to the wind in an open field to know that they do not like the penetrating blast of a cold winter's wind any more than you or I. Protection from wind and rain is welcome to both man and beast; it prevents body temperatures from dropping, so retaining energy levels, which enables all animals to convert their food more efficiently into whatever form it is required, be it milk or meat.

Arable and grass crops, or higher value crops of fruit and vegetables, also benefit from the protection of a good hedge or windbreak. Wind increases the rate of transpiration across the surface of the leaf, which responds by respiring at a higher rate to both cool and retain the turgidity of its cells. This draws more water up the plant from its roots, so reducing the available soil moisture.

Beyond the physical benefits of a hedge to the farmer and grower, there is the much wider aesthetic value to the nation as a whole. Only a small percentage of the population continue to live and work on the land, whilst the majority work within the confines of a factory, shop or office, denied the beauty of our landscape.

The appeal of the countryside varies according to taste. Some love the wild open moorlands, others prefer the closer confines of a woodland. The patchwork of our fields, surrounded by hedges or walls, is a feature of the English landscape which is cherished beyond our shores and, like other elements of our heritage, it needs to be appreciated by us rather than taken for granted.

In the same way that architectural styles of the past are copied and incorporated into new buildings because of their enduring qualities, so we now need to take stock of those qualities which have enabled the English hedgerow to survive into the age of mechanised farming.

The public and farmers have become aware of the damage that has been done to our rural heritage by a rash of ugly asbestos and concrete block structures; planning controls on farm buildings have arrived, preservation orders have been placed on many trees and, thankfully, an increasing number of landowners are taking a great interest in restoring some of the lost variety of our countryside. In so doing, conservation and landscape advisers have taken a fresh look at the fabric of the farming landscape to reassess both aesthetic and wildlife requirements for the future. Downland, woods, ponds and old buildings are now under intense scrutiny. This scrutiny has recently spread to assess the value of field margins, of which the humble hedge is an integral part.

J. C. Beddall summed up the value of our hedges in the opening paragraph of his book *Hedges for Farm and Garden*, written in 1950:

> Who can think of England without thinking of a land of fields and hedges? Nowhere else are there hedges quite like our English ones, nowhere else are they such a feature of the landscape, for the hedges hold the very spirit of our countryside. Like the mesh of a far-flung net, they frame the pattern of our fields, that maze of meadow and arable, orchard and copse which lies over hill and vale in this fair and lovely land.

Chapter 1

The Hedge in History

Generations pass while some tree stands
and old families last not three oaks
SIR THOMAS BROWNE

The 'bocage' (hedgerow) region of Normandy in France illustrates how much of rural England looked at the turn of this century. Roads bordered by banked hedges wander through a patchwork of small fields, coppice and oak woodland. Lush meadows and a mixture of arable crops grow in harmony to provide the balanced farming economy which England has now lost for ever.

Northern France has been the battleground of Europe for centuries, yet it was not until the devastation of the entrenched battles during the First World War that large areas of Picardy lost their hedgerows and woodland. England has remained free from invaders since the Norman Conquest, yet a combination of civil wars and an enduring interest for fighting in other people's wars has left its mark upon our countryside in more subtle yet equally lasting ways.

The initial colonisation of Britain, even in remote upland regions, began during the prehistoric period and by the late Iron Age (500 BC) the country was already extensively settled and well cultivated (Figure 1.1). The Roman (AD 40–400), Saxon (AD 400–1066) and Norman invaders initially had to fit into the existing pattern of settlements with their fields and connecting tracks.

THE NORMAN CONQUEST

Once William the Conqueror had subjugated the Saxon population, he instigated the Domesday survey of the kingdom in 1086 to provide him with a rural inventory upon which he could base taxation. It was part of the introduction of the feudal system,

FIGURE 1.1 An artist's impression of a Bronze Age settlement on the banks of the River Thames near Oxford. The settlers cleared the woodland to provide land for cropping and grazing cattle. The woodland strips and cattle enclosures were early beginnings of our hedgerow heritage.

whereby the king took over the ownership of all land, transferring it in turn to his knights and barons in recognition of their services. The countryside was then more densely wooded, with large areas cleared around villages and towns to provide open fields for cultivation and grazing. The Saxons had evolved a combination of 'dead' hedges, made of stakes and brushwood, and ditches (dykes) to delineate village and district (hundred) boundaries.

Relative peace in the 12th and 13th centuries led to improved farming prosperity and more woodland was cleared, with the forest edges often retained to mark the boundary of the newly claimed land.

The Black Death in 1349 claimed nearly half the population and led to a severe depression. With so few people left to till the soil, arable cropping declined, hedges and fences fell into disrepair and simple stock farming was all that became possible.

THE WAR OF THE ROSES

The 15th century saw little relief from this depression. The Hundred Years' War with France was quickly followed by a civil war between those of Lancastrian and Yorkist persuasion. The continuing shortage of labour led to many common arable fields being enclosed with hedge and fence to provide smaller fields for grazing sheep and cattle. The enclosing of common land further affected the rural population as there was less need for the shepherd and swineherd to tend the common flocks.

The 16th century witnessed a great upheaval in the ordered existence of the countryside, with the decision of King Henry VIII to confiscate all the monastic and abbey land, taking it from the church and giving it to his favourite courtiers. His courtiers had little respect for the tenant farmers, whom they in turn dispossessed of their land and stock to further enclose the open fields for more grazing sheep (Plate 1.1). This was a simple and less labour-intensive means of extracting a greater profit from the land at a time when the price of wool was high and had been stable for a long period.

Our knowledge of early farming practices is based on the Saxon chronicles, the Domesday book and a mixture of manorial records and royal statutes, together with information which can be drawn from the careful interpretation of early maps. From the mid-16th century onwards, writers emerged who conveyed in detail the farming patterns of their day, and made critical observations on long-standing agricultural practices. Thomas Tusser wrote his well-known *Five Hundred Points of Good Husbandry* in 1557, which was a record, written in verse, of his farming experiences in Essex and

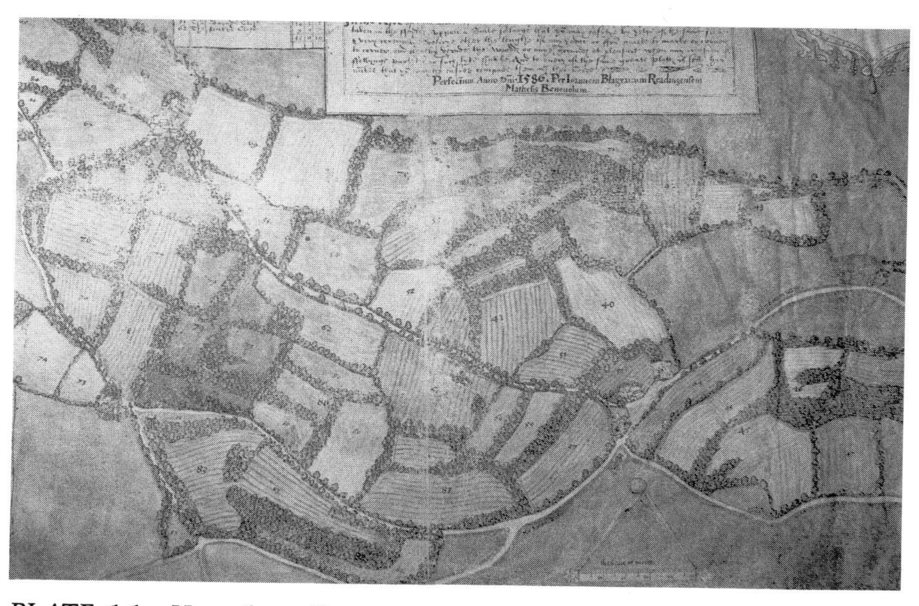

PLATE 1.1 Harpsden village, near Henley-on-Thames, 1586. A tithe map drawn onto vellum, by Mathesis Benevolum, showing the richness of hedges and woodland strips which bordered many of the small fields.

Suffolk. We have William Mavor to thank for updating the rhyming couplet form of the original text in 1812, and adding footnotes as necessary to explain to the modern reader what Tusser was saying. The book is set out in monthly chapters giving the reader all the information and observations necessary for the sequence of the farming year.

Tusser informed us that he was an advocate of enclosure as opposed to open fields (formerly called 'champion' country). His comments on hedges, their cultivation and care are as follows:

October's husbandry
Sow acorns, ye owners that timber do love,
Sow haw and rye with them, the better to prove
If cattle or coney may enter the crop
Young oak is in danger of losing his top.
Mavor's note: This advice is excellent, and it is to be lamented that so few acorns are sown. The first year a thin crop of rye will protect them, after which the plantation should be fenced against cattle and rabbits, even though the hawthorn are sown with them.

Where speedy quickset for a fence ye will draw
to sow in the seed of the bramble and haw . . .
Mavor's note: Brambles might be planted and trained as vines for their fruit. Haws, needless to say, are the fruit of the hawthorn.

January's husbandry
Leave grubbing or pulling of bushes, my son,
Till timely thy fences require to be done . . .
Mavor's note: To leave a sufficiency of bushes in order to fill up gaps in hedges is obviously right.

In every green if the fence be not thine
Now stub up the bushes, the grass to be fine . . .
Mavor's note: It would be a beneficial practice if hedges were constantly kept trimmed and clipped at a height of four feet. Not only would the fences be more durable, but grass or corn would thrive better in their vicinity.

February's husbandry
Buy quickset at market, new gather'd and small
Buy bushes or willow, to fence it withall . . .
Mavor's note: Quickset [hawthorn] should not be too old before they are planted, and except in mending gaps they are now usually secured by post and rails.

CIVIL WAR

In 1549 Robert Kett, a Norfolk farmer, led the last attempt of the labourers to contain the power of the lords of the manor, who continued to enclose land whenever they could find some justification, regardless of the added hardship it caused poor cottagers. From then on until the Civil War between King Charles I and Oliver Cromwell's Protestants in 1642–48, farming for the wealthy prospered at the expense of the poor. The first Poor Law of 1601 began the process of providing food and shelter for the needy of each parish. However, the Civil War once more brought upheaval to the land, and a decline in its care and maintenance.

John Worlidge from Hampshire, writing in 1669, stated that the enclosures gave employment to the poor and sustained three times the rural population than had been possible with the old open field systems. He noted that large areas of open land which had been in common use, had become low in fertility, yet were soon shown to be good land when enclosed and managed properly (Plate 1.2).

The 18th century witnessed a substantial investment of capital in communications by wealthy industrialists and in farming by landowners.

AN AGE OF CHANGE

In 1773 Jethro Tull of Shalbourne in Berkshire published his book *Horse Hoeing Husbandry*, following his invention of the corn drill. Such a radical change in the cultivation of cereals could not possibly be utilised on the old open field strip system of farming; it was designed to meet the change to large enclosed fields, where new hedges protected crops from the wanderings of a neighbour's stock.

The pace of enclosure eased until the early 18th century, when the arrival of the Hanovarian kings coincided with the 'flowering' of English agriculture.

The following gives some indication of the scale of hedge planting during the 18th century:

Queen Anne	1704–14	2 acts enclosing 1,439 acres
George I	1714–27	16 acts enclosing 17,960 acres
George II	1727–60	220 acts enclosing 318,778 acres
George III	1760–97	1,532 acts enclosing 2,804,197 acres

The end of the 18th century saw the start of the Napoleonic Wars, which continued until 1815, bringing added prosperity to farmers.

WAR WITH FRANCE

Napoleon Bonaparte had noted that England was 'a nation of shopkeepers', which might be brought to heel by a maritime blockade; however, he miscalculated the strength of the navy under Nelson, and the ability of the English farmer, with his enclosed and 'improved' lands, to produce all the food necessary to feed an industrial nation at war.

The end of the war heralded a serious depression in agriculture. This was further aggravated by the repeal of the Corn Laws in 1846, which had protected home production from the cheaper imports of Russian and North American quality grain. A growing industrialised society needed cheap food to feed its factory workers, and, if England's landed gentry could not provide grain for bread, it could easily be transported across the Atlantic in the multi-masted grain clippers. The acreage of wheat fell steadily throughout the rest of the 19th century as the land reverted to increased stock grazing, providing a continuing stimulus to enclose land.

THE AGE OF THE CANAL

The winding, rutted roads and the wide open drovers' tracks were becoming anachronisms in a busy and more ordered countryside. The Duke of Bridgewater built the first canal, from Manchester to Worsley, in 1755, to be followed by the works of Thomas Telford, the famous canal- and road-building engineer.

The heyday of canal building stretched from 1760 to 1830, by which time over 3,000 miles of inland waterways had been constructed. The greater proportion of these canals were built to serve the needs of the industrial towns of the north and Midlands. Many miles of canal stretched across open countryside, changing field shapes which required new fencing and hedging.

THE IMPACT OF THE RAILWAYS

The pace of canal building had begun to slacken when the railway boom began in the second-quarter of the 19th century. The railway network spread quicker and further, being cheaper to construct. By the latter part of the 19th century nearly every town in the country was served by either a main or branch line. All this trackway had to be well fenced or hedged to prevent cattle and sheep straying onto tracks.

In a more visible way the railways made the greatest impact upon the appearance and order of the landscape (Plate 1.3), only to be upstaged by the scars of today's motorway builders.

W. J. Malden, writing in the 1899 RASE Journal, gave a full account of the specification for the Midland railway hedges:

> Double rows are planted in parallel lines, the lines being 4 in apart and the plants 8 in from one to the other in the rows. The planting is done so that one row 'breaks joint' [is staggered] with the other. 100 plants to the chain [22 yds] – 3-year-old

PLATE 1.2 Part of Brunel's Great Western line from London to Bristol, at Wantage Road Station, Oxfordshire. Notice how it runs through fields in the upper right-hand section of the photograph. No attempts have been made to grub out hedges to incorporate field remnants into adjacent fields.

> quicks (hawthorn) are purchased at 11s per 1,000. The quicks are cut back at planting, left untrimmed till they attain a height of 6–8 ft, when they are layered, being subsequently trimmed in late autumn–early winter.

Such a description indicates the high standard and density needed to provide a thick stockproof hedge which would ensure the safety of both the farmer's stock and the railway traveller passing swiftly by.

The Industrial Revolution poached much valuable farm land in the north and Midland regions, and the beautiful Welsh valleys were scarred with mining pitheads and slag heaps. There were increasing numbers of cases where old banked hedges around small or awkwardly-shaped fields were grubbed up and a new hedge planted around the resulting larger field.

HEDGEROW REMOVAL

Professor Buckman, writing in 1865, stated that he would recommend banking up the ground for a new hedge on its crown only where the soil was of poor quality or shallow depth. On most fertile or deeper loams he recommended that the new hedge be planted direct into the existing soil level. He went on to give a description of the removal of banked hedges surrounding 15 tiny fields on his own farm to form one field of over 50 acres:

> As regards the loss of land by the division into smaller fields, we cannot do better than to copy the former outlines of an arable field on our own farm. This, which is now one field of over 50 acres, was formerly in 15 fenced fields, each with a ragged hedge – of anything but quicks – planted upon raised mounds. Now, the gain in the removal of fences, indicated by the dotted lines [Figure 1.2] may be explained by the following calculations:

	Acres	*Rds*
Ground, 2 yards wide, occupied by the mounds and hedges, about	1	2
One foot and a half on either side of the mounds which cannot be ploughed, about.....	0	3
Total of gain in 50 acres	2	1

We must not blame today's farmers for hedge removal any more than their predecessors, who had been engaged in a continuing

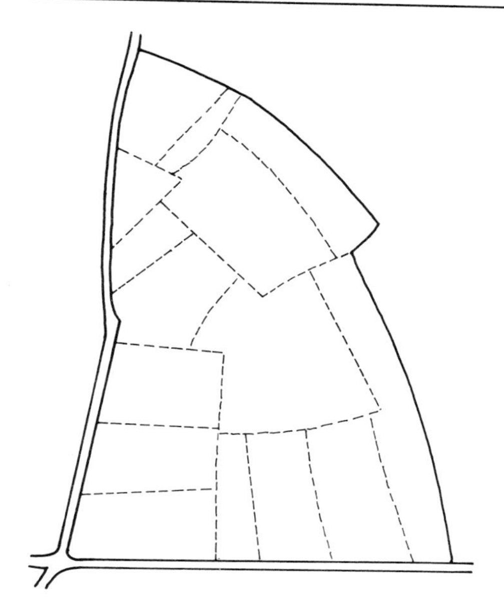

FIGURE 1.2 Field with its old divisions, now removed, as marked by the dotted lines.

process of enclosing the large, open common fields as well as grubbing out old banked hedges around fields that were becoming too small for an increasingly mechanised age.

Enclosure orders went on until near the end of the 19th century, by which time many of the orders were little more than a gentleman's agreement for the sensible reallocation of lands within a parish. This allowed the principal farmers to exchange their scattered strips on the open fields for compact blocks of land, preferably near their own farmhouse, or if not, they could build a new home and a modern range of buildings within their reallocated lands, which were often hedged to establish their new boundaries.

THE FIRST CENSUS

Accurate statistics on agricultural output should have been a government priority with the improvement and expansion of farming in the 18th century, but it was not until 1793 that the efforts of Sir John Sinclair MP persuaded the government to establish the Board of Agriculture to gather statistical information and stimulate improvements in farming practices through a series of county surveys, which are still valuable to historians and farmers today. In 1866 a bill was successfully introduced empowering the Board of Trade to collect information on crop outputs from uncooperative farmers. These records show the changing pattern of farm crops over the past 125 years. There is no comparable information on the planting and removal of hedgerows since their heyday in the 18th century. The enclosure acts and awards rarely gave any account of the length of hedges planted and the Ministry of Agriculture Fisheries and Food (MAFF) is reluctant to release information on grant-aided hedge removal since the Second World War.

The overall amount of hedgerow planting or removal during the period 1860–1940 is likely to have been minimal at a time of little agricultural progress interspersed with years of depression.

Examination of enclosure awards can be most revealing to the knowledgeable viewer; a greater understanding of these documents is gained from regular research or by a practical knowledge of local field patterns.

It must not be assumed that the maps were all correctly drawn up, as can be illustrated by a detailed map of Frilford parish dated 1846 owned by the author. This map was drawn up by Commissioner Edward Driver to indicate the line of a new road to bypass the main part of the village. It showed a field boundary to the north of West Field which is still in existence today. Yet this hedge and ditch line were completely omitted from the equally detailed map drawn up by the commissioner appointed to handle the Frilford Enclosure Award in 1860, none other than Edward Driver's nephew Robert Collier Driver, who had copied directly from his uncle's earlier map! It is recommended that research from old maps is corroborated by evidence on the ground wherever possible. Aerial surveys can reveal the line of old hedges, ditches and roads, particularly if the photograph is taken either when the ground has been freshly ploughed or in dry summer conditions under a grass or cereal crop.

Photography was invented in 1835, so by the latter end of the 19th century there was an excellent photographic record of farming practices and country scenery. The horse and ox were still the motive power for all machinery on the land until the steam engine took over the tasks of threshing and some ploughing on larger fields.

In 1971 Dr Hooper announced a method for assessing the approximate age of old hedges.

Historians had been aware of the many miles of single species hawthorn hedges planted during the 18th and 19th centuries as a result of the enclosure awards, but there had been no known way of

PLATE 1.3 An 18th century toll house beside the main Oxford-to-Swindon road at Longworth near Abingdon. The colour shades in the old hedge indicate a rich mixture. It contains 13 species over a length of 400 yards and 8 specimens in random 30 yard sections, indicating an age of about 800 years.

determining the age of earlier hedges. Dr Hooper's studies into medieval hedgebanks, which could be dated accurately from Saxon charters, has led to a wide acceptance of his method for dating old hedges (Plate 1.2).

This is based on the principle of taking random 30 yd stretches of an old hedge, counting the number of different species to be found in each stretch, then calculating an average from the counts taken in each stretch. Each species represents approximately 100 years. Thus, a hedge which has an average of 2.3 species within each 30 yd random stretch indicates that the hedge was planted approximately 230 years ago, in about 1762. It is important to verify such a conclusion by the study of old parish maps, land deeds or other estate records, which may be held in the local county council archives.

WAR IN EUROPE

The advent of the First World War was to mark the start of the most dramatic change in the face of the countryside for two centuries. Not only did the land give up its male workforce for the fields of

Flanders but, once again, it had to feed a nation under siege.

In the early part of the war, the government gave little encouragement to increase home production until the losses of British merchant shipping began to mount, due to the success of the German U-boats. In 1917 the government introduced the Corn Production Act, which provided a guaranteed price for wheat, oats and potatoes. Production picked up and, early in 1918, control of all basic food supplies was centralised until after the end of the war.

From that point until the clouds of war gathered again, agriculture went steadily into a deep recession. Many acres of 'strong' land were allowed to become overgrown with scrub because the soil was too heavy to be worked easily with horsepower. Hedges and ditches fell into disrepair and the well drained and irrigated water meadow systems became overgrown. Arable production continued on the lighter, easily worked soils, which did not necessarily produce the highest yields, so compounding the loss of productivity. During this period there was little incentive to plant or remove hedges, both the operations costing money and time which could not be justified.

THE 'WAR AGs' (COUNTY WAR AGRICULTURAL COMMITTEES)

At the outbreak of the Second World War there were approximately 2.5 million acres less arable land than in 1914. Unlike during the First World War, the management of agricultural production was firmly controlled from September 1939 onwards by the establishment of the 'War Ags' or County War Agricultural Committees, which undertook the task of increasing output by directing cropping and the reclamation of derelict land.

In Leicestershire the percentage of arable land went from 15 to 50% in four years and nationally it was increased by 4,500,000 acres. Whilst much scrubland was brought back into cropping, there was little direct hedge removal, as it was not felt necessary to alter field boundaries.

AIRFIELDS

Considerable areas of land were requisitioned to build aerodromes and training camps. C. S. Orwin in his book *The Future of Farming* (1930) illustrated the ease of hedgerow removal by citing the consequences of building a new aerodrome at Abingdon in Oxfordshire. Two-and-a-half miles of hedgerow were removed to clear the necessary 432 acres. At nearby Grove airfield, built at the onset of the Second World War, 5 miles of hedgerow were grubbed to convert good dairy land into a vast, open expanse for the three runways and connecting perimeter track (Plate 1.4).

Across southern-central England and up into the eastern counties airfields were constructed, with many operational bases having their own satellite airfield nearby in case the main runways were bombed whilst the squadrons were airborne. This safety measure added substantially to the areas of farmland requisitioned to prepare for the

PLATE 1.4 Construction of the main runways at Grove airfield, Wantage, Oxfordshire. The aerial photograph, taken in 1942, shows how the airfield imposed itself upon the small fields. The dark lines across many fields are flooded ridges and furrows, probably resulting from interrupted draining due to the runway building.

1944 Allied offensive to free Europe.

The area occupied by the average wartime airfield varied between 150 and 450 acres and most were built on prime agricultural land.

By 1945 there were over 600 airfields covering 360,000 acres. In addition approximately 4,500 army camps were built, many of a temporary nature for the run-up to D-day.

The overall effect is best summed up by the joke of United States pilots who said they 'could taxi the whole length of the island without leaving a runway!'

Since the end of the war little of this land has been returned to its original state, remaining bleak, wind-swept areas of corn and concrete.

MECHANISATION

The post-war rise in numbers of tractors and combines of ever-increasing horsepower and size led to the extensive grubbing of hedgerows in arable areas to provide the optimum field size which would maximise the potential of these machines. So we have arrived at another crisis. Farming has reached a peak in its efficient use of land resource, and now stands accused of producing too much food, after nearly 50 years of steady exhortation to feed the nation 'from our own resources'. The countryside is productive and well-managed; but it is no longer as beautiful to behold as it once was.

War and the demands it set in train have taken a permanent toll on the appearance of our landscape. The farmers are not to blame; they have achieved what was requested of them. It is now up to the government to provide a similar strong lead for the future wellbeing of the land that has always served us well when needed.

REFERENCES AND FURTHER READING

Buckman, J. (1865), *Science and Practice of Farm Cultivation.*

Carter, G. (1927/8), *Outlines of English History* (The Educational Supply Association Ltd., London).

Cobbett, W. (1825), *The Woodlands.*

Curtler, W. H. R. (1909), *Short History of English Agriculture* (Oxford at the Clarendon Press).

The Harmsworth Encyclopaedia (circa 1910) (The Amalgamated Press Ltd. and Thomas Nelson & Sons, London).

HMSO (1968), *A Century of Agricultural Statistics – Great Britain 1886–1966.*

Hoskins, W. G. (1955), *The Making of the English Landscape* (Hodder and Stoughton Ltd., Sevenoaks, Kent).
Orwin, Christabel and Whatham, E. H. (1971), *History of English Agriculture* (David and Charles Ltd., Newton Abbot, Devon).
Orwin, C. S. (1930), *The Future of Farming* (Oxford at the Clarendon Press).
Tusser, T. (1812), *Five Hundred Points of Good Husbandry.*

Chapter 2

The Choice of Trees and Shrubs

Gives not the Hawthorn bush a sweeter shade
To shepherds, looking on their silly sheep,
Than doth a rich embroidered canopy
to kings that fear their subjects' treachery

HENRY VI, PART 3 WILLIAM SHAKESPEARE

Ask yourself the question, 'Why do I want to plant a hedge?' The answer will fall into one of the following categories:

- To contain and give shelter to livestock.
- As a boundary to mark the division between one's own land and that of a neighbour.
- As a windbreak to protect growing crops, particularly valuable cash crops of vegetables, flowers or fruit.
- As a conservation hedge to join up existing hedges to each other, or to join together hedges and woodland to form a continuous corridor for the safer movement of wildlife across open farmland.
- To act as a dividing line between different soil types; hence differing cropping patterns.
- As an attractive feature beside a road or leading up to a house or building.
- To form a partial screen around some unsightly building, the earthworks of a slurry lagoon, silage clamp or a dispersal area for debris and machinery.
- To control soil erosion, particularly on farms growing cash crops which are being planted regularly into weed-free conditions, so subjecting the soil surface structure to the damaging effects of rainfall or frequent irrigation.

The reason for planting a hedge will determine the choice of suitable species.

W. J. Malden, writing in the RASE Journal of 1899, gave a good and concise appraisal of the points to be taken into consideration before choosing the most suitable species. Not all his points will apply in every case, but the list is as relevant today as it was over 90 years ago.

Hedges and Hedgemaking
Important points to be considered:
- To produce a stockproof hedge in a reasonably short time.
- For the hedge to be long-lived.
- To be capable of easy repair if neglected.
- To be uniform in the vigour of growth.
- To be easily kept within bounds.
- For the hedge to present a compact front.
- To be strong enough to resist the efforts of animals to escape, which will be made easier if the hedge has thorns or strong prickles.
- To choose plants which are suited to the soil type.
- The species chosen to be frost-hardy.
- To offer shelter to animals from cold winds.
- To produce shoots close to the ground, so containing both small and larger animals.
- To be resistant to fungal diseases.
- Not to possess suckers which can spread out into the adjoining crop or pasture.
- Not to be edibly attractive to the animals within the field, or to game sheltering in the hedge.
- If requiring laying at a later stage, the species need to be those which will regrow vigorously from a close-cut stump.

The following list gives a description of trees and shrubs and their suitability for hedgerow use. This is followed by a concise list of those species which should NOT be chosen, and why they are to be avoided.

Trees and shrubs in lists appear in alphabetical order according to their scientific names and are listed in that order even when only the common name is cited.

SPECIES SUITABLE FOR A HEDGEROW

Field Maple (*Acer campestre*)

A small deciduous 5–10 m (16–33 ft) tree, more commonly found as a shrub in hedgerows, where it is an excellent plant, responding well to trimming, although its shoots are somewhat brittle and tough.

FIGURE 2.1 Field maple.

The field maple is a native species found on a wide variety of soil types and will tolerate dry sandy conditions.

The leaves have three to five toothed lobes and are a dull green colour, which turns to a very attractive bright yellow-orange in autumn.

It carries a few flowers in early April, which appear before the leaves and become pairs of winged seeds (called 'keys') which stretch out horizontally to look like a bird in flight.

The young and older bark is sandy-brown in colour with flaky longitudinal fissures.

Hornbeam (*Carpinus betulus*)

An attractive tree, up to 20 m (66 ft) in height, with a round bushy crown, sometimes conical. More often planted as a hedge. It responds well to trimming and will hold its leaves long into winter.

It grows well on the sandy and loamy soils of central and southern England, but does not like dry conditions or frost-prone sites.

FIGURE 2.2 Hornbeam.

Dogwood (*Cornus sanguinea*)

A dense hedgerow shrub commonly found in southern England. Its dark, dull green, oval leaves are pointed and borne opposite to each other on purplish twigs.

Clusters of cream/white flowers are carried on older wood in May–June to become bunches of black berries in the autumn.

Its blood-red young growth turns to a greenish-brown as the bark ages.

The vigorous and fibrous root system prefers light lime soils, but will grow well on sandstone and other soils.

Hazel (*Corylus avellana*)

An excellent hedgerow plant of strong and vigorous habit, producing a bushy, small, 5 m (16 ft) high tree formerly coppiced for hurdle-making and used in house-building for roof and wall lathes. It is valued by gardeners for pea and bean poles.

Hazel grows well in damp and acid-to-neutral soils.

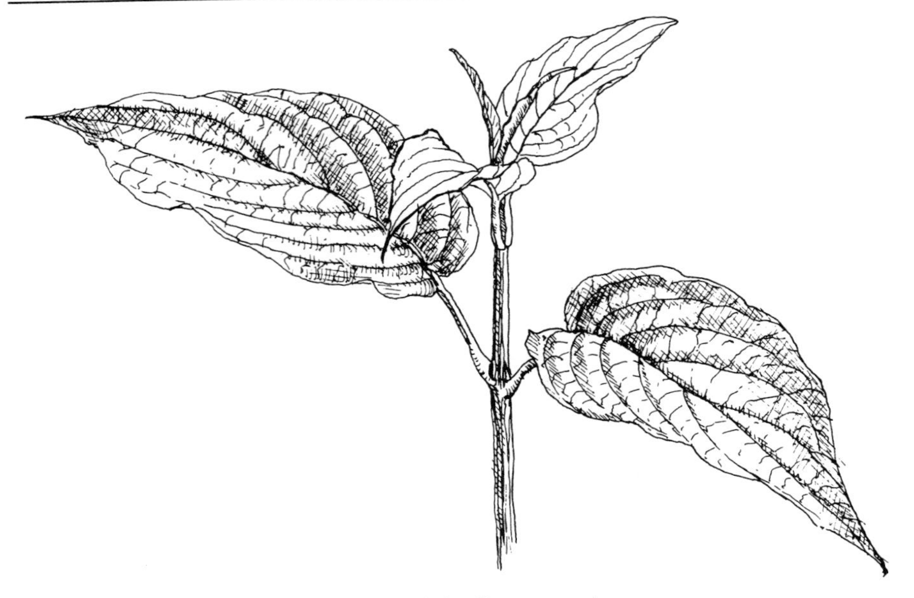

FIGURE 2.3 Dogwood.

FIGURE 2.4 Hazel.

Its oval-to-round leaves are slightly pointed and heart-shaped at the stem. The shoots are brown and hairy, with the main trunk bark being a shiny copper-brown colour with a tendency to papery peeling.

It flowers in March–April before the leaves open. The male catkins appear earlier in groups of four. The later female flowers break out above the catkins as spikes with red styles. The fruits are round, edible, hard-shelled nuts, each enclosed in a green covering which has an irregular flame-like edge.

Hawthorn (*Crataegus monogyna*)

A thorny, quick-growing shrub, which can grow into a small gnarled tree 5 m (16 ft) high with age, if given the freedom of a scrubland setting.

A very tough, hardy, native plant which can survive and colonise derelict land across a wide band of soil types. It is the perfect and proven plant for stockproof hedging.

FIGURE 2.5 Hawthorn.

FIGURE 2.6 Spindle tree.

FIGURE 2.7 Common beech.

The hawthorn has dark yellowish-green leaves which are small yet variable in size. Each leaf has three–five lobes which narrow to the leaf stem.

It carries many thorns on both shoots and branches. The bark is pale grey when young, becoming browner and fissured with age.

The dense clusters of white flowers appear in May to become bunches of blood-red oval berries in the autumn, each berry containing one hard seed.

The hawthorn must be regarded as the 'king' of the hedgerow plants as it meets every important need of the landowner.

Spindle Tree (*Euonymus europaeus*)

It is usually found as a small bushy shrub, but can grow into a small 5 m (16 ft) tree when situated in a woodland fringe.

Attractive for its grey and green bark with corky, lined ridges along the stems and in the autumn for its leaf colours and pink, heart-shaped seed cases.

The leaves stem opposite each other, being oval-to-oblong spear-head in shape, with finely-toothed margins. Their deep green colour turns to a dark reddish-yellow in the autumn.

The spindle bears yellow-green flowers in the leaf axils during May–June and these become bright pink berries containing four seeds, each in a vivid orange covering.

It is found throughout England, although is not regarded as a common hedgerow plant. It adapts well to a wide range of soils, having a very fibrous root system.

This is a plant which deserves to be more widely planted, being attractive in all seasons.

Common Beech (*Fagus sylvatica*)

It can be grown as a hedgerow plant or a tree, responding equally well to both options. It is a common plant for garden hedges and is also found in farm hedges, particularly on chalk upland or limestone soils. It will not tolerate a wet site.

Beech is not recommended for use in a hedge where livestock are present as they will browse on its foliage and tender young shoots.

It responds well to tight trimming to produce dense growth.

The leaves are broad, smooth and ovate in shape, pointed with a wavy edge. The foliage is bright green in early summer, darkening towards autumn to become yellow and brown in winter.

In May the beech bears clusters of small green flowers, with up to three clusters of female flowers at each shoot tip; the male flowers hang in long tassel-like bunches. The fruit is the familiar beech 'mast', a rough case containing two triangular small nuts in the late autumn. The bark is smooth and silver-to-grey in colour.

FIGURE 2.8 Sea buckthorn.

Sea Buckthorn (*Hippophaë rhamnoides*)

A very hardy maritime shrub, commonly found on sandy foreshores or in coastal gardens, where it makes an attractive windbreak for an exposed position.

Its distinctive long, thin, silvery leaves stem from sharp, spiny shoots with a silvery bark.

The sea buckthorn produces a multitude of flowers in late April and, if pollinated, will form clusters of small, bright orange berries in the autumn. Being a single-sex plant, male plants must be planted with the female ones in the ratio of one-to-five to obtain good pollination.

It produces suckers from which further plants can be established.

FIGURE 2.9 Holly.

Holly (*Ilex aquifolium*)

A small, slow-growing, evergreen tree, which also makes a good hedgerow shrub.

A native plant found throughout Britain on a wide variety of soil types. It prefers to grow in calcareous soils with adequate moisture, but does not like wet sites.

Its dark green glossy leaves are hard and leathery, oval-to-oblong with deeply undulating edges that bear spiky points which make it an ideal plant for a stockproof hedge.

Male and female flowers are borne on separate trees and appear in May within the leaf axil.

The white flowers, if pollinated, will become bright red berries in the autumn and are much loved by birds. Heavily berried trees must be netted to prevent bird damage if one wishes to cut the berried sprigs for the Christmas decoration trade.

The young shoots are dark green and smooth, with the main stem bark being smooth but becoming grey-green with age.

FIGURE 2.10 Common privet.

Common Privet (*Ligustrum vulgare*)

A semi-deciduous shrub 5 m (16 ft) high seen in hedges and scrubland, particularly on chalky soils. It is now more commonly seen as a garden hedge plant in its *L. ovalifolium* form.

Its longish-oval, dull green, smooth leaves with pointed tips stem opposite each other from smooth light brown shoots. The bark is similarly smooth and a dull brown.

Privet responds well to trimming to form a thick hedge. Its vigorous and fibrous root system adapts to most soil conditions and will tolerate salty, polluted and windswept sites.

Crab Apple or Wild Crab (*Malus communis* or *silvestris*)

The wild crab is a long established native found as a dense, small tree 5 m (16 ft) high growing on the edge of woodland or in a hedgerow.

Its small, oval, bright green and shiny leaves stem from thorny twigs.

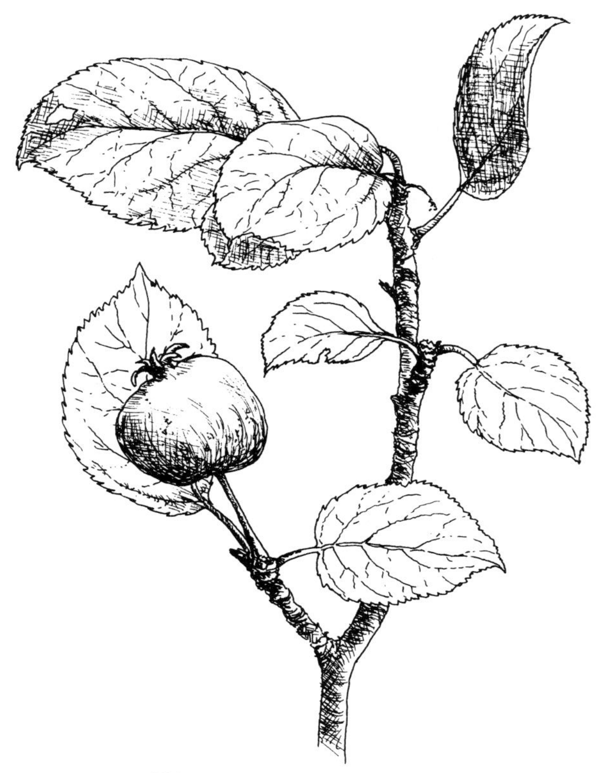

FIGURE 2.11 Crab apple.

The white-to-pale-pink flowers with yellow stamens bloom in early May. The fruits are yellow-to-green with dashes of red and look like miniature apples.

Myrobalan, Cherry or Wild Plum (*Prunus cerasifera*)

A small 6 m (20 ft) high tree or a hedgerow plant, introduced from Central Asia; cultivated forms include damsons and gage fruits.

The glossy, dull green leaves are longish-oval-to-lance-shaped, tapering at each end with a deep main rib and a finely notched margin.

There are some thorns on the reddish-green young growth and on the mature grey wood.

The wild plum produces solitary flowers which appear with the young leaves in early May and, if pollinated, will become small greenish-red plum-like fruits in late summer.

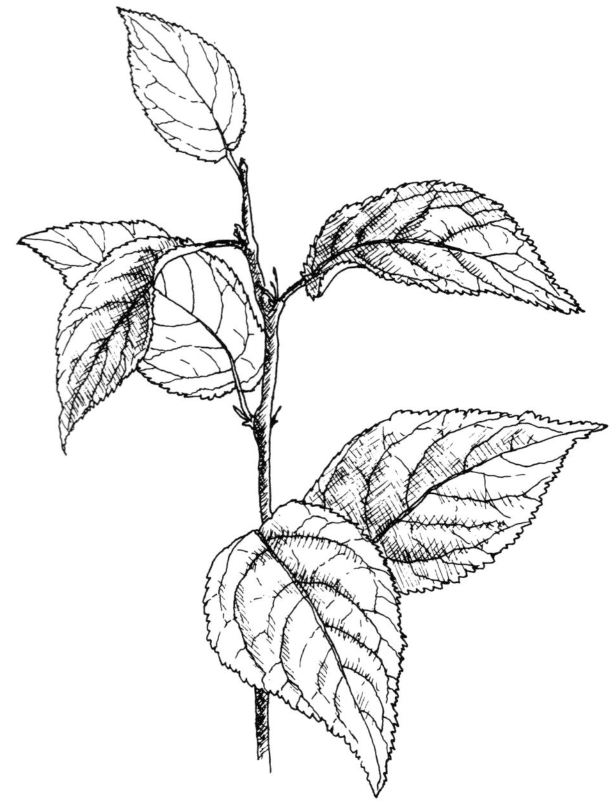

FIGURE 2.12 Wild plum.

It has a tendency to produce a number of suckers around the base of the trunk. It will grow in a wide range of soils and situations to form a good stockproof hedge.

Blackthorn or Sloe (*Prunus spinosa*)

A good shrub or bushy tree for use in trimmed or free-growing hedges. Widely grown and especially suited to coastal sites where it can tolerate salt-laden mists and windy conditions. Hardy and robust enough to grow in any soil type, but prone to producing suckers which will form a thicket if not controlled.

The blackthorn responds to trimming to form an excellent stockproof hedge, either on its own or with gorse for coastal sites and with hawthorn for inland areas.

Its long, pointed, mid-green leaves spring from green-to-purple shoots. A mass of white flowers appear in March before any leaves and, if pollinated, will form small dark blue, damson-like fruits in the autumn. These are excellent when soaked in gin to form the rich liqueur sloe gin.

The blackthorn's multi-branched wood has dark grey-brown smooth bark.

FIGURE 2.13 Blackthorn.

Purging or Common Buckthorn (*Rhamnus cathartica*)

A deciduous shrub which grows into a small 5 m (16 ft) high tree. It is found on calcareous soils growing in hedges, and also favours peat or scrubland conditions.

It has broad, egg-shaped leaves stemming opposite each other, which are a dull green colour, turning yellow with a finely-toothed edge.

The purging buckthorn bears yellowish-green flowers in late May–

FIGURE 2.14 Purging buckthorn.

June, to become clusters of poisonous black berries in the autumn. Thus it is not suitable in a stockproof hedge.

Its grey-brown shoots are spurred or thorny and stem from a trunk with smooth, dark brown-to-orange bark, which becomes fissured and sooty with age.

Alder Buckthorn (*Rhamnus frangula*)

It is usually found as a ditch- or stream-side shrub, never growing into more than a small, bushy 2 m (7 ft) high tree. It is not a common hedgerow plant, but is an attractive addition for moister sites.

The alder buckthorn has small, oval, alder-like smooth-edged and pale green, shiny leaves which stem from dark brown-to-violet, hairy twigs.

In May–June it produces clusters of greenish-cream flowers, which

FIGURE 2.15 Alder buckthorn.

later can turn into small, red, berry fruits, which darken upon maturity to become almost black.

Its bark is smooth and purple-brown when young, becoming grey-brown on old stems with white corky cells.

Dog Rose (*Rosa canina*)

A longer stemmed bush rose with spiky, hooked thorns.

Its long, oval-to-elliptical leaves are dull grey-green and have toothed margins.

The pink-to-white flowers become long, lobed, red hips in the autumn, containing many seeds in a pulpy centre.

The dog rose is the most common wild rose to be found in most hedgerows, where it will colonise very quickly.

Ramanas Rose (*Rosa rugosa*)

A dense, prickly-stemmed bush with large, oval, green, paired leaves which are hairy on the underside.

FIGURE 2.16 Dog rose.

FIGURE 2.17 Ramanas rose.

Pink or white flowers in early summer turn into the familiar bright red oval-to-globular hips in the autumn, each of which contains many seeds in a pulpy centre.

Gorse (*Ulex europaeus*)

Gorse will thrive in poor, dry conditions and windy sites. It is commonly found on the top of a turf or wall bank, as well as on moorland slopes.

It grows as a low, compact, spiny shrub. The green branches have dark grey-to-black hairs and stiff spines.

Gorse bears a profusion of bright yellow pea-like flowers with small, smooth yet scaly leaves. It will flower from March through to May.

FIGURE 2.18 Gorse.

Wayfaring Tree (*Viburnum lantana*)

A bushy deciduous shrub found in hedgerows on chalkland and the drier soils of England; it is not so common in northern Britain.

It is noted for oatmeal, downy stems and distinctive large oval leaves, which are opposite one another, dull green in colour with finely toothed margins and a white downy underside. The leaves turn a dull bruise-red colour in the autumn.

The wayfaring tree bears broad clusters of white flowers in May, which become shiny, oval, red berries in the autumn, turning to black later in winter. Its bark is a light brown colour and smooth.

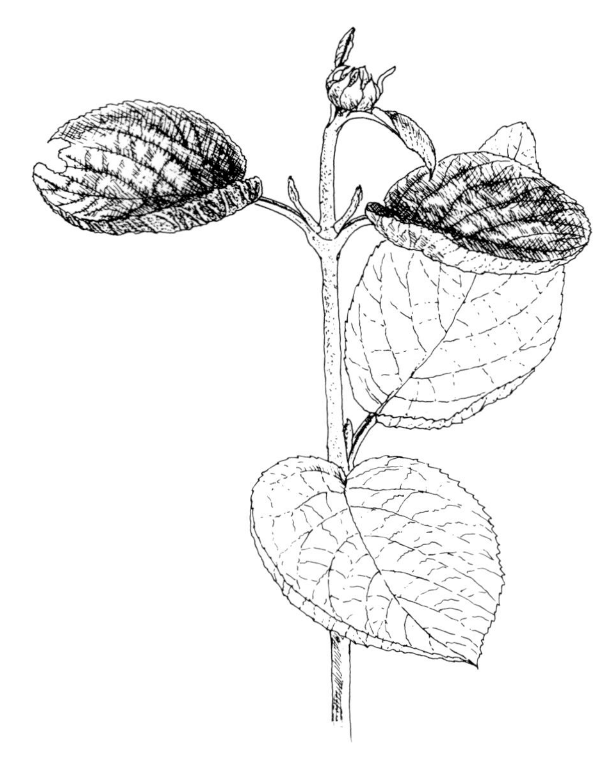

FIGURE 2.19 Wayfaring tree.

Guelder Rose (*Viburnum opulus*)

A slow-growing, small, bushy shrub found commonly in English hedgerows.

It has green, maple-like leaves. Clusters of white flowers in May–June will become bunches of blood-red berries in the autumn, by

FIGURE 2.20 Guelder rose.

which time the leaves have turned to a deep crimson-red. It has thin, grey twigs and grey bark.

SPECIES TO BE AVOIDED IN ANY HEDGE

Box (*Buxus sempervirens*)

Most commonly seen as a low border hedge in formal gardens or the old walled kitchen garden. It will grow into a small tree if left untrimmed. It is not suited for growing in a hedge because of its slow growth rate and its foliage is poisonous to cattle, particularly if withered clippings are left about after hedge trimming.

Broom (*Cytisus scoparius*)

Normally associated with a dry bank, wall or dry, sandy conditions. It is not recommended for general hedgerow use on account of its poisonous foliage.

Laburnum (*Laburnum vulgare*)

A hardy, small tree or shrub, which is found in old hedgerows throughout Wales. All its parts are highly poisonous; its use is not encouraged.

Rhododendron

A genus with many species, mostly evergreen. It was introduced from Asia, notably the Himalayas, China and India, first appearing in England in the mid-17th century. It was not until the mid-19th century that Sir Joseph Hooper brought back a selection of varieties from his Himalayan travels.

The rhododendron has become associated with the driveways and grounds of large country estates, notably in the moister, milder climate of the west country. It will grow in most conditions, but does not thrive on chalky or dry soils.

It is another plant whose foliage is poisonous to stock, so it is not commonly used for hedging.

Common Elder (*Sambucus nigra*)

A vigorous-growing and invasive shrub which, if allowed to establish itself within a hedge, will soon dominate its position (Plate 2.1), growing more intrusive for a number of years, to become a small tree if left unchecked. It will tend to die back slowly, leaving an unsightly gap upon its demise (Plate 2.2). It has a use for planting upon waste sites, where it can establish well under adverse conditions. It is loved by both birds and amateur wine-makers alike for its bunches of purple-black berries in the autumn, providing food for the former and elderberry wine for the latter.

Yew (*Taxus baccata*)

An evergreen tree or shrub, noted as an aged churchyard tree or a close-trimmed hedge in the grounds of country mansions.

The yew will tolerate most soils; although slow-growing it will

PLATE 2.1 Elder's invasive establishment within a hawthorn hedge planted in 1978 at Collins Farm, Frilford, Oxfordshire.

PLATE 2.2 The gap left by the demise of elder in a 19th century hawthorn enclosure hedge.

continue to grow actively over several centuries when well maintained.

Its foliage and seeds are poisonous to most stock; thus it is not recommended for planting in any position accessible to horses, cattle or sheep.

Common Elm (*Ulmus procera*)

The English elm was, until recently, a dominant feature of the English lowland landscape. During the 1970s Dutch elm disease reduced the elm population to little more than skeletal trunks and unsightly stumps, as a vast population of fine, mature trees were killed by the fungi *Graphium ulmi* or *Ceratocystis ulmi* which was spread quickly by a bark beetle.

However fine the mature elm looked, it was no friend to the farmer. Its broad spreading canopy reduced crop levels within its shadow, and an ability to produce a multitude of suckers soon converted a single tree into a thicket. Foresters and nurserymen alike have made no effort to encourage its return, but already many a country lane is witnessing a revival of this ancient tree, from a 'reservoir' of suckers.

CHOICE AND REQUIREMENTS

The correct choice of plants for a new hedge will be dictated by the requirements to be met and by one's own preferences. When selecting plants, there can be no better guide than to look at neighbouring hedges on a similar soil type and choose those species which are flourishing.

A Stockproof Hedge

Time and trial have proved the hawthorn and, to a lesser extent, the blackthorn to be the most appropriate and robust plants which will defy the most determined escapee. Both are vigorous and bushy in growth and have an abundance of sharp thorns which will deter escape and discourage browsing.

Hawthorn is the most common and popular, and is recommended as the main constituent in a hedge in all areas except Kent. Hawthorn is susceptible to the bacterial disease fire blight, which affects apple and pear trees, so fruit growers try to minimise the risk of infection by removing hawthorn hedges and substituting alder windbreaks.

The percentage mixture of hawthorn and blackthorn should be in favour of the former. Blackthorn, through its ability to put out suckers, can become invasive at the expense of even the strong-growing hawthorn. A suitable compromise is to plant one blackthorn to every two or three hawthorn.

If one wishes to add other plants to give more variety and retain the stockproof strength of the hedge, holly and wild crab are good choices. Both have thorny defences to deter browsing and the holly will give colour to an otherwise bare winter appearance.

A Boundary Fence

A greater variety of plants is possible, allowing one's own preferences to be matched by those plants which are growing well in the immediate vicinity.

Hawthorn should still be the main variety, alongside blackthorn, because one may well need to keep a neighbour's stock from free-grazing one's crops or grass! At least 25% of the hedge can include alternative plants such as field maple and hazel, plus a few holly.

A Windbreak For Growing Crops

The emphasis should be on vigorous growth to provide a tall hedge which will leaf up early in the spring to provide the earliest protection. Hawthorn can take a less dominant role, allowing the use of more leafy plants such as hazel, field maple and wild plum.

If height is important in a windbreak hedge which will be trimmed regularly, then consider using tree species such as the alders – *Alnus incana* (grey alder), *Alnus glutinosa* (common alder) or *Alnus cordata* (Italian alder). *A. cordata* leafs up earlier in the spring than its brethren, but does not have a particularly strong root system, so it is not ideal for an exposed site. All three varieties of alder can be trimmed to good effect and will provide an attractive hedge quickly.

Coastal Sites

Blackthorn, sea buckthorn and gorse have a good track record for survival in exposed conditions, and are the mainstays for protection from wind. Willows, hawthorn and field maple are also suitable and can be mixed with the former three species if away from the seashore to give a little more variety on deeper soils. For a semi-evergreen hedge, privet is often found to be successful.

A Conservation Hedge

The choice of species depends on their ability to attract, sustain and shelter wildlife, and a much wider selection of plants is needed to meet these demands. The faithful hawthorn is still a strong contender, as it will produce plenty of edible fruits which are popular with birds in the autumn. Squirrels love hazel and beech for their nuts and a wide range of birds feed upon blackthorn sloes, rose hips and other berry fruits.

The flowering time of common hedgerow shrubs in order of blossoming is as follows:

January	Wild plum
February	Hazel (catkins)
March	Blackthorn
April	Crab apple
May	Wayfaring tree, hawthorn, spindle
June	Guelder rose, privet
June–July	Dog rose

Many of these flowers will form fruits in the autumn which provide food for the hard winter months that follow. When this harvest of hedgerow berries falls to the ground, it provides food for mice, shrews, voles and other mammals.

A conservation hedge of native species should combine good berry producers with good protection for nesting birds and an all-year-round habitat. A proven composition consists of:

- Hawthorn 50%
- Field maple 20%
- Blackthorn 15%
- Others 15% – to include dogwood, wayfaring tree, buckthorn, guelder rose, goat willow, hazel, crab, wild cherry and bird cherry.

Aspects of conservation and wildlife are dealt with in more detail in Chapters 4 and 10.

A Division Between Different Soil Types

The use of a hedge as a division between different soil types presents a problem in making a correct choice as differences in soil type will favour different species. Hawthorn and blackthorn grow well on a wide range of soil types, so they are an automatic choice. Also field maple, holly and dogwood which grow well on a wide range of soils. For a wider selection it is best to be guided by those species which are growing well in the immediate vicinity, regardless of how unusual the plant may be. If a particular plant thrives well and appears to be common in the area, then its selection is recommended highly. For greater detail see Chapter 3.

An Approach Feature Leading to a Farm, House or Buildings

Neat, compact and uniform growth is required. A single species hedge is perfectly acceptable and, once again, the hawthorn will rank highly alongside the much slower growing beech or hornbeam. Hawthorn is very much cheaper to buy than beech or hornbeam, but the latter varieties are more attractive and hold their leaves longer into winter. Their autumn colour is a bonus.

A mixed species hedge, with its variety of leaf colour and shapes combined with different growth patterns, will provide a more interesting view and give every appearance of a long established hedge.

For a mature or rustic appearance, aim for the wide selection of varieties found in the so-called Saxon hedges. Include crab apple, the wayfaring tree, guelder rose and one of the buckthorns, in addition to the more common field maple, hazel and dogwood.

A Screen Hedge

Look for qualities of vigorous and bushy growth to provide good cover at an early stage. Such a hedge should not be trimmed regularly; allow each species to grow into its natural shape to provide a better camouflage. Include crab apple, wild plum, hazel and wayfaring tree to give a mixed-bag effect alongside hawthorn and blackthorn.

Control of Soil Erosion

Shrubs that have a vigorous and fibrous root system help bind the soil and provide a good anchor for themselves in sands. Dogwood, hazel, hornbeam and the ubiquitous hawthorn should be the first choice. For more loamy and moist conditions, the spindle, field maple and willow varieties are good additions, together with blackthorn because of its suckering habit. For more detail see Chapter 3.

The Use of Evergreens

Evergreen trees such as privet, holly or the holm oak will give winter colour and contrast to an otherwise bare appearance. All three species will stand mechanical pruning and retain good bushy growth within a trimmed hedge. They are all trees in their own right which can be allowed to grow up within the hedgerow if desired.

Less Common Plants

Some conservation advisers are conservative in their recommendations, often on the reasonable grounds that they wish to retain a traditional appearance to the landscape, using a limited range of species according to the locality. However, there is a strong case for the bolder use, on a modest scale, of a wider choice of trees and shrubs.

Consider greater use of the spindle tree, ramanas rose, alder and purging buckthorns and wild plum. One or more of these dotted along a new hedge gives more contrast and interest for future generations of farmers, ramblers and naturalists. One reads of landscape architects turning up their noses at the horse chestnut because they do not want problems arising from children who use sticks to knock the conkers down and make a mess on the ground, all of which does minor damage. What spoil-sports some have become in denying children the joy of conker fights, which they undoubtedly enjoyed in their youth! So provide a few pleasant surprises in a hedge for future generations.

REFERENCES AND FURTHER READING

Beddall, J. L. (1950), *Hedges* (Faber and Faber Ltd.).

Harz, Kurt (1980), *Trees and Shrubs*, Chatto Nature Guides (Chatto and Windus Ltd.).

Malden, W. J. (1899), *R.A.S.E. Journal.*

Pollard, E., Hooper, M. D. and Moore, N. W. (1974), *Hedges* (William Collins Sons & Co Ltd.).

Chapter 3

Effect of Soil Type and Topography

I owne I like definite form in what my eyes
are to rest upon. And if landscapes were sold,
like the sheets of characters of my boyhood
one penny plain and twopence coloured,
I would go the length of twopence
every day of my life

FATHER APOLLINARIS ROBERT LOUIS STEVENSON

The great joy of the English landscape is its infinite variety within the small confines of our island shores. A closer examination of this diversity reveals that the landscape of lowland England can be divided very broadly into two distinctive types:

- *'Ancient' countryside* (Plate 3.1) Woodland and pasture (bocage) with hamlets, winding roads and small, irregular-shaped fields enclosed by earth banks, walls and mixed hedgerows.
- *'Planned' countryside* (Plate 3.2) Large, regular fields bordered by compact hawthorn hedges, formerly called 'champion' country – a vista of large villages joined by straight roads, again bordered by single-species hawthorn hedges. This is very much a result of the surveyor's art during the 18th and 19th century enclosures.

Modern farming practices have tended to highlight these two groups.

Cornwall, Devon, Somerset, Dorset and the Welsh counties retain many characteristics of ancient countryside, whilst the corn boom of the 1970s and '80s has left its mark on the eastern counties of Suffolk, Essex, Norfolk and Lincolnshire, together with Hampshire and Wiltshire in the south. It is this latter group which could benefit from the return of the hedgerow to improve the visual appearance of the countryside (Plate 3.3).

Farming has been the primary use of our land right up to the present day. Past generations of farmers have used their inherited

PLATE 3.1 The Vale of the White Horse in Oxfordshire. A patchwork of irregular fields, woodland and winding roads, the remains of 'ancient' countryside.

PLATE 3.2 The surveyor's art. Nineteenth century enclosure fields in the Cotswolds; a precise layout of square fields and straight hedges.

wisdom to choose the right plants for hedgerows on or around their farms.

It is not dodging the question to state at the outset that the best choice of plants for a new hedge will be found by looking at the growth and vigour of existing hedges in the immediate locality. Whilst noting the primary use of hawthorn, blackthorn, field maple

PLATE 3.3 A change in the soil colour (down-slope from the left tree belt on the skyline) indicates where a hedge has been removed on the Marlborough Downs to further bleaken the landscape.

and hazel, make a careful note of the less obvious plants which have found their way into an old hedge, either as a seed dropped or eaten by a bird or mammal. Soil types can vary within a field, yet a locality of several square miles will be given a basic soil category upon which to make a preliminary plant selection:

Light sandy loams and gravel soils
Blackthorn
Gorse
Hawthorn
Field maple

Loamy and silt soils
Beech
Blackthorn
Crab
Hawthorn
Hazel
Hornbeam
Holly
Field maple
Wild plum

Chalk and limestone soils
Beech
Dogwood
Hazel
Hawthorn
Holly
Field maple
Privet
Guelder rose
Spindle
Wayfaring tree

Damp or boggy sites
Alder buckthorn
Willows

Windy and exposed coastal sites
Blackthorn
Sea buckthorn
Hawthorn
Holly
Gorse
Privet

Heavy and clay soils
Blackthorn
Crab
Hawthorn
Holly
Wild plum

A questionnaire was sent out to conservation advisers across the country. Table 3.1 on pages 48 and 49 sets out their recommendations for hedgerow shrubs and trees.

The unanimity of choice for certain species corresponds closely to the suggestions already made. Hawthorn and blackthorn are regarded as the dominant species for a 'working' hedge. The choice of suitable trees for planting in a hedgerow equally favoured ash and the English oak.

The table shows how each part of the country makes use of species which have proven their worth in particular soil or climatic conditions. Cornwall has rightly given a recommendation for the use of the oval-leafed privet in exposed hedges, alongside a wide selection of species which occur in its many miles of old banked and walled hedges. A higher concentration of bank-hedged small fields in the West Country stems from early enclosures in a climate which begs protection from the wind and driving rain coming in from the English Channel to the south and the Atlantic Ocean (Plate 3.4) and the Bristol Channel to the north.

In practical terms, a hedge or hedgebank on level terrain will provide full wind protection for a distance equivalent to five times its height. Thus a 3 m (10 ft) high, semi-permeable hedge will provide 15 m (50 ft) of full protection from wind on its leeward side. Thereafter the shelter value declines gradually until the full wind speed is restored at a distance equivalent to 12 times the height of the hedge, at 36 m (118 ft).

Protection from both the force and chilling factor of wind in exposed fields not only provides welcome shelter for stock, but also aids the establishment of crops in early springtime, such as early potato production in Cornwall and South Wales.

All arable and vegetable crops benefit from wind protection. There will be a small crop loss immediately beside the hedge unless a field margin has been created. From a distance of about twice the height of the hedge out into the crop to a distance equal to 12 times the hedge height, there will be a gain in yield and quality above the overall field average (Figure 3.1).

PLATE 3.4 The effect of high winds from the Atlantic on a Cornish hedgebank.

Allowing hedges to grow taller will have a direct benefit upon wildlife and the care of crops or stock.

Modern wide-cut hydraulic hedge trimmers are very versatile and can cope with heights in excess of 3 m (10 ft). Therefore do not waste the ability of modern hedge cutting machinery by continuing to trim hedges each year to the common height of 1.5 m (5 ft). Allow them to grow gradually to twice that height and make the hedge work for you.

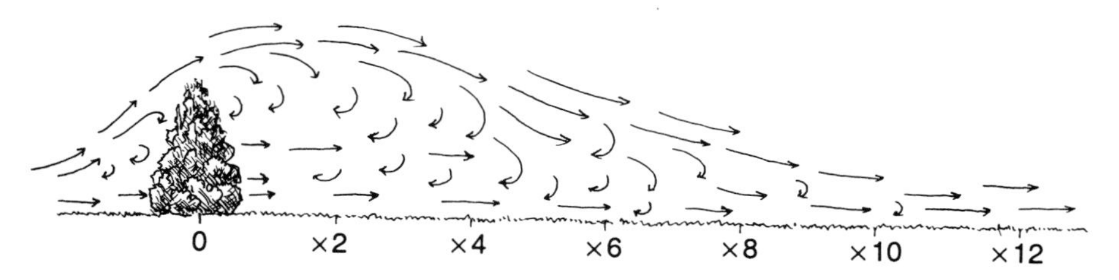

FIGURE 3.1 The shelter value of a hedge.

Table 3.1 Shrub and Tree Species as Recommended by Conservation Advisers Throughout Britain

SHRUBS	Field maple	Hornbeam	Dogwood	Hazel	Hawthorn	Spindle	Common beech	Sea buckthorn	Wild plum	Blackthorn	Alder buckthorn	Purging buckthorn	Wild rose	Wayfaring tree	Guelder rose	Common privet	Holly
Cornwall	✓	✓		✓	✓		✓	✓		✓	✓	✓		✓	✓	✓	
Devon	✓	✓		✓	✓		✓			✓							
Somerset	✓		✓	✓	✓	✓	✓		✓	✓		✓	✓	✓	✓		✓
Avon	✓		✓		✓	✓	✓	✓	✓	✓	✓		✓	✓	✓		
Glos.	✓	✓		✓	✓	✓	✓			✓	✓	✓	✓	✓	✓		
Hereford	✓		✓	✓	✓	✓				✓			✓		✓	✓	✓
S. Wales	✓			✓	✓					✓							
M. Wales				✓	✓		✓			✓			✓				
N. Wales				✓	✓					✓							✓
Hants.	✓	✓		✓	✓				✓	✓							
Oxford	✓			✓	✓	✓			✓	✓		✓	✓	✓	✓		
Essex	✓	✓	✓	✓	✓	✓	✓			✓	✓	✓	✓	✓	✓		
Norfolk	✓		✓	✓	✓	✓			✓	✓			✓	✓	✓		
Shrop.	✓		✓	✓	✓	✓				✓			✓	✓	✓		
Leeds	✓			✓	✓					✓					✓		
Lancs.	✓		✓	✓	✓		✓			✓	✓	✓	✓		✓		
Cumbria	✓			✓	✓	✓		✓		✓	✓	✓	✓		✓		
N. Yorks	✓		✓	✓	✓					✓	✓		✓		✓		
Dumfries & Galloway					✓		✓	✓		✓			✓		✓		
Totals	16	5	8	17	19	9	9	4	5	19	7	7	13	8	14	2	3

TREES	*Sycamore*	*Common alder*	*Common beech*	*Common ash*	*Holly*	*Wild cherry*	*Bird cherry*	*Common pear*	*Crab apple*	*English oak*	*White willow*	*Goat willow*	*Mountain ash*
Cornwall	✓			✓	✓	✓			✓	✓	✓	✓	✓
Devon			✓	✓	✓					✓			✓
Somerset			✓	✓	✓					✓			
Avon		✓		✓	✓	✓	✓	✓	✓	✓		✓	
Glos.	✓	✓	✓	✓	✓	✓	✓	✓	✓	✓	✓	✓	✓
Hereford			✓	✓	✓	✓	✓		✓	✓			✓
S. Wales				✓	✓	✓				✓			✓
M. Wales	✓		✓	✓	✓	✓				✓			✓
N. Wales				✓	✓						✓	✓	
Hants.				✓		✓				✓			✓
Oxford				✓		✓		✓	✓	✓			
Essex				✓		✓			✓	✓			
Norfolk				✓	✓	✓		✓	✓	✓			
Shrop.				✓	✓					✓			
Leeds				✓						✓			
Lancs.		✓		✓	✓			✓	✓	✓			✓
Cumbria				✓	✓		✓		✓	✓			
N. Yorks		✓	✓	✓	✓		✓			✓			✓
Dumfries & Galloway			✓	✓						✓			✓
Totals	5	4	8	19	14	10	5	4	9	18	3	4	10

Where protection for crops or stock was required as quickly as possible, it was the practice to form a bank of earth along the intended hedge line and to plant the shrubs on the bank ridge, so the young plants gained from the greater depth of good, free-draining loam taken as topsoil from either side to form the bank. In many cases the bank was raised solely to obtain an adequate planting depth of good soil on sites of either very wet or shallow soil. Thus the formation of a bank serves a dual purpose and gives the hedge a head start. Devon, Cornwall and many areas of Wales are noted for their high banked hedges and for hedges planted on top of stone walls.

Stock will need to be kept away from both the bank and its crowning hedge to prevent damage to the immature bank until it has formed a good grass cover. Sow a grass mix or lay the turfs saved from the adjacent area when digging out earth for the bank. The ditch formed will serve as a drainage channel for both the field and bank area.

Those who cultivate the land for a living develop an intimacy with the soil. They get to know its good and bad points, its reactions to the seasons and how to win the most from it without damaging its fragile texture. The less land a farmer owns, the more likely he will have chosen to farm on a soil which is capable of providing higher returns from a succession of cash crops in any one year. The estate owner, farming hundreds of acres with a limited range of cereal and seed crops and the minimum of labour, accepts a wider variation in soil quality. Some crops may not be ideally suited to parts of the large fields within which they are sown.

The same can be applied to hedge planting: on short runs of new hedging for a particular need, species can be selected which will respond well to the localised soil type, whereas on long runs around a large field the planter will be faced with a more limited choice to suit the overall soil type. There is likely to be the occasional instance where the soil is so poor that little can thrive, however hardy or drought-tolerant.

For a hedge-planting scheme carried out by the author for a farmer in a local parish, it was decided to use only hawthorn for a particular stretch beside a main road. The overall soil classification was a light sandy loam, yet within one year of planting and constant summer watering, there were some areas where the hawthorn had put on over 2 ft of extension growth and others where the plant had struggled to make 2 inches of growth. Three years after planting the difference had become even more marked, with the best hawthorn plants nearly 5 ft in height and on the thinner soil barely 3 ft. In

Chapter 11, dealing with weed control, measures are outlined which can help redress these differences in growth due to soil type and the ability to retain moisture.

SOIL SURVEYS

It is recommended that a landowner contemplating hedge planting obtains a soil survey map covering his fields to familiarise himself intimately with the soil classifications, their advantages and disadvantages. Most towns have bookshops which are agents for the full range of Ordnance Survey maps. The soil survey of England and Wales is based on the seventh series one-inch maps dated 1967 and 1968. Each map, in glorious colours to indicate the myriad of soil series to be found, covers an area approximately 10 miles by 15 miles at a scale of one inch to the mile. This scale will give a very good indication of the areas of each soil series to be found in any particular field of reasonable size.

Advisers for a hedge-planting scheme of any size should physically examine the soil texture and depth on site with an auger to confirm the occupier's opinion of the site.

With the increasing use of irrigation for intensive crop production, growers are turning to specialist firms that offer an irrigation management service. The first requirement of such a service is to carry out a detailed soil survey of the land to be irrigated, to determine its available water capacity. This ensures that future irrigation applications to a particular field are directly related to the soil texture and to its ability to retain and make soil water available for plant root uptake and, hence, plant development.

Figure 3.2 shows one such survey carried out at Frilford in Oxfordshire. The soil type of the locality is referred to as 'a light sandy loam overlying outcrops of coral rag limestone'. The detailed survey shows three distinct variations of that blanket definition. The dark shaded area shown as G3 is classified as Marcham Series of loamy texture over sandy limestone (Jurassic). The largest single central area, shown as E3, is classified as Fyfield Series of coarse loamy texture, loose sands or sandstone (Jurassic and Cretaceous), and the four fringe areas lightly shaded as F3 are classified as Kingston Series of loamy or loamy over clayey texture, interbedded clays with loams (Jurassic and Cretaceous). These latter areas give the best crop growth at the expense of being harder to work in winter months; not always a welcome feature for year-round intensive cropping, but ideal for longer term tree and shrub growth.

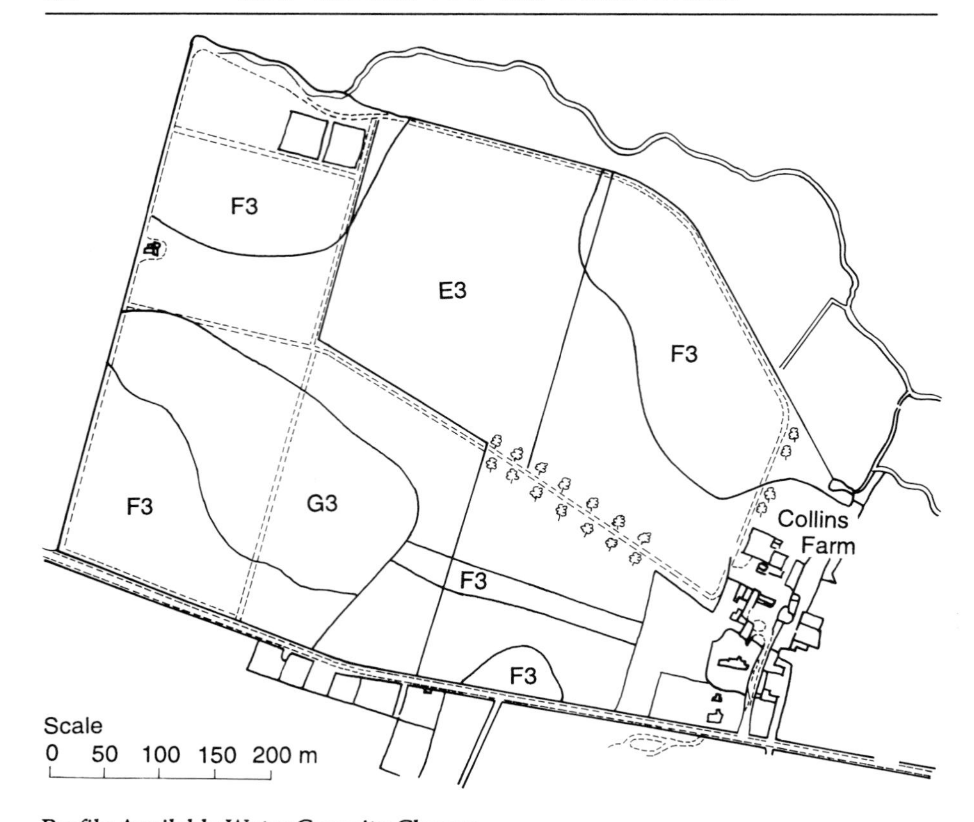

Profile Available Water Capacity Classes:
A 226–250 mm; B 201–225 mm; C 176–200 mm; D 151–175 mm;
E 126–150 mm; F 101–125 mm; G 76–100 mm; H 50–75 mm

Available Water Capacity Classes for Top 30 cm:
1 >75 mm; 2 50–75 mm; 3 <50 mm

FIGURE 3.2 Soil map of Frilford, Oxfordshire. (Irrigation Management Services Ltd)

The moral is that the quickest way to come to a good choice is to examine local hedgerows for the variety and vigour of suitable species. To a landowner with a longer term interest in his soil and its ability to support the crops grown, and to ensure the best position of a new hedge, a detailed soil survey of the appropriate soil map, or by a soil management analysis, will be of considerable value. One will be surprised at how often the analysis explains why an irregular patch has appeared in a crop, usually when under stress from disease or drought.

The constant trimming of older hedges will have removed most of the visible variations in growth rate due to soil factors. Be prepared for some interesting differences in the growth of a new hedge according to plant and soil type, particularly if one has allowed personal preference to override choice according to soil type. The freedom of choice will sometimes be in conflict with a soundly based selection of suitable plants.

REFERENCES AND FURTHER READING

Beddall, J. C. (1950), *Hedges* (Faber and Faber Ltd., London).

Irrigation Management Services (1985), *Soil Survey for M. Maclean, Frilford, Oxon.*

Ordnance Survey (1968 & 1967), *Soil Survey of England and Wales.*

Pizer, N. H. (1931), *The Soils of Berkshire* (Bradley & Son Ltd., Reading).

Chapter 4

Conservation Considerations

The poetry of earth is never dead.
When all the birds are faint with the hot sun
And hide in cooling trees, a voice will run
From hedge to hedge about the new mown mead
ON THE GRASSHOPPER AND CRICKET JOHN KEATS

Early advocates of hedges for enclosing open land were criticised by farmers who often blamed hedges for harbouring all the pests and diseases which afflicted their crops. The farmers reasoned that if no hedges were present, there was less risk of bird damage to ripening corn, of rabbits grazing into the edges of the field and of all the fungal diseases and weeds lurking in the hedge bottom waiting to infect their lush growing crops.

This attitude has been hard to dispel in many predominantly arable areas, but a rational approach to the reality of what a hedge can harbour will show that there is likely to be a predator for most pests, if the hedge's ecology is in balance.

BIRDS

A good hedge may provide an adequate nesting site for many small birds, but it will also need to provide a good and varied insect population upon which the birds can feed themselves and, more especially, their ravenous young. In turn the insects will need host plants in adequate numbers to feed on. Thus a simple life cycle within the hedgerow becomes a necessity if all the inhabitants are to survive and thrive within their own territory.

The presence of trees within a hedge will add to the range of birds present, such as rooks, crows and pigeons. The form of the hedge will influence the selection of inhabitants. Hedge sparrows, robins and wrens prefer a hedge which is thick at the bottom. This provides the cover they prefer for scratching about in its depths for insects, particularly in winter when the open ground may be frozen hard. The bottom of the hedge, with its carpet of dead leaves, will remain unfrozen and thus a rich source of food. Song birds such as the blackbird and thrush sing from the top of the hedge, nest in its midst and join others in scratching about in the bottom for snails, seeds, worms and grubs according to their taste.

Taller shrubs growing in a hedge, such as wild crab or plum, provide the higher vantage and nest sites preferred by the wood pigeon. Such a vantage point will also serve as a song post for the blackbird and songthrush, amongst others. Trees within the hedgerow provide nesting sites for rooks, crows, pigeons, buzzards and kestrels. These may be viewed with mixed feelings by lovers of small birds in the hedge below, which will be prey to the kestrel and the buzzard.

Table 4.1 Value of Hedges for Common Birds

Bird	*Nesting Site*	*Feeding Area*	*Shelter*
Hedge sparrow	✓	✓	✓
Robin	—	—	✓
Blackbird	✓	✓	✓
Wren	✓	✓	✓
Blue & great tits	✓	✓	✓
Greenfinches (bullfinch & chaffinch)	—	✓	✓
Starling	—	—	—
Linnet	✓	✓	✓
Thrush	—	—	—
Skylark	✓	✓	✓
Cuckoo	✓ In other birds' nests	—	—
Pigeon	✓ Tall hedge	✓	—
Moorhen	✓ Tall hedge	✓	✓
Magpie	✓ Tall hedge	✓ Eat eggs and young birds	—
Whitethroat	✓	✓	✓
Yellowhammer	✓	✓	—
Collared dove	✓	—	—

Many of the above birds will equally be found in woodland margins, where a mixture of bushes, shrubs and small trees provide similar levels of cover and shade with easy access to their feeding ground, be it on the woodland floor, out in the open field or the grassy edges of fields and hedgerows.

The abundance of wildlife in Victorian hedgerows can be illustrated by a pair of bird catching nets owned by the author. Used by farm lads, they helped to prevent flocks of sparrows from damaging growing crops.

A large piece of close-mesh netting was attached between two 12 ft long canes, which were joined (at the tapered end) with a piece of leather thong to form a large hinged arch (Figure 4.1). The thick ends

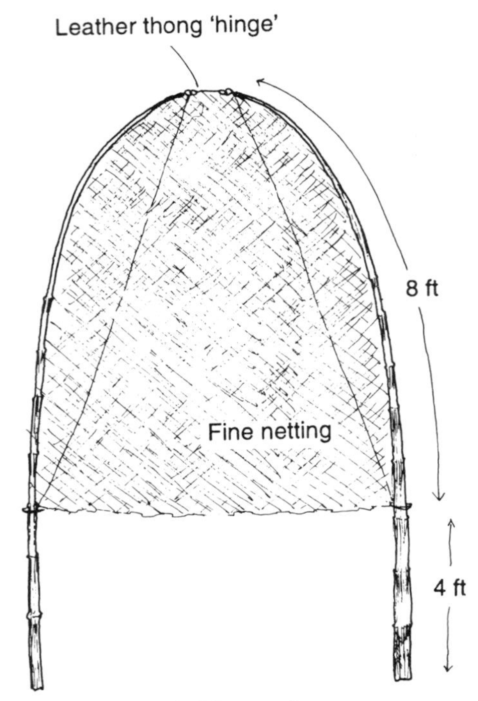

FIGURE 4.1 A Victorian bird-catching net.

of the canes were held up by one man, the outstretched arched net being held aloft, banner-like. He proceeded to walk up the side of a hedge, while another man carried a similar open net opposite him on the other side of the hedge. As they walked up the hedge, so one or more men would be walking down the hedge from the other end, beating the hedge with sticks, shouting or whirling a rattle to scare all the sparrows, linnets, finches and other small birds out of the hedge (Figure 4.2). The birds would fly forward down the line of the hedge in short flight hops, until unwittingly they would land up caught in the net, whereupon the two men holding the open nets would close them like a book, trapping the birds inside. They would

FIGURE 4.2 The bird-catching net in use.

be killed, and either earned a reward from the farmer or were eaten, as this was a time when farm labourers could not afford meat and were forbidden from taking even a rabbit home for a stew.

The 12 ft length of the canes makes it likely that these trap nets were used for working along the tall unmanaged hedges common during the depressed Victorian farming period, up to and following the First World War. Since that time hedgerow removal or close trimming has become widespread in all but the more intensive stock- and dairy-producing areas of the country (Plate 4.1), where a hedge is still valued for its shelter.

Such an abundance of small birds in Victorian hedges may not be welcome today any more than it was then, but we do need to redress the imbalance created in the past 40 years.

The presence of birds in hedgerow will be the most visible sign of life, yet what is less obvious to the human eye will be the mammals, insects and other invertebrates which colonise or visit the hedgerows.

PLATE 4.1 A West Country hedgebank of overgrown hawthorn and young oak with a flower-rich bank and meadow.

MAMMALS

Before the arrival of myxomatosis in the late 1950s, the rabbit was the scourge of the hedge, living deep amongst the hedge's roots and slowly undermining and destroying many hedgebanks. Its damage to both the hedge and adjacent crops was often the reason why farmers lost their patience, brought in a bulldozer and set a match to the grubbed hedge piles, so removing the problem clinically and quickly. The return of rabbits is often checked once they begin to dig out old, deeper warrens which appear to be the source of reinfestation of myxomatosis for the colony.

The hedgehog may have acquired its name originally because of where it was commonly found, but today it is more likely to be seen in gardens and overgrown areas, which provide its diet of beetles, grubs and small invertebrates.

The main hedgerow mammals are mice, voles, shrews and the

mole. All are insect- or worm-eating animals which live either underground, like the mole, or in shallow runs below the leaf litter and other herbage of the hedge bottom and its environs. Whereas voles will find their food solely at ground level, mice will climb up into the hedge to reach berries of the rose and hawthorn and will nibble into hazelnuts on the branch.

All these mammals will be preyed upon by the kestrels and buzzards perched or nesting in the trees above the hedge line. The bank vole will not venture from the shade of the hedge; mice and shrews, on the other hand, will forage further afield into the adjacent crops, particularly if edible.

There is one unwelcome addition to the list of mammals – the brown rat. Increasingly banished from the farmyard by changing farming patterns and highly effective poisons, the rat finds itself inhabiting field margins. Rats can become a problem where they burrow into hedge and ditch banks, causing structural damage to both.

Good populations of all these smaller mammals are of great benefit to such birds as owls, kestrels and crows, the latter only going for the smaller mice and voles.

The stoat and weasel will be regular visitors to the hedgerow in search of food in the form of mice, voles and the chicks of game birds. The latter makes them the enemy of gamekeepers.

Banked hedges on the sandy and heath lands of south-west and eastern England provide a home for native species of lizards and snakes. The lizards live on a diet of insects and spiders while the snakes are carnivorous, eating frogs, mice and small birds. Hedges provide them both with breeding, feeding and hibernation cover.

INVERTEBRATES

The largest group of creatures which live on and off hedges are the invertebrates, a vast group of insects, beetles, aphids, flies and mites, all of which are a very important link in the cycle of life within the hedge and its surroundings. It is this group which causes nearly as much concern to farmers as the stock of 'misplaced plants' (weeds!), upon which many will feed and live, in hedge margins.

The farmer's enthusiasm for the spraying machine as the panacea for all pest and weed problems has, in the past 30 years, led to a serious imbalance in the flora and fauna of the hedgerow. Today the cost of chemicals, combined with falling produce prices, has led to a complete reappraisal in farming circles of the benefits which can accrue from a more cautious and restrained use of herbicides and insecticides.

The role of beneficial insects in controlling crop pests can be best illustrated by the accepted value of the larvae of the hoverfly and ladybird, together with lacewings, in controlling infestations of aphids on a wide range of arable crops. In certain cases, where the aphid carries a damaging virus infection, spraying may need to take priority over the slower results achieved by the likes of the ladybird, because the quick spread of the virus within the crop will affect the quality and value of any seed to be saved from the crop for future production. Good examples are mosaic disease and leaf roll in potatoes, both caused by viruses transmitted throughout the life of the aphid.

The transmission of virus diseases in potato crops is common in southern and eastern regions of Britain, where the warmer summer conditions are conducive to the rapid multiplication spread of aphid infestations. It is for this reason that the raising of potato seed stock can best be carried out in the cooler summers found in northern England and Scotland, particularly on higher ground away from the conditions required for good aphid spread.

The removal of hedges in lowland Britain will not prevent the spread of aphid attacks and in fact is very likely to lead to heavy crop infestations being left unchallenged by predators waiting in the adjacent hedges to feed on any such luscious visitors.

A mixed species hedge with an uncropped and unsprayed strip between it and the adjacent field crop provides an excellent source of predator insects, which will move into the crop in the spring months to live, breed and multiply, feeding on incoming pests, be they aphids, mites or caterpillars. The anthocorid bug is an excellent predator of the red spider mite, as is the ladybird. The earlier use of DDT insecticide to control the cabbage root fly was found to be killing off the predatory rove beetle, which fed on the pupae of the root fly. In the past 20 years great strides have been made in understanding the role of beneficial insects, which has led to the banning of many broad-spectrum insecticides in favour of newly developed selective ones, which leave the pests' natural predators unharmed.

Slowly the farming community is moving down the road already trodden by glasshouse growers, making full use of introduced predators and/or providing the necessary conditions for pest predators to live on or adjacent to the crop requiring protection. Farmers have the benefit of their own hedges for constructive control of crop pests.

The most visible hedgerow invertebrates are the wide range of butterflies and moths, which will colonise a mixed species hedge with a good selection of wild flowers and plants in its shadow. Single species hedges of hawthorn or blackthorn will only harbour those insects which feed on them; broaden the selection of plants in a hedge and so broaden the range of insects attracted to live and feed there. The ermine moth caterpillar is particularly fond of the hawthorn and spindle, feeding voraciously on the young spring leaves. The brimstone is found feeding on the flowers of the buckthorn, but the presence of many moths and butterflies along a hedge in summer is due to the proximity of the wild flowers upon which they feed. The flowers of hedge ivy are attractive to a wide range of moths and flies, but a good population of butterflies will require a more diverse range of plants in the uncultivated area beside the hedge. Peacock, comma, red admiral and tortoiseshell butterflies feed on the flowers of the annual nettle, while the hedge brown feeds on grasses and the orange tip on garlic mustard.

The state of the ground immediately adjacent to a hedge is a major factor in determining and realising the full wildlife potential of the hedge. As an analogy, compare a house without a garden to a hedgerow without an adjacent field margin. One can live in a house without a garden, but its presence greatly enhances the quality and scope of life. Likewise, a variety of wildlife will inhabit a hedge, but the variety and opportunities for that wildlife will be enhanced substantially if there is a wide margin between the hedge and the field crop, within which flowering plants, grasses and further wildlife can flourish to the benefit of the hedgerow inhabitants and for the control of pests in the adjacent crop.

This concept would have been alien to many farmers striving to gain every extra yard of ground possible to grow more acres of cereals and other cash crops. But with surpluses of most farm produce throughout western Europe, prices have begun to fall steadily, forcing farmers to trim production costs. They have become receptive to conservation measures which can help maintain output at a lower cost. Land 'set-aside' schemes, woodland planting, traditional downland restoration and other conservation measures (with increasingly attractive financial inducements) are encouraging farmers to be better stewards of the land.

Prior to the introduction of inorganic fertilisers, insecticides, fungicides and herbicides, farmers had no choice but to farm in harmony with nature to obtain consistent, good crops. Many of their day-to-day practices, which we now term 'conservation measures', were simply inbred good husbandry techniques which had evolved over centuries and been honed with the experience of successive generations.

In the same way that one can describe a hedge as being a thin strip of woodland, so the adjacent field margin can be called a strip of meadow. Both analogies draw attention to the conditions one is trying to incorporate into the restricted area between fields of saleable crops.

FIELD MARGINS

To encourage the formation of an uncultivated strip of land between the crop and field boundary, reintroduce the wide range of annual and perennial grasses and flowering plants, commonplace before the invention of weedkillers which extinguished many species of wild flowers. Weedkillers have similarly decimated the fauna that relied upon the diversity of plants for feeding and breeding.

A field margin, sown with a wild flower mix or managed in such a way as to encourage the regeneration of former plants, is greatly enhanced if an old or new hedge is adjacent to provide a balanced and complete ecology. Local ADAS (Agricultural Development and Advisory Service) and FWAG (Farming and Wildlife Advisory Group) conservation advisers are well acquainted with the types of seed mix required for a field margin, according to the locality and soil type. With the choice of plants for the hedgerow, there is an equal need to choose the correct mix of plants to complement the hedge and existing wild plants established in the hedge bottom.

An important management aspect for both hedges and field margins is the total exclusion of inorganic fertilisers, insecticides and herbicides, each of which affects the ecological balance.

If fertiliser applied to the field crop is allowed to fall onto the uncultivated conserved edge, it will encourage the growth of aggressive plants such as cleavers, couch and sterile broom at the expense of the more fragile plants such as cornflower, daisy and primrose. Similarly, herbicide drift will adversely affect those plants which fall within its scope of activity.

The use of insecticides for controlling crop pests will also eliminate those insects living in the field edge and hedge bottom. Once they are killed, the birds and other insects which rely upon them as a food source will have to move away to another area in search of food or die from starvation. Failure to avoid spray drift by blanking off an end nozzle on the sprayer boom when going round the crop edge can have a devastating and knock-on effect on all wildlife of the hedgerow. Fertiliser spreaders can be fitted with a baffle plate to prevent the granules falling beyond the crop edge.

The conservation of the flora and fauna of hedgerows and their immediate surroundings is only possible if their needs are considered and fully respected by landowners. The discouragement and regulation of straw and stubble burning has been the saviour of many miles of hedgerow which would otherwise have perished at the touch of a match.

Changing fortunes and attitudes in farming now present the hedge with its best prospects for survival since the end of the Second World War and, when allied to the interest in establishing field margins, the English hedgerow can be revived to its former glory and again grace many acres of the present-day bleak arable landscape.

REFERENCES AND FURTHER READING

Mellanby, Kenneth (1981), *Farming and Wildlife* (Collins, London).

Pollard, E., Hooper, M. D. and Moore, N. W. (1974), *Hedges* (Collins, London).

Porter, Valerie (1990), *Small Woods and Hedgerows* (Pelham Books/Stephen Greene Press).

Chapter 5

 Raising Shrubs and Trees from Seed

The winged seeds, where they lie cold and low
Each like a corpse within its grave, until
Thine azure sister of the spring shall blow . . .
ODE TO THE WEST WIND JOHN KEATS

Tree and shrub seed strains remain largely free from the manipulations of man, probably because the market for seed is small in comparison to the thousands of tons of cereal seed required each year by farmers, or the smaller quantities of more expensive flower and vegetable seeds used by growers. The farmer and grower's desire to produce heavier yields of uniform, quality crops continues to provide the new plant breeder with the stimulus and outlet for any new crop variety which will help to meet an increasingly discerning market.

Tree growers do not enjoy the same level of authenticated reliability in either seed quality or the ultimate performance of their crop as their agricultural counterparts. This can be accounted for mainly by the relatively short history of tree improvement in comparison to cereal breeding. Conifer producers in this country are able to benefit from only around 70 years of effort designed to improve the genetic quality of their stock, and broadleaf growers are in an even less fortunate situation. The emphasis of forestry research in the United Kingdom on conifers has meant that much of the broadleaf seed grown in this country is collected from unimproved stands of variable quality. Broadleaf seed is also often imported from the European continent where it is sometimes mixed with other seedlots prior to sale.

The Forestry Commission instigated a seed improvement programme in the early 1920s. Seed was collected from forests in Canada and the United States, where man had not yet influenced original native tree species by the introduction of new species from other areas, affecting the purity of the former.

Breeders are able to return to the source of origin of certain conifer species to obtain the purity of the parent seed source each time they need the original material for a breeding programme.

For small-scale seedling production, it will be possible to gather seed of most hedgerow plants locally, particularly where hedges have not been trimmed for a number of years, thus allowing the plants to grow into small trees or large rambling bushes, according to type.

The production of seedlings is a skilled occupation, which can be fraught with problems as variable as the types of seed handled. It is a job which is best left in the hands of the dedicated professional or the enthusiastic amateur. The complexity of differing seed treatments according to seed type, and the problems which can occur (Plate 5.1)

PLATE 5.1 Bare, patchy seedbeds in the foreground show the layout and grit-covering to prevent soil capping and erosion. They also indicate the risks of growing tree seedlings; seeds do not always germinate.

and which vary with different seasons, make the task a nightmare for the faint-hearted. The information set out in this chapter is for the guidance of those who wish to undertake small-scale plant raising on a non-commercial basis for their own interest and to meet their 'home-grown' needs.

Those who wish to raise plants on a commercial basis will need to consult many more detailed publications, some of which are listed at the end of the chapter. They must be prepared to learn a considerable amount from the pains of experimentation and failure. As the saying goes, 'Only perseverance pays'.

It will take a number of seasons' seed collection to find reliable sources of uniform and viable seed. Once a good seed source has been located, it is important to keep an eye on its development and collect the seed as soon as it is mature, preventing vermin such as squirrels and birds from gathering it first. Nature knows when its winter food supply is ready for collection or eating. A heavy crop of seed, once mature, can vanish within a few days.

The seed must be collected from a plant which is growing well, in good health and free from any visible disease. Initially choose plants that are carrying good quantities of seed which are within easy reach from the ground by a ladder. Apple picking buckets strapped to the shoulders allow the collector to use both hands for seed gathering. An ordinary plastic hand bucket is also adequate but has to be held with one hand or hooked onto the side of the ladder or picking frame.

For collecting higher in the tree a simple, tractor-mounted collection cage is a great asset and can be simply manufactured by welding two old steel stillages one on top of the other, and welding a strip of angle iron across the top of any open side to form a chest-high guard rail. Plate 5.2 shows such a cage. Empty and full buckets of seed can be stored on the shelf of the bottom stillage, together with any wet-weather or discarded clothing, leaving room for two collectors to work unencumbered in the upper cage. Collection buckets are hooked onto the outside of the top rail, allowing them to collect seed with both hands, or to hold a branch steady with one hand and collect with the other. A third person will need to be on the ground in charge of the tractor, to move it around the bushes and trees.

It is safer to collect seed either from the ground or from the hoist cage, both of which enable the collector to stand securely and reach out to arm's length without the risks encountered while standing at the top of a long ladder.

Once collected, the seed should be transferred into hessian or polypropylene net bags to be hung up to dry fully.

It is best to collect the sample as cleanly as possible, free of leaves

PLATE 5.2 A safety lift cage fitted onto a tractor-mounted fork-lift. Two operators can safely gather seed up to a height of 6 m (19 ft).

and twigs, at the outset. This helps ensure that the sample does not heat up in the storage bags due to the presence of leaf and other organic matter; this could harm the seed's viability by litter-induced fungal attack upon a damp sample. It also makes the later cleaning task easier.

Once dry the seed samples should be examined and cleaned of debris as soon as possible. In many cases they will then be put into a stratification medium to begin the germination process.

All seed must be labelled and catalogued for future reference. This will enable the seed collector to build up a record of seed sources, their reliability and performance year by year. Poor performers can be eliminated and problems can be traced back to the seed source.

The cost of collecting seed will, in most cases, be higher than buying in the seed from the Forestry Commission or one of the other United Kingdom or European seed houses. Try to contract out the collection to part-time or weekend collectors, who will be happy to be out in the fresh air and less concerned with monetary rewards. If one's staff are used, it must be done on the basis that they are more gainfully employed doing such work than on other activities which are of less importance in the late summer and autumn. Collection of the full range of hedgerow seed species will take place from August to November, according to the individual seed maturity dates.

SEED TREATMENT

Each seed type requires a different treatment to bring it to the point of germination for a set date; some only require a period of cold storage (vernalisation), while others need a period of warm stratification prior to the cold treatment.

Table 5.1 Tree and Shrub Seed Stratification and Pre-germination Treatments Necessary for Mid-April Sowing and Germination

	Warm treatment (20–25°C (68–77°F))		*Cold treatment (3°C (37°F))*
Field maple *Acer campestre*	4 weeks from 9 Nov		18 weeks from 7 Dec
Norway maple *Acer platanoides*	—	—	14 weeks from 4 Jan
Sycamore *Acer pseudoplatanus*	—	—	9 weeks from 8 Feb
Horse chestnut *Aesculus hippocastanum*	Autumn sown into free-draining soils only	- or -	17 weeks from 14 Dec
Italian alder *Alnus cordata*	—	—	4 weeks from 15 Mar
Common alder *Alnus glutinosa*	—		4 weeks from 15 Mar
Grey alder *Alnus incana*	—	—	4 weeks from 15 Mar
Common white birch *Betula pubescens*	—	—	4 weeks from 15 Mar
Hornbeam *Carpinus betulus*	4 weeks from 12 Dec		12 weeks from 18 Jan
Sweet chestnut *Castanea sativa*	Autumn sown into free-draining soils only	- or -	16 weeks from 21 Dec
Common dogwood *Cornus sanguinea*	10 weeks from 23 Nov		10 weeks from 1 Feb
Hazel *Corylus avellana*	—	—	14 weeks from 4 Jan
Hawthorn *Crataegus monogyna*	6 weeks from 23 Nov		14 weeks from 4 Jan
Spindle *Euonymus europaeus*	10 weeks from 7 Nov		12 weeks from 18 Jan

	Warm treatment (20–25°C (68–77°F))		Cold treatment (3°C (37°F))
Common beech *Fagus sylvatica*	Autumn sown into free-draining soils only	- or -	17 weeks from 14 Dec
Ash *Fraxinus excelsior*	—	—	8 weeks from 14 Feb
Sea buckthorn *Hippophaë rhamnoides*	—	—	12 weeks from 18 Jan
Common walnut *Juglans regia*	Autumn sown into free-draining soils only	- or -	16 weeks from 21 Dec
Crab apple *Malus communis*	2 weeks from 21 Dec		14 weeks from 4 Jan
Wild cherry *Prunus avium*	2 weeks from 23 Nov		18 weeks from 7 Dec
Bird cherry *Prunus padus*	3 weeks from 16 Nov		18 weeks from 7 Dec
Wild plum and blackthorn *Prunus cerasifera* and *P. spinosa*	12 weeks from 14 Sep		18 weeks from 7 Dec
Wild pear *Pyrus communis*	2 weeks from 21 Dec		14 weeks from 4 Jan
English oak *Quercus robur*	Autumn sown into free-draining soils only	- or -	16 weeks from 21 Dec
Red oak *Quercus rubra*			
Common and alder buckthorns *Rhamnus cathartica* and *R. frangula*	—	—	8 weeks from 14 Feb
Dog rose *Rosa canina*	8 weeks from 7 Dec		10 weeks from 1 Feb
Ramanas rose *Rosa rugosa*	—	—	14 weeks from 4 Jan
Whitebeam *Sorbus aria*	2 weeks from 14 Dec		15 weeks from 28 Dec
Mountain ash *Sorbus aucuparia*	2 weeks from 21 Dec		14 weeks from 4 Jan
Wayfaring tree *Viburnam lantana*	8 weeks from 21 Dec		8 weeks from 14 Feb
Guelder rose *Viburnam opulus*	8 weeks from 21 Dec		8 weeks from 14 Feb

Pages 70–79 detail how to raise hedgerow shrubs and trees from seed. Figure captions indicate the scale of magnification of the seeds. Some species can be used as either shrubs or trees, but are more commonly classified as follows.

HEDGEROW SHRUBS FROM SEED

Field Maple

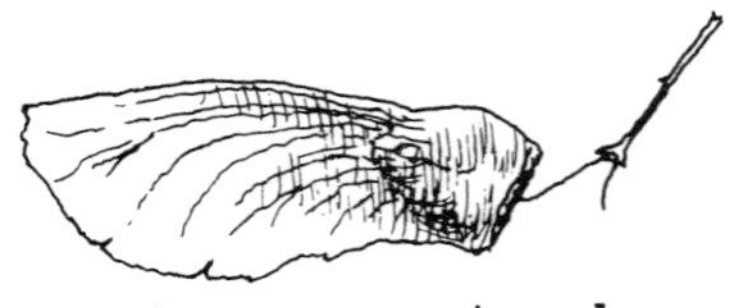

Acer campestre × 1

Collect the winged seeds during late September/October whilst they are still a yellow to light brown colour, before they form the hard seed coat condition which can delay germination.

Once picked and cleaned, sow the seed immediately in the autumn. If one wishes to store the seed for sowing the following spring, mix the semi-ripe seed with a peat/sand compost and cold-store at 3°C (37°F). Inspect the seed regularly, remixing to maintain in a moist but aired condition.

Hornbeam

Carpinus betulus × 2

Mature bushes and trees produce heavy crops of seeds every two or three years. Collect the seed when the wings are a pale green to brown colour and partially dry. At this stage the seed should not have formed a hard seed coat, allowing the cleaned seed to be sown directly in the autumn.

For sowing the following spring, mix the seed with a moist compost and store at 3°C (37°F).

Common Dogwood

Cornus sanguinea × 4

Collect the berried fruits as soon as they change colour from green to black in late summer – August/September – before birds can strip them from the bushes. The onset of bird damage is a good indication that the seed is ripe for collection. The berries can be sown immediately to allow their fleshy exterior to rot off in the ground over winter.

If cleaned seed is bought in during the summer prior to spring sowing, it will have formed the hard seed coat condition, which will need lengthy pre-treatment to soften and enable germination to take place.

Soak the seed in water for several hours before mixing into a peat/sand compost and warm store for two to three months at 20–25°C (68–77°F), before moving to cold storage for a further two to three months at 3°C (37°F). This will bring the seed to the point of germination for warm spring soil conditions.

Hazel

Corylus avellana × 1

The seeds can be picked as early as late August from bushes and trees, before they are robbed by squirrels and other rodents. Lay out to dry adequately to remove the husks.

Immerse the seed in water after cleaning and dispose of any that float, as these contain air. Air can enter the seed case only if there has been insect damage or if the seed has not formed properly within its case.

Sow in autumn, allowing the cold damp winter conditions to both soften the hard seed case and maintain the seed in a lipid state.

Soak bought-in dried seed in water for two days prior to cold storing in compost for 12 to 16 weeks at 3°C (37°F) in preparation for sowing in the spring.

Hawthorn

Crataegus monogyna × 4

In most years, untrimmed bushes will produce a reasonable crop of berries, which should be collected when they are a bright blood-red colour in October–November.

The hawthorn seed has a very hard coat, which will need a complete season's stratification in a sand/peat mix to decompose the outer flesh and prevent the hard case from drying. By the following autumn the seed can be sown or alternatively kept in cold storage for a second winter at 3°C (37°F) for spring sowing.

Some nurserymen collect the seed and bury them in an earth-filled pit, leaving them for a year to allow nature to carry out the stratification process.

Spindle

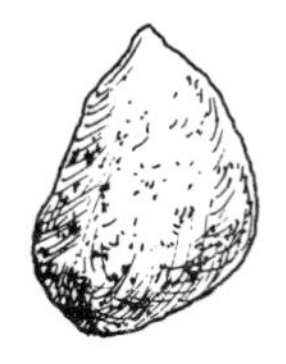

Euonymus europaeus × 4

Collect the bright orange, three- to four-celled lobed clusters in late September/October and lay out to dry for a week or two in a greenhouse or a warm room. Once dry, the seed can be extracted easily by beating in a bag or rubbing through a coarse sieve to separate the chaff.

Once cleaned, sow the seed in the autumn or store in damp sand at 3°C (37°F) throughout the winter months for sowing the following spring. Ensure that the sand does not dry out or become too wet. This will maintain the thin-coated seed in good condition and prevent it from drying, which will severely reduce its viability.

Common Beech

Fagus sylvatica × 1.5

Collect the seed in September/October when the 'masts' (seeds) turn brown. Sweep them up from underneath the trees, extract all rubbish by coarse sieving and immerse in water to remove any remaining trash, together with any empty seed cases.

Whilst beech produces seed regularly, it does not produce a crop of *viable* seed every year. A water flotation check is an important measure to ensure one is collecting viable seed.

Once cleaned, mix the seed with moist peat to maintain its lipid condition and cold store at 3°C (37°F) until sowing.

The seed can be autumn sown or cold stored for sowing the following spring.

Sea Buckthorn

Hippophae rhamnoides × 4

Collect the orange/yellow pea-sized fruits in September/October before birds and rodents can strip them from the bushes.

Remove the outer pulpy flesh by maceration, mix the cleaned seeds into moist peat and hold in cold storage for

12 to 15 weeks at 3°C (37°F) prior to spring sowing. The seed can also be autumn sown immediately after cleaning.

Holly

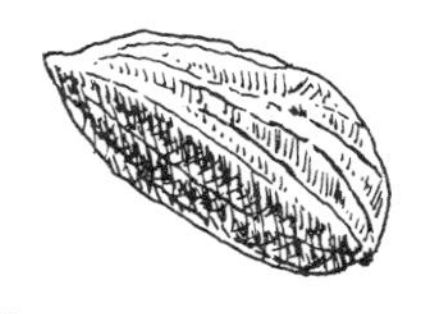

Ilex aquafolium × 4

Although holly can be raised from seed in the usual way, it is commonly propagated from cuttings taken throughout the summer months.

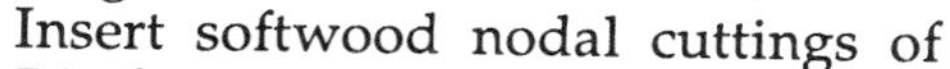

Insert softwood nodal cuttings of 4–5 in from the current season's growth into a peat-sand mix in a cold frame. Once rooted, line out in the field or put into pots, with careful watering to ensure they grow into sturdy seedlings by the autumn.

Hedge Honeysuckle

The honeysuckle can be raised from seed, but as the number required for hedgerow planting is relatively small, it is easier to raise plants from cuttings.

Take 3–4 in inter-nodal cuttings in June from fresh growth and raise in a cold frame, with a plastic cover to retain moisture, to provide strong seedlings in the autumn.

Wild Plum

Prunus cerasifera × 2

Collect the fruits in September as they begin to turn a darker blue to black colour. Remove the pulpy flesh by maceration or by mixing the complete fruits in a peat-sand mix to allow the flesh to rot off slowly in warm storage at 20–25°C (68–77°F) for about 12 weeks. Once the flesh has rotted off, direct sow the seed in late autumn or hold through the winter in a compost mix at 3°C (37°F) for sowing the following spring.

If it is bought in as dried seed, soak in water for several days prior to beginning the stratification process.

One advantage of spring sowing is the reduction of possible damage to the seed by rodents or birds due to the shorter period the seeds are in the ground prior to germination and growth. Losses can be severe if the seedbed is not well netted to prevent access.

Prunus spinosa × 2

Blackthorn

The sequence is the same as outlined for the wild plum.

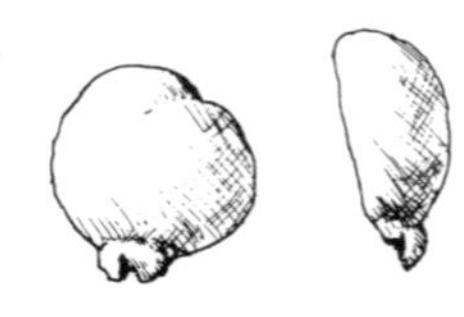

Rhamnus frangula × 3
(Alder buckthorn)

Rhamnus cathartica × 3
(Common buckthorn)

Alder Buckthorn and Common (or Purging) Buckthorn

Both members of the buckthorn family can be treated the same way. Collect the fruit from the bushes in late summer, before the birds find them ripe and attractive.

Remove the fleshy exterior by putting through a macerator or allow the flesh to rot for a few days before rubbing off. Cold store the cleaned seed in peat or moist sand for eight weeks at 3°C (37°F) or longer if required for sowing the following spring.

Rosa canina × 4
(Dog or wild rose)

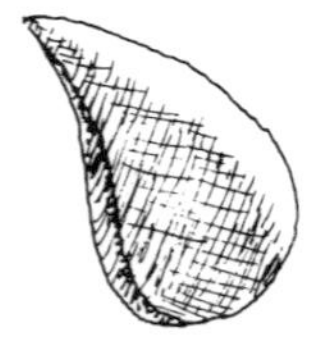

Rosa rugosa × 8
(Ramanas rose)

Dog or Wild Rose and Ramanas Rose

Collect the rose hips as soon as they turn from a green to reddish hue. Mash them in water to separate the seed from the bulk of the pulp and skins.

Directly sow the fresh seed in autumn or mix into peat and sand and stratify in cold storage at 3°C (37°F) for sowing the following spring. If the seed is dried for long-term storage, it will require soaking, followed by eight weeks' warm stratification in a peat-sand mix at 20–25°C (68–77°F), prior to the usual cold treatment before sowing.

Wayfaring Tree and Guelder Rose

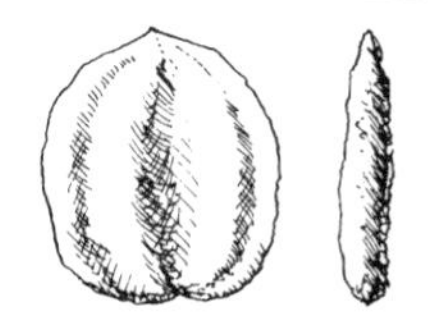
Viburnum lantana × 3
(Wayfaring tree)

Viburnum opulus × 3
(Guelder rose)

It is equally difficult to obtain good germination from both of these.

Collect the berries early in August when they are still a yellow to red colour (wayfaring tree) and a translucent red (guelder rose). This will ensure that they have not formed the hard seed coat condition. Remove the flesh from the seed by maceration and then float off in water. Do not allow the berries to ferment as a means of removing their fleshy exterior; this can reduce their viability.

Once extracted, the seed can be sown immediately into the warmth of early autumn soil conditions, which will eliminate the need for a warm pre-treatment period of six to eight weeks prior to the usual cold treatment of a further six to eight weeks through the winter months. If dry, bought-in seed is used, spring sow after carrying out the above warm and cold vernalisation periods with the seed mixed in moist peat.

TREES FROM SEED

Raising selected tree species from seed for use within hedgerows follows similar patterns to those set out for hedgerow shrubs.

Norway Maple and Sycamore

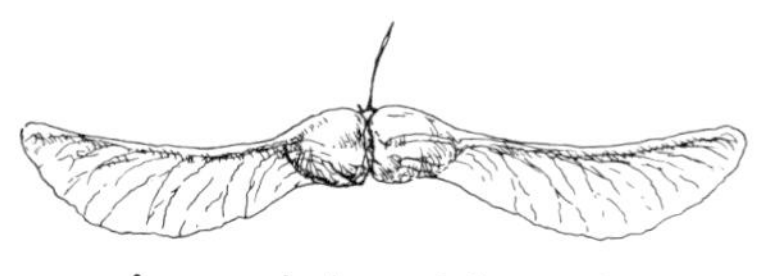
Acer platanoides × 0.5
(Norway maple)

Acer psuedoplatanus × 0.5
(Sycamore)

Collect the winged seeds in late summer, when they are turning from green to brown, preferably when the wings have turned light brown but the seed is plump and bright green.

Remove all twigs and other leaf matter, but do not attempt to remove the wings. Cold store over winter in a peat/sand mix for sowing the following spring or sow immediately in the autumn.

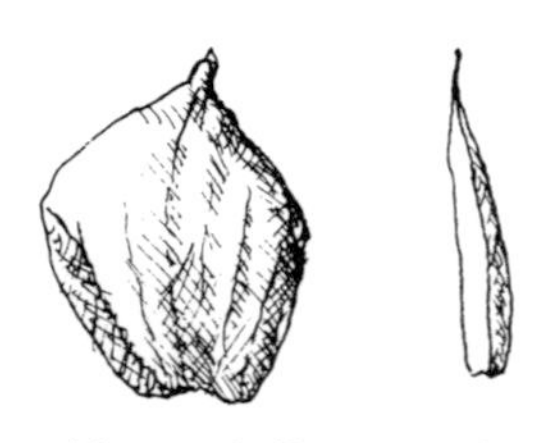

Alnus glutinosa × 8

Alder

Collect the small cones (strobiles) before they begin to open on the tree. Lay them out to dry for a week or two and then shake to release the small, fine wing-edged seed.

The seed can be sown immediately or stored dry for later spring sowing. If stored for later sowing, the seed will only need a short period of cold pre-treatment at 3°C (37°F). It needs little stratification. Simply soak the dry seed in a plastic bag filled with water for a day. Remove the water by cutting a small hole in the bottom corner of the bag, allowing it to seep out slowly leaving the damp seed behind. Shake the bag regularly to keep the damp seeds aerated and cold store for about eight weeks prior to sowing.

Castanea sativa × 0.75

Sweet Chestnut

Gather the fallen fruits from the ground or pick them off the trees, if easily accessible, to ensure that they are all freshly collected.

Collection should begin once the burs (nuts) begin to break open. It is important to collect fallen fruits regularly to prevent them drying out and to keep them from the clutches of squirrels and other rodents.

Spread the cleaned seed out to surface dry in a shaded, well-ventilated building; one week should ensure that they have not lost too much moisture.

The seed can be autumn sown or cold stored at 3°C (37°F) through the winter, mixed in a moist peat/sand mix. Keep the mix regularly turned to aerate the seeds and to ensure that they are neither too wet nor too dry during storage. Sow in March/early April when spring conditions arrive.

If the seed is bought in, soak them in water for at least 24 hours to restore any lost moisture before sowing or mixing into the moist peat/sand mix for storage.

Common Beech

Beech responds equally well to the restriction of being trimmed to

restriction of being trimmed to contain it as a hedge or given the freedom to grow into a mature tree. Hence it can be classified as a shrub or a tree. See instructions given on page 72.

Common Ash

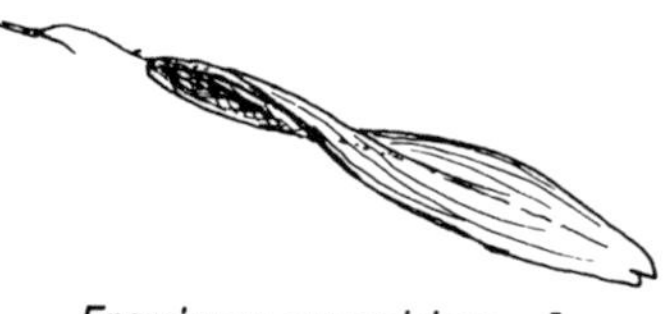

Fraxinus excelsior × 1

Collect the bunches of winged seed in early autumn, when they are beginning to turn from pale green to light brown, usually in early October, to avoid the hard seed coat condition.

Once cleaned, the seed should be mixed with a peat/sand compost and cold stored at 3°C (37°F) or alternatively sown immediately in the autumn.

For longer-term storage, spread the seed out to dry before hanging up in hessian sacks away from vermin. Dried seed will have developed the hard seed coat dormancy condition, thus needing an eight to ten week vernalisation period at 3°C (37°F) to bring it to germination, when mixed in moist peat and sand.

Walnut

Juglans regia × 0.75

Collect the nuts when they fall, remove the fleshy skin and wash them clean before sowing direct in the autumn.

The seed coat of the walnut is relatively thin and not very resistant to internal drying of the seed, so store the nuts in a moist peat/sand mix if there is any delay in sowing. Store at 3°C (37°F) prior to sowing.

Crab Apple or Wild Crab

Malus sylvestris × 3

The hedgerows contain many differing types of crab apple, most of which will have grown from a discarded apple core, so care must be taken to select fruits from a tree which bears the hallmarks of a true crab. It is advisable to hunt for the correct wild crab in hedgerows away from main or minor roads or in known old woodlands.

For small batches of seed, collect ripe fruits, cutting open each fruit to remove its complement of five to ten seeds. This is somewhat laborious, but is to be preferred to attempting to macerate the whole fruit without proper extraction equipment which will float off all the pulp, such as a cider mill. The small, fleshy, soft-coated seeds are vulnerable to damage when extracted in a cider or other press.

The freshly-extracted seed can be autumn sown or stored over winter in a peat/sand mix and held in cold storage at 1–3°C (34–37°F) for a 12 to 16 week period, when the seed will have completed its vernalisation for spring sowing and early germination.

Prunus avium × 2

Wild Cherry

Collect the fruits from hedgerow trees in late summer. It may be necessary to collect as early as July to prevent birds eating them first.

Mix the fruits into a moist peat/sand compost, which will rot off the flesh as well as provide the necessary two to three week period of warm stratification. After cleaning, move the bags of seed and compost into cold storage for a further 12 to 18 weeks at 2–3°C (36–37°F) to complete their vernalisation.

The seed can be autumn sown or held in cold storage at 3°C (37°F) for sowing the following spring.

If dry seed is bought in soak in water for several days to allow the seed to imbibe fully prior to carrying out the above-mentioned warm and cold spells of stratification.

Prunus padus × 3

Bird Cherry

Collect the small black berry fruits in late summer before birds attack them.

The cleaning and stratification procedures are the same as outlined for the larger wild cherry seed.

Pyrus communis × 3

Wild Pear

Collect the small pear fruits when ripe, during September–October. They are treated in the same manner as crab apple, small quantities of seeds being collected by cutting open the fruits and extracting the pips (seeds).

Larger quantities can be extracted by careful maceration in a cider mill and floating off the pulpy flesh.

Mix the freshly extracted seed with peat and sand prior to stratification in a cold store at 1–2°C (34–36°F) for 10 to 14 weeks prior to sowing in the spring. The seed can be sown in the autumn immediately after extraction without stratification. The cold winter seedbed conditions will complete the seeds' vernalisation.

Oak

The seeds of all oak varieties are treated in the same manner. Collect the ripe acorns from the ground or from the trees during the period September–November; early collection will reduce the risk of theft and damage by squirrels and other rodents.

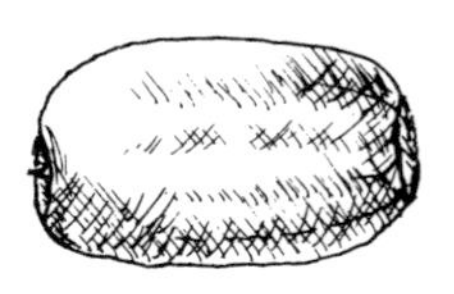

Quercus robur × 1
(English oak)

Place the seeds in water and remove all those seeds which float, to eliminate any which have been damaged by weevils or which are not fully formed.

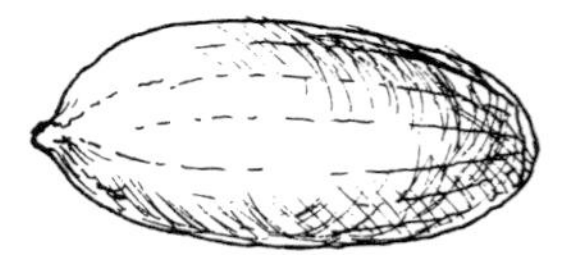

Quercus petrea × 1
(Sessile oak)

Keep the seed cool and moist after collection by storing in damp sand and peat at 1–2°C (34–36°F).

Autumn sowing is preferred. If spring sowing is chosen, examine the cold stored seeds regularly to keep them turned and aired, ensuring that they have not begun to germinate. If signs of germination are seen the seed must be sown immediately to ensure that the emerging radicle is able to grow straight down into the soil.

Quercus rubra × 1
(Red oak)

In the absence of adequate cold storage space to hold quantities of acorns stratifying in peat/sand, place them in small onion nets and bury in the soil at least ½ m (1½ ft) deep, to ensure they are held over winter in moist conditions at a cool even temperature. If they are not covered adequately they may suffer from frost damage or dry soil conditions. Bury only into light, free-draining soils.

Other large seed species, such as horse chestnut and walnut, can be stored over winter in a similar fashion (Plate 5.3). Inspect the bags regularly as springtime approaches to ensure the seed has not begun to germinate.

PLATE 5.3 Walnut seed contained in a nylon onion net and stored over winter in free-draining soil at a depth of 0.6 m (2 ft). The seed has begun to sprout and should have been sown earlier.

No explanation of seed coat reducing techniques using the chemicals sulphuric acid and hydrochloric acid will be given. The author has no experience of these methods, and from discussion with nurserymen who have experimented with this means of 'eroding' and thinning hard-coated seed, he is of the opinion that such measures should not be attempted until one has gained a wider experience of raising a full range of tree and shrub seeds under normal stratification conditions, gaining a 'feeling' for each seed type and its particular requirements.

CHOICE AND PREPARATION OF A SUITABLE SITE

The soil should be a light to medium, free-draining loam. Avoid light, sandy soils which can dry out quickly, unless adequate irrigation facilities are available to apply small amounts of water on a regular basis to maintain the necessary moist soil conditions in the topsoil. Heavy clay and silt loams should also be avoided, as these soils are slow to warm in spring, are not normally free-draining and are prone to surface capping if irrigated too regularly. They can 'pack down' tight, making it difficult for the developing seedling to put down a fibrous root system.

Other physical attributes of a good site are adequate windbreaks to create a warm environment around the seedbeds and a gentle, south-facing slope to drain off excess water and gain the full benefit of sunny conditions.

It will not always be possible to find all these ideal seedbed conditions within the confines of one's land, but so long as one is aware of the seedlings' requirement for warmth, moisture and good growing conditions, then measures can be taken to create these conditions if they are not present.

Windbreaks of Netlon or other man-made woven fibres can be erected around and within the seedbed area to combat the cold, damaging and drying effects of wind. Good dressings of well-rotted farmyard manure or the incorporation of peat into the seedbed soil will enhance the moisture-retaining capacity of a sandy soil and, conversely, will help aerate a clay or silt loam.

The potentially high value of a good crop of seedlings warrants having the soil tested to determine its nutrient status, and further tests should be carried out to determine the levels of soil nematode infection.

SOIL STERILISATION

Once the chosen site has been prepared and wind-protected, soil sterilisation can be carried out (Plate 5.4). It is vital that the seed is sown into a soil which is free from weed seeds and damaging soil pathogens.

The sterilisation of soils carrying high value crops has been commonplace in the glasshouse industry for many years. Formerly steam sterilisation was the most widely used method. In recent years several chemicals have become available to supersede the lengthy process of steam injection.

Chloropicrin (tear gas)

This highly toxic and unpleasant liquid fumigant can only be injected into glasshouse and open-ground soils by a qualified contractor. It is the most effective and expensive soil nematode sterilant, but has limited effect on weed seed control. The next crop may be planted within one week.

Metham-sodium

This is a liquid dithiocarbamate fumigant sterilant for injection into

PLATE 5.4 Soil sterilisation injection equipment, rig-mounted on a tined cultivator. The chemical is injected into the soil under pressure from compressed air.

glasshouse and open field soils. It gives some control of soil-borne diseases, soil insects and nematodes. It also controls weed seed germination at relatively low rates. The chemical takes longer to disperse in the soil than other soil sterilants. Carry out a cress growing test with some field soil to check for full dispersal. If the sterilant has not fully dispersed it will kill the cress, and conversely, once the chemical has dispersed, cress will be able to germinate.

Methyl bromide

Another toxic soil fumigant, which can only be injected by a qualified contractor. It will control soil insect nematodes and weed seed germination more effectively, but at a higher cost, than metham-sodium. The next crop can be planted within one week.

Dazomet

A granular soil fumigant for both glasshouse and field use. It is a very effective control for soil-borne diseases, nematodes, soil insects and weed seed germination. It can be purchased and applied by any competent person without specific qualifications.

For small-scale use the finely ground granules can be applied by a small 1 m (3 ft 3 in) wide, hand-pushed 'SISIS' lawn sand and fertiliser distributor. For larger areas there is a wider tractor-mounted version.

Dazomet is the most widely used form of soil sterilisation for tree seedling production. The manufacturer's label instructions should be followed closely for the correct, safe and approved uses of the chemical. Dazomet takes four to eight weeks to disperse fully. A cress growing test with some of the field soil can be used to check for full dispersal.

The seedbed ground should be prepared to a fine tilth prior to the application of the granules, which must be incorporated into the soil to a depth of 6–8 in immediately after application. Once the granules have been incorporated by a Rotavator or by a deep working power harrow, the treated beds are covered with a thin, photo-degradable polythene film, using a polythene laying machine to lay the film to cover the treated bed width.

The granules act by releasing methyisothiocyanate fumes upon contact with moist soil. If the soil is below 50% of its water-holding capacity, the ground should be irrigated before treatment. To ensure that sterilisation of the soil is completed effectively and quickly, the soil temperature should be above 7°C (45°F).

Treatments of soils for tree seedbeds are best undertaken in late summer (August/September) to ensure optimum control in the short time prior to autumn sowing. The polythene covers must be removed and the ground harrowed following the treatment period before preparing the beds for sowing. If sowing is not to take place until the following spring, it is recommended that the polythene covers be left on as long as possible in order to reduce the risk of the ground becoming re-infected by weed seed blown in from adjacent land.

SEED SOWING

Small seeds (alder, birch) should be broadcast to produce an even distribution across the bed, whereas the larger seeds (oak, chestnut, walnut) are sown in drills into the soil.

Very small seeds are easier to sow if they are bulked up by mixing with sand or perlite to ensure even distribution. They are best broadcast thinly onto a fine, open-textured seedbed and then carefully raked into the soil surface before rolling in. The rolled beds are dressed with a thin 1½ cm (½ in) layer of fine 'pea' grit. Check with the supplier that the grit is washed to ensure that its pH (lime content) is neutral, particularly if it has been extracted from a limestone quarry.

For hand sowing larger seeds, draw out 4 cm (1–2 in) deep drill lines using a toothed rake with the teeth spaced to give the required row spacing of 15–22 cm (6–9 in). Cover the seeds with the rake to the desired sowing depth. When machine sowing, cover well to ensure that the seed is deep enough to prevent it drying out.

Seed sowing data

Table 5.2 on page 85 sets out the approximate seed counts per kilo, sowing rate per square metre of prepared seedbed and sowing depth, together with final covering medium.

The sowing recommendations are based upon the author's experience where possible; otherwise a consensus has been taken from a range of sources and the recommendations given reflect experience of related seed types. It must be stressed that variations in seed yield, size, quality and viability make it necessary for the plant raiser to use his or her experience in determining the best procedure to be adopted for each seed type.

When sowing larger quantities of seed into long beds, it is important to ensure that the seed rate is maintained at the required constant density. This can be achieved by dividing the seed lot into ten equal parts and dividing the seedbed into ten equal lengths; thus the sower only has to concentrate on sowing one-tenth of the seed onto one-tenth of the total seedbed area at a time.

Once the seed lots have been carefully sown into moist, fine seedbed conditions in autumn or spring, the beds should be rolled. After rolling, apply a thin covering of 5 mm pea grit, 10–15 mm (½ in) in depth. If applied by hand, rake over to ensure the covering depth is even across the bed.

With the sowing, rolling and grit covering completed, the seeds are protected against the elements, but not against vermin and bird damage. There is not much that can be done to deter small rodents such as mice, who can get under the lightest netting, but good precautions must be taken to keep squirrels, rabbits and birds from damaging the dormant or emerging seed.

The most effective protection against these predators is wooden frames (Plate 5.5) or galvanised wire hoops fixed across the bed at 2 m (6–7 ft) intervals, and covered with a close-mesh, woven-fibre netting which is pegged down at the edges at regular intervals to prevent animal entry and ensure that the protective netting is not blown off by strong autumn winds. Snowfalls must be brushed or shaken off to prevent damage to the netting or the hoops.

HEDGEROW FLOWERS AND FRUITS

◀ *Field maple seeds*

Common dogwood fruits ▶

◀ *Common dogwood flowers*

◀ *Hazel fruits (nuts)*

Hawthorn flowers ▶

◀ *Hawthorn fruits (berries)*

◀ *Spindle flowers*

Common privet flowers ▶

◀ *Common privet fruits*

◀ *Crab apple fruits*

Crab apple flowers ▶

◀ *Wild pear fruits*

◀ *Blackthorn blossom*

Blackthorn fruits (sloes) ▶

◀ *Wild plum fruits*

◀ *Alder buckthorn flo*

Alder buckthorn fruits ▶

◀ *Purging buckthorn fruit*

◀ *Dog rose fruits (hips)*

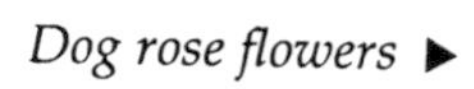

Dog rose flowers ▶

◀ *Ramanas rose flowers*

◀ *English oak fruits (acorns)*

Guelder rose flowers ▶

◀ *Guelder rose fruits*

Table 5.2 Seed Sowing Rates for Hedgerow Shrubs and Trees

SHRUB/TREE	*Seed count per kg (average) (cleaned seed)**	*% viability of seed**	*Sowing rate per m²*	*Sowing method and depth*	*Covering medium*
Field maple	13,000	55	300	Sow in drills 1 in	Thin peat & grit topping
Common hornbeam	24,000	50	300	Broadcast & roll in to ½ in	Thin grit
Common dogwood	30,000	75	400	Broadcast & roll ¼ in	Thin grit
Hazel	800	60	250	In drills ½–1 in	Grit
Hawthorn	10,000	75	375	In drills ½ in	Grit
Spindle	25,000	70	300	Broadcast & roll in ½ in	Grit
Beech	4,500	60	350	In drills ½ in	Grit
Sea buckthorn	40,000	70	500	Broadcast & roll in ¼–½ in	Thin grit
Wild plum	2,000	60	250	In drills 1½ in	Grit
Blackthorn	5,500	85	320	In drills 1 in	Grit
Alder buckthorn	27,000	—	350	Broadcast & roll in ½ in	Grit
Purging buckthorn	19,000	—	300	Broadcast & roll in ½ in	Grit
Dog rose	75,000	50	250	Broadcast & roll in ½ in	Grit
Wild rose	75,000	80	250	Broadcast & roll in ½ in	Grit
Wayfaring tree	20,000	60	300	Broadcast & roll in ½ in	Grit
Guelder rose	29,000	60	300	Broadcast & roll in ½ in	Grit
Sycamore	9,500	80	250	In drills 1 in	Grit
Common alder	350,000	40	300	Broadcast & roll in ¼ in	Thin grit
Common ash	13,000	60	350	Broadcast & roll in ½ in	Thin peat & thin grit
Walnut	150	70	200	In drills 1½ in	Grit
Wild cherry	5,000	75	320	In drills 1 in	Grit
Bird cherry	14,000	50	375	Broadcast & roll in ½ in	Grit
Wild pear	35,000	70	400	Broadcast & roll in ½–1 in	Grit
Crab apple	61,000	60	550	Broadcast & roll in ½–¾ in	Grit
English oak	300	80	300	In drills 2 in	Grit

* Seed count and viability will vary according to season and provenance.

PLATE 5.5 Wooden frames supporting protective netting over seedbeds.

FERTILISERS FOR EMERGING AND GROWING SEEDLINGS

The soil analysis undertaken before the seeds were sown will have indicated any deficiencies of the major nutrients N (nitrogen), P (phosphate), K (potash) and Mg (magnesium).

A low nitrogen compound, organic-based fertiliser can be applied to the soil prior to sowing or later in the growing season. Organic-based compounds have less risk of scorching emerging seedlings, whereas a concentration of inorganic nutrient salts can scorch the emerging tender shoots and restrict the development of fresh root growth.

This risk can be avoided by applying regular sprays of a low concentration foliar feed, which can be mixed with any sprays required to control mildews on susceptible species such as hawthorn, crab, field maple and wild/dog roses.

At the beginning of the chapter it was stated that the raising of seedling trees and shrubs is not for the faint-hearted. However, the control over quality and the guarantee of the necessary seedlings available for transplanting is a great asset.

For those wishing to raise small quantities of seedlings from locally collected seed, it can be an inexpensive and satisfying experience, as well as providing the plants needed. It requires a lot of hand labour, but fixed costs for machinery and sundries are low, making it a possible side-line for producing the trees and shrubs needed for on-farm hedge and woodland planting.

DEFINITION OF WORDS USED IN SEEDLING PRODUCTION

Acid 'digestion'	The use of concentrated sulphuric acid to reduce the thickness of the hard seed coat, so speeding up the process of imbibing and subsequent germination.
Dormancy	An inactive state; the state prior to germination.
Embryo	The undeveloped plant form (fertilised ovule) contained within the seed.
Fruit	The bulky and/or pulpy flesh surrounding the seed, or group of seeds, which protects the seed to ensure its full development and help maintain its viability.
Genetics	The study of the inherited characteristics of an organism.
Imbibe	To absorb moisture. Dry seed needs to absorb moisture into its seed case to soften the case and so allow the process of germination to commence.
Impermeable	Not allowing the uptake of water and/or oxygen.
Lipid	A fat or fat-like substance.
Maceration	Softening or separation as a result of soaking.
Provenance	The original geographic area from which the seed was obtained.
Seed	The fertilised ovule which develops to form a plant upon germination.
Seed coat	The covering around the embryo which protects it until germination.
Stratification	The mixing of seed with another medium (peat or sand) to aid and encourage germination.
Vernalisation	The treatment of seed by cold storage to accelerate and encourage early germination.
Viability	The ability (of the seed) to germinate and live.

REFERENCES AND FURTHER READING

Aldhouse, J.R. (1975), *Nursery Practice* (Forestry Commission Bulletin No. 43) (HMSO).

Brown, James (1882), *The Forester* (William Blackwood & Sons).

Cobbett, W. (1825), *The Woodlands* (William Cobbett, Fleet Street, London).

Forest Service – United States Department of Agriculture (1974), *Seeds of Woody Plants in the United States* (Agriculture Handbook No. 450).

Gordon, A. G. and Rowe, D.C.F. (1982), *Seed Manual for Ornamental Trees and Shrubs* (Forestry Commission Bulletin No. 59) (HMSO).

McMillan Browse, P.D.A. (1979), *Hardy Woody Plants from Seed* (Grower Books).

Yule, John (1815), *Naturalisation of Trees* (Caledonian Horticultural Society).

Chapter 6

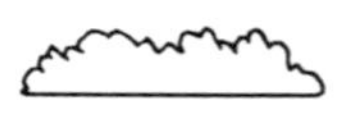

From Seedling to Transplant

The seeds ye sow, another reaps . . .

PERCY BYSSHE SHELLEY

It is possible to raise a new hedge from seedlings; but the level of care and maintenance required may not be appreciated by those not used to giving regular attention to small plants.

The raising of seedlings has been discussed fully in the preceding chapter. Those who have raised their own seedlings in the spring will be able to lift these plants in the winter months and replant them early the following spring directly into the proposed hedge lines, or they may follow the commercial practice of growing the seedlings on for a second year.

It is recommended that seedlings are planted out at a wider spacing than that recommended on page 98 to grow on for a further season to become larger and more robust 'transplants'.

Well-rooted transplants have a greater chance of survival when planted into the average field edge of grass sward. Tender, one-year seedlings need to be planted into clean, cultivated soil and maintained in a weed-free state for at least two years to allow them to establish and grow adequately to match the potential of well-grown transplants.

The customary use of transplants remains the most acceptable approach for growing new hedges; it is cheaper and less demanding upon the landowner.

Plates 6.1 and 6.2 show established hedges on the author's farm grown from seedlings. A stockproof and mature hedge can reach 2 m (6 ft) high in eight years.

Some nurserymen in the United Kingdom produce their own seedlings for growing-on into transplants. They will also sell some of their crop to other nurserymen who grow them on for one or two years to produce 'transplants' in one year or 'feathered whips' in two

PLATE 6.1 A young hawthorn hedge, grown from three close-spaced rows of seedlings, after three years. Collins Farm, Frilford, Oxfordshire, 1984.

PLATE 6.2 The same hedge after eleven years' growth, providing a good windbreak for cash crops.

years. Each extra year increases the size and sturdiness of the plant enabling it to survive in more demanding conditions, where care after planting is increasingly limited.

The following description of the commercial production of transplants from seedlings details the procedures necessary to ensure that a 20 cm (8 in) seedling will be transformed into a well-rooted, sturdy 60–90 cm (2–3 ft) transplant. Good growing conditions and attention to the plants' needs throughout the season will ensure that most hedgerow species reach a size of 60–90 cm (2–3 ft).

The first problem encountered by expanding nurseries is the availability of fresh, disease-free land. Many nurseries are too small to practise a proper rotation of land, particularly as they are monocropping their land – growing only the one crop of trees – year after year. Without recourse to adequate land to carry out a rotation, soil pest and disease levels soon build up, seriously affecting growth and vigour, preventing the seedlings from attaining the necessary growth in one season.

The easiest solution is to rent land from a neighbour on a rotational basis, resting the nursery's own land, which can be sown with a grass cover for one or two years. Prior to the autumn or spring planting of seedlings, the land should be dressed with well-rotted farmyard manure if its fertility and structure need improving.

In an arable situation it is possible to plan rotations ahead, ploughing in the chopped straw resulting from cereal crops or by following it with a grass ley to gain a good, friable soil structure.

SEEDLING SOURCE

If the nurseryman has not raised his own seedlings, it is likely he will purchase them from Holland or Denmark, as the number of United Kingdom nurserymen producing quantities of seedlings for sale is limited. Danish stock tends to be of a higher quality, and more expensive, than Dutch seedlings.

In Holland, the traditional approach continues, with many family-owned nurseries working on small individual sites, particularly around Boskoop and Breda, each producing small batches of a limited range of species. This stock is sold to the large export companies, who can bulk these batches of plants together to meet seedling orders from Germany, France and the United Kingdom.

Growing conditions on the low-lying polder soils produce excellent seedlings at very competitive prices, making it difficult for

United Kingdom nurserymen to compete.

The regularity of severe winter conditions in the Low Countries requires many nurseries to undercut the beds of seedlings in late summer to stop them growing-on into the early autumn. The seedlings are then lifted in late autumn and cold stored prior to despatch. Stock which is not delivered until early spring should be carefully checked upon arrival. Ensure that there has been no drying out, and consequently death, from being stored for long periods at too low a temperature or too low a humidity. Some cold stores are not very sophisticated.

Bought-in seedlings should be given a good soaking in water upon arrival and heeled into trenches to await planting.

GROUND PREPARATION

Subsoil the land to a depth of 45–60 cm (18–24 in) to break up any panning and open up the subsoil to facilitate good air and root penetration for the coming crop.

Throughout late summer and early autumn spray any perennial weed patches with glyphosate or paraquat according to weed type and severity.

During the winter, plough the land to a depth of at least 30 cm (12 in) using a plough with semi-digger bodies and an attached furrow press. This will ensure that all surface weed is buried and the land is left level, requiring minimal pre-planting preparation.

Commence planting in late February or early March when soil conditions allow. Only prepare adequate ground for one to two weeks' planting at a time. This ensures that the ground is friable and free of germinating weed seeds. The soil will flow freely around the planter shares to be easily and properly firmed by the following press wheels.

The way the overwintered ploughed land is prepared for planting will be dictated by soil type and the range of cultivation machinery available. If a furrow press was used when winter ploughing on light soils, all that is required is the rolling of the ground into beds. The word 'bed' refers to the area of prepared ground between the tractor's wheel marks which is planted with the crop. The system allows tractor access over the crop throughout the life of the crop and enables any particular bed (crop area) to be harvested prior to its adjacent neighbours.

Straight rolling of the land into beds of the same width as the planter relieves the tractor driver of the need to concentrate on keeping the beds straight when creeping along in a very low gear at planting time. Heavier land may require one pass of a power harrow to prepare the land before rolling into beds.

Aim to achieve open-textured soil beneath a firm surface; neither too 'puffy' to impair traction, nor too firm to impede the planter share from working at a depth of 25 cm (10 in), with the soil able to flow around the share to envelop the roots of the seedling as they are released from the planter's grip.

PLANTING

At planting time, from February onwards according to ground conditions, the day's requirement of seedlings are lifted direct from the seedbeds or from the heeling-in trenches and placed in large, heavy-duty plastic bags to prevent drying of the seedling's tender root.

The initial bulk size of seedlings can be reduced by root pruning of tree and shrub species (Plate 6.3), prior to planting out. This pruning discourages the formation of tap roots in favour of more fibrous, spreading, new root growth.

Shrub species such as hawthorn, blackthorn, hazel and dogwood can also receive a degree of pruning of their aerial parts to encourage a spreading habit by the initiation of secondary growth breaks from the pruning cuts. Tree species should not receive such pruning; good straight growth is required from the terminal bud.

The four-row tandem machine planter should average over 1,000 plants per operator per hour – so achieving at least 30,000 plants in a full working day.

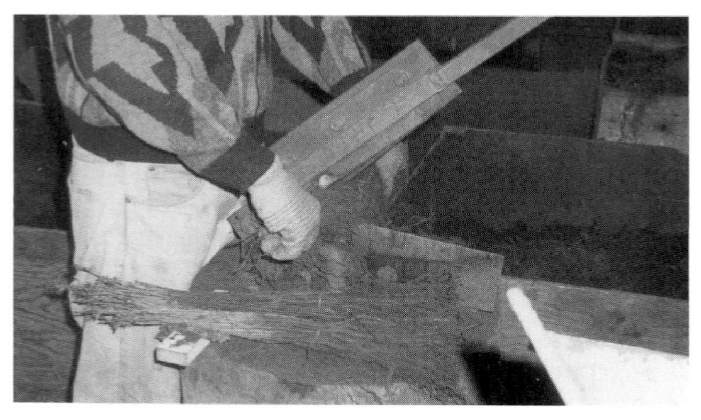

PLATE 6.3 A home-made guillotine for trimming the roots and tops of hawthorn seedlings ready for planting, mounted on a heavy elm log for stability.

MACHINE PLANTING

No planters currently available have been specifically designed for handling tree and shrub seedlings. The three most widely used machines each have a different way of placing the plants into the soil in an upright position.

Alpha Accord

The planting unit consists of two supple metal discs, with rubber rims, that are inclined together and press lightly against each other

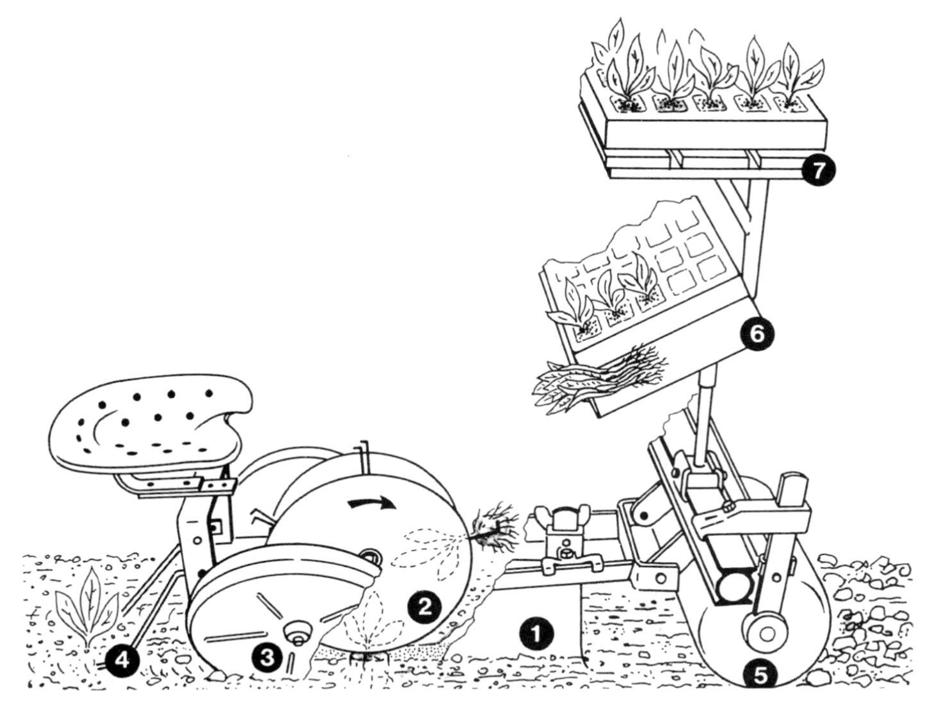

FIGURE 6.1 Accord transplanter. (Ferrag Ltd) The firming wheel in front of the planter unit (5) (optional) firms and levels the planting bed. The plant is inserted into the feed discs (2) at marked positions. As the discs rotate it is carefully set into the furrow made by the opening coulter (1). The wheels of the planter unit, the press wheels (3), press the plant into the soil. The coverers (4) behind the planter unit place loose soil crumbs up to the root neck. For the storage of seedlings and block (or rootballed) plants the inclined platform (6) is fixed at a suitable height, and the stock platform (7) can be mounted to carry further cases of plants.

for nearly half their circumference. The operator places each plant into the inclined grip of the two discs which revolve, taking the plant down into the ground opened behind the share. The plant is released into the grip of the soil, which folds back under pressure from two inclined press wheels (Figure 6.1).

Super Prefer

The planting unit comprises a revolving disc with a number of mechanical grippers around its circumference. Each gripper simulates two fingers, closing around the plant's stem as the operator places it in its grasp. The plant is held until the fingers are mechanically parted at the chosen point to release the plant's root into the soil (Figure 6.2).

Stanhay-Webb Ranger T50

This machine is a variation of the gripper finger system. A number of long metal fingers, each with a cushioned folding pad, are connected to a chain conveyor. The operator places the seedling into the open fold of the pad, which closes around the plant as it is carried down into the ground on the conveyor chain. The folding pad on each finger opens mechanically to slide the plant into the soil (Figure 6.3).

The Alpha Accord and the Super Prefer planters have a number of similar features.

On both machines the drive for the planter unit comes from one of the two inclined press wheels, over which the operator sits. The operator faces forward in the same direction as the machine travels.

The Stanhay-Webb Ranger's planter unit is chain driven from two landwheels at the front of the machine. The operator sits over the opening share, facing the planter unit, but with his back to the direction of travel and, likewise, the tractor driver.

All three machines have been designed to handle a wide range of plants, including bare roots, small soil blocks and modules. Whilst they do the work of planting tree and shrub seedlings adequately, improvements can be made, with a little ingenuity, to deal with the specific needs of longer, stiffer-stemmed seedlings.

Alpha Accord offers a wide range of accessories to enable the grower to adapt a basic machine to meet his particular requirements. The Alpha Accord has the least mechanical parts of the three planters and is the least likely to suffer from problems in the field. Against these advantages, it may be less accurate in placing plants

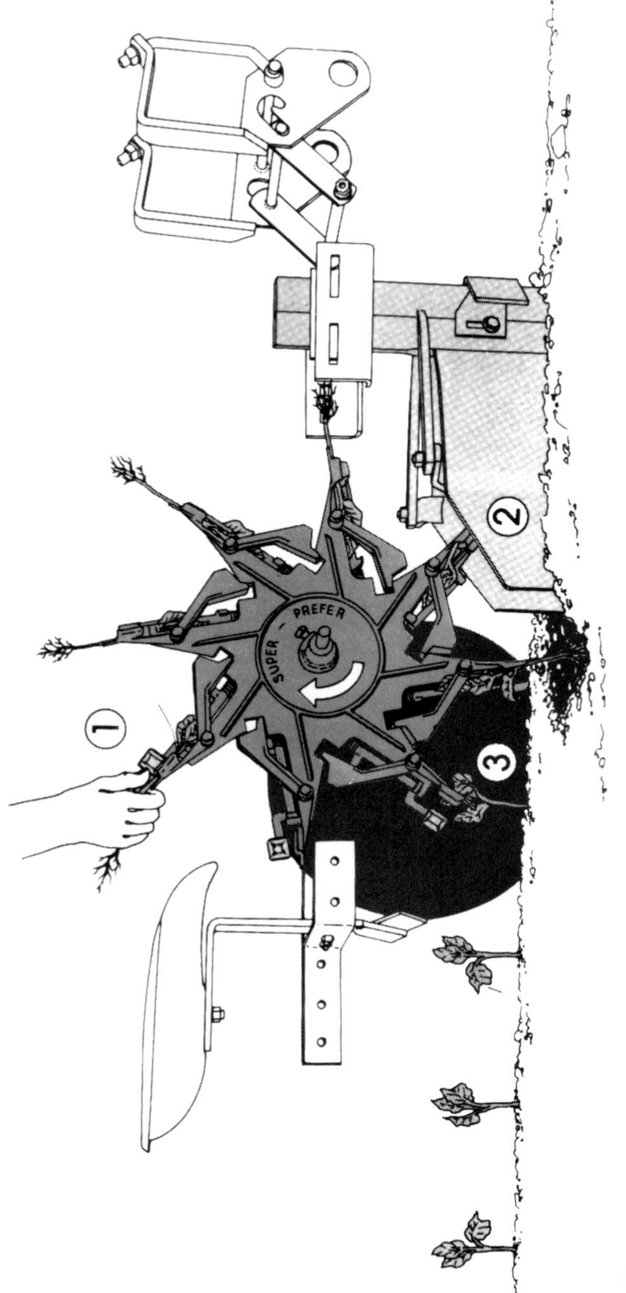

1 The gripper is opened automatically, and is closed by light manual pressure when the operator places the plant onto the gripper.

2 The rotation of the distributor transports the plant into the furrow previously formed by the share. The gripper then automatically releases the plant into the returning soil ahead of the presser wheels.

3 The operation is finished by the V-inclined press-wheels which firm the earth around the roots to ensure efficient growth of the plant.

FIGURE 6.2 Super Prefer transplanter. (Plumtree Nursery Equipment Ltd)

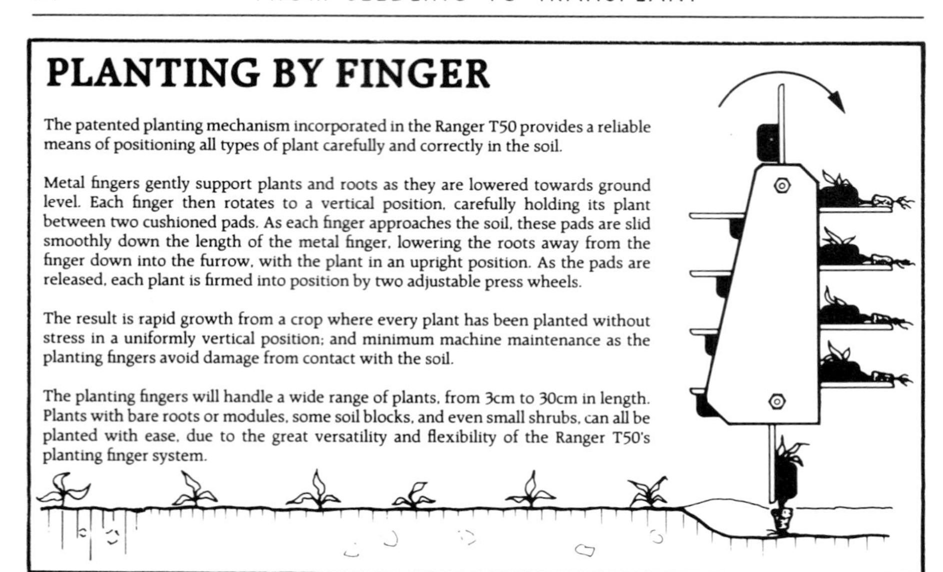

PLANTING BY FINGER

The patented planting mechanism incorporated in the Ranger T50 provides a reliable means of positioning all types of plant carefully and correctly in the soil.

Metal fingers gently support plants and roots as they are lowered towards ground level. Each finger then rotates to a vertical position, carefully holding its plant between two cushioned pads. As each finger approaches the soil, these pads are slid smoothly down the length of the metal finger, lowering the roots away from the finger down into the furrow, with the plant in an upright position. As the pads are released, each plant is firmed into position by two adjustable press wheels.

The result is rapid growth from a crop where every plant has been planted without stress in a uniformly vertical position; and minimum machine maintenance as the planting fingers avoid damage from contact with the soil.

The planting fingers will handle a wide range of plants, from 3cm to 30cm in length. Plants with bare roots or modules, some soil blocks, and even small shrubs, can all be planted with ease, due to the great versatility and flexibility of the Ranger T50's planting finger system.

SPECIFICATION

THE STANHAY WEBB RANGER T50

Models – single bar	: **1–5 rows**
– tandem	: **2–7 rows**
Minimum row width – single bar	: **50cm (20")**
– tandem	: **25cm (10")**
Toolbar length – 2 row single bar	: **2.00m (78")**
– 4 row single bar	: **2.60m (102")**
Spacing range in row – 10 fingers	: **23–85cm (9"–33")**
–15 fingers	: **16–57cm (6"–22")** **(13 options in each range)**
Height	: **125cm (50")**
Weight – 2 row	: **318kg (700lb)**
– 4 row	: **541kg (1190lb)**
A-frame	: **Cat 1 and 2**

ADDITIONAL EQUIPMENT

- Bout markers – for matching adjacent bouts.
- Front cultivator tines – eliminate tractor wheelings and break up hard, compacted soil.
- Watering device – applies controlled squirt of water on each plant.
- 5 Planting fingers – for converting row unit to 15 fingers.
- Soil block racks – for carrying six 33cm wide soil block trays.
- Granyl Applicator – for application of granular soil pesticides.

Descriptions and illustrations are not binding and are subject to change without notice. Options and accessories may vary in different countries.

FIGURE 6.3 Stanhay-Webb Ranger T.50 transplanter. (Stanhay Webb Ltd)

upright into the soil and at the required spacing as this is dependent on the individual operator's skill.

On the Super Prefer and the Stanhay-Webb Ranger the position and spacing of each plant are mechanically controlled and uniformly accurate, so long as each finger is working. Sandy or dusty conditions can interfere with the efficiency of the finger operation on the Super Prefer. The chain drives on the Stanhay-Webb Ranger must be kept in correct adjustment to achieve constant accuracy.

All machinery working in close proximity with loose soil must be regularly maintained to achieve constant quality and uniformity in planting. A four-row planter only has to have one unit break down to result in the complete team of five people waiting while a repair is completed!

BED SIZE AND PLANT SPACING

There are no hard and fast rules for the width of beds and the number of rows to plant. The width of a bed will depend upon other crops grown and their effect upon tractor wheel spacing.

The most common bed widths in horticulture are 1.5 m (60 in) and 1.9 m (75 in), the former for nursery stock producers and the latter for vegetable growers. Assuming that one opts to work on a 1.5 m (60 in) bed width, the number of rows down each bed will vary from three to five, according to personal preference and the quality of stock required (Figure 6.4).

If land is not at a premium and one wishes to produce stock with a good stem girth, it is advisable to settle on a three-row bed. With land and its subsequent management at a greater premium, opt for a four- or five-row bed. The closer the plants are spaced the more there will be a proportional decrease of the stem girth and final quality of each plant, due to increased competition for available light, moisture and nutrients.

The author, in common with a number of other growers, has opted for the compromise of a four-row system on a 1.5 m (60 in) bed

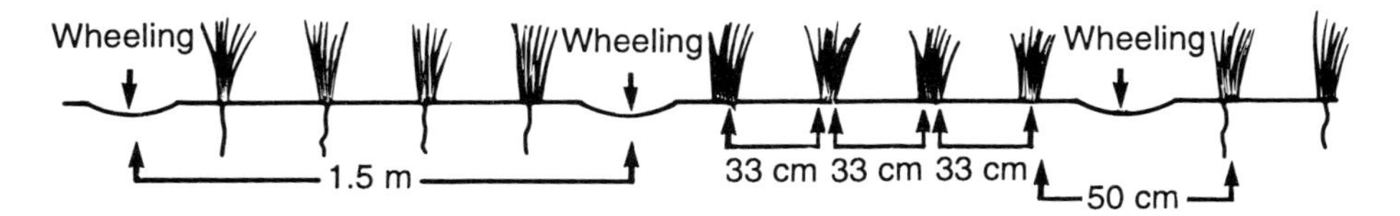

FIGURE 6.4 Bed size and plant spacing.

width. The spacing of the four rows across the bed will be influenced by the space needed for each wheel to pass down either side of the bed at lifting time. To ensure adequate traction and minimise soil compaction, most growers use radial tyres, which have a wide contact area with the soil. Wheel size must be taken into consideration to avoid damaging side shoots on the outer rows of each bed when lifting the mature crop.

Spacing the four rows 33 cm (13 in) apart means that it is only 1 m (40 in) from row one to row four. On 1.5 m (60 in) wheel centres, there is a 50 cm (20 in) space between the outer rows of each bed to accommodate the tractor wheel and allow for overhanging shoots of the mature crop.

The grower has to decide on plant spacing down each row of the bed, based upon plant-to-plant competition and the possible planting speeds of a good gang. The faster the gang can work, the closer the plants can be set in the row, assuming that the range of forward speed gears on the tractor will accommodate the necessary 'creep' speed.

Zetor tractors are fitted with a creep range of gears as a standard feature on their two- and four-wheel drive tractors, while this is an optional extra with Ford tractors.

It must be remembered that the speed of quality planting is influenced by the slowest operator on the planter. However good the team, some operators work faster than others, so the tractor driver must set a speed that will stretch the slower team member, yet be easily within the capability of the swifter members.

The author uses a Ford tractor fitted with a 5.7:1 reduction (creep) ratio, enabling the tractor to proceed at 0.4 mph, yet at an acceptable 1,500 rpm engine speed.

A slow forward ground speed attained by running the tractor at very low engine rpm will soon damage the engine, so fit a reduction gear ratio to give a wider range of slow speed options at acceptable engine rpm levels. The creep speed option will be valuable at lifting time. Mechanical undercutting and lifting machinery, which shakes all the earth from the plants as it lifts them from the ground, requires running at a slow forward ground speed, coupled with a reasonable engine speed.

The planting of a four-row bed with a mechanical planter requires a tandem layout; rows one and three of the bed are planted by two planter units mounted in front of two further units planting rows two and four. Each unit has a simple bar blade coverer to pull soil around the collar of the planted seedling. The efficiency of these coverers is limited, so the author has fitted a further ridging unit across the back of the planter frame (Plate 6.4) to ridge up more soil along each line of plants to hold the young seedlings firmly in the soil, to prevent rain or irrigation erosion around the collar and aid water run-off along each line of seedlings.

The spacing of plants along each row of the bed is dictated by the number of rows in the bed and depends upon the ability of the tractor to go slowly enough for the operators to set the seedlings quickly into the gripper fingers. The most common combination is a four-row bed, each row set 30 cm (12 in) apart and with individual seedlings spaced 15 cm (6 in) along each row. At such a spacing, each plant occupies 450 sq cm (½ sq ft) or 18/20 plants occupy 1 sq m (1 sq yd), which multiplies up to a total of 215,000 plants per hectare (87,000 per acre). In reality the figure will be reduced by lost planting areas at each end of the field, missed plants along each plant line as operators reach for a fresh bundle of plants from the carrying trays and differing operator planting speeds. A realistic number of plants is in the region of 161,000 plants per hectare (65,000 per acre).

In deciding plant spacing and bed width, it is most important to take account of the machinery which will be used to harvest (lift) plants the following autumn.

PLATE 6.4 *Machine planting seedlings into a four-row bed. At the rear of the planter, coverers ridge earth up to each row of plants for added stability. The plastic canopy protects the operators from inclement weather and the plant roots from drying.*

WEED CONTROL

During the past 20 years there has been a considerable increase in the range of chemicals available for the pre-emergence control of weeds on newly planted seedling trees and shrubs. Varying weather conditions each season affect the performance of these chemicals, many of which are also influenced by differing soil types. It will take several years to assess the true capabilities of each chemical on a range of soils in different seasons.

During the early 1980s many nurserymen were still only using the triazine herbicide simazine, which had proved very effective at preventing the germination of a wide range of weed seedlings on most soil types. The addition of an equal amount of the herbicide propyzamide (Kerb) improved the spectrum and persistence for pre-emergence weed control with minimal crop damage at the recommended low dose rate, 1 kg (2.2 lb) of each of the products per hectare. By the mid 1980s growers in various parts of the country were simultaneously noticing that simazine, and the related triazine herbicide atrazine, were no longer controlling groundsel. The reality of a plant's ability to become resistant to a particular herbicide soon cast shadows over chemical weed control. In 1986 the Control of Pesticides Regulations came into force. These regulations immediately placed restrictions on the wider use of many chemicals which had not been subject to MAFF clearance. All uses for both existing and new chemicals now require MAFF approval, and are illegal until such clearance for use has been granted.

One result of this legislation is that chemical manufacturers cannot justify the costs necessary to obtain approval for small-scale use of some existing and new chemicals. Prior to the legislation growers were able to experiment with the use of chemicals that had been approved for use with other crops. If a particular chemical had been cleared for pre-emergence use on lettuce, a delicate and sensitive seedling, it was likely to do no harm to a robust tree or shrub seedling – so the chemical diphenamid (Enide) was used by the nursery trade. Under the new legislation, the chemical has to undergo specific trials prior to its clearance for use on trees and shrubs.

The chemical oxadiazon (Ronstar) has a long-established use on the Continent for the pre-emergence control of weeds in vineyards. Growers in the United Kingdom found that at low dose rates it proved to be an effective herbicide for use on tree and shrub seedlings, as long as it was sprayed over the crop prior to bud break, after which it caused scorch on emerging buds. This chemical underwent approval trials and was cleared for use on transplant and liner trees (the next stage up from transplant).

The application of any chemical to control the emergence of weeds following the planting of seedlings should be delayed for several days to allow the freshly moved soil to settle down. Once the chemical is applied to the weed-free soil it will act like a coat of paint, when the spray layer is uniform and complete, preventing weed germination and emergence.

Most chemicals used to control the emergence of weeds require moist soil conditions prior to and after application, to ensure they remain active in the topsoil. Frequent applications of small amounts of irrigation during dry conditions following planting will maintain the continued efficiency of chemical weed control and provide a suitable micro-climate around the seedlings during the sensitive stage of their initial establishment.

Most chemicals used after planting work by binding to the particles of the soil surface and do not move down through the soil profile. Simazine can be washed further down if subjected to heavy rain or excessive irrigation, where it can damage the roots of the young seedlings. Care must be taken to avoid over-watering at this stage of the crop's development.

A further reason for the restrained use of irrigation in the weeks after planting is to minimise surface rooting at the expense of deeper anchorage roots, which the young plants must develop at an early stage if they are to be capable of giving adequate support for the plant's rapid growth during June and July. It is important that the young seedlings establish quickly following planting, so they are able to maximise the benefits of a warm soil and long daylight in high summer.

Pre-emergence weed control applied after planting will remain fully effective for six to eight weeks. To maintain a good level of weed control, it will be necessary to apply a top-up dose of a suitable chemical to continue the suppression of weed germination. The range of chemicals suitable for use (as an overall spray) on the growing crop is more limited than those available following planting – simazine, propyzamide, metazachlor and diphenamid are options for selection, according to soil type and weed spectrum.

An alternative means of weed control is to machine, or steerage, hoe down the rows of each bed. If weed control has been good, it is preferable to maintain the position with a further overall spray. However, if there has been a flush of seedling weeds or a particular weed has not been suppressed by the initial spray application, it may be necessary to resort to steerage-hoeing the rows.

Most modern steerage hoes can be bought with an inter-row spray attachment. The hoe unit carries a small tank, a power-take-off-mounted pump supplying the dilute spray to individually guarded jets, which are adjustable to spray each row as required. Each jet is mounted underneath a shoe-shaped guard which prevents the herbicide splashing or drifting onto adjacent plants. With this level of protection, it is possible to use the contact desiccant herbicides diquat or paraquat in preference to a further top-up of a residual (soil-acting) herbicide.

PEST AND DISEASE CONTROL

The control of pests on the wide range of tree and shrub species is treated as the problem occurs, different species being susceptible to different pests at varying times of the year. In today's climate of restricted chemical use, the role of beneficial insects (present on the crop at the same time as their predators) needs to be assessed carefully. For instance, if small quantities of aphids are noted and colonies of ladybirds, with their larvae, are also present, give the ladybirds a chance of clearing up the problem before going over the crop with the spraying machine.

There are some specific pests which need to be watched out for and dealt with immediately they appear.

For example, the tarcenomid mite appears on ash shoots in May and, if left unattended, attacks the growing point. The terminal bud is damaged, adjacent leaves turn a dry, rusty-green colour, and further shoot growth is prevented. An early attack of this mite is a serious risk to the growth and quality of ash, so spray immediately any mites are seen, using an approved insecticide.

Watch out for aphids on *Rosa* and *Prunus* species, and the woolly aphid is liable to attack *Malus* species.

Under nursery conditions – growing a wide range of tree and shrub species side by side – pests do not usually present a major problem, thanks to the diversity of the stock allied to the presence of beneficial insects. The current range of insecticides includes ones which will not harm beneficial insects, so there is a better chance of controlling any problem pest without upsetting the ecological balance in the crop.

The control of diseases in seedling and transplant stock is a subject which needs to be taken very seriously. If mildew and rusts are allowed to develop during favourable weather conditions, they soon reach epidemic proportions and can become impossible to control. The damage done to a young seedling from a bad attack of mildew can destroy its saleable value.

To ensure that young seedlings remain free of infection from mildew or rust, a preventative spray programme must be drawn up and adhered to throughout the growing season.

Nurserymen have followed the experience of apple and pear growers, who for many years have been carrying out fortnightly preventative sprays against infections of mildew and scab.

NUTRITION

A soil analysis should be taken prior to planting to determine the nutrient status of the soil. The results will enable the grower to apply the correct amount of each of the major elements – nitrogen, phosphate, potash and magnesium – usually in the form of a compound inorganic fertiliser, to provide the necessary nutrients to sustain the development of the plants through the growing season.

In many arable and grassland areas, regular heavy dressings of inorganic fertilisers have raised soil fertility levels to the point where further applications of one or more elements may not be necessary. Phosphate and potash pass slowly through the soil and do not present major problems of leaching through to the water courses lower in the soil profile.

There are many areas of lowland Britain where the excessive use of inorganic nitrogen has led to leaching into water courses, causing problems in the purity of domestic water supplies. To alleviate the problem, inorganic nitrogen should be applied in small quantities throughout the growing season, rather than in one heavy dose early in the season, which could leach into the subsoil under heavy rain or irrigation, before the crop has developed a root system adequate to absorb and utilise the nitrogen fully.

Assuming that fungicide sprays are being applied to the growing crop every two weeks to prevent mildew or rust infections, a liquid foliar feed can be applied with the fungicide, to supply the plants with small amounts of nitrogen on a regular basis.

These small regular doses are a valuable addition to any inorganic nitrogen applied in granular form.

IRRIGATION

Records show that in most seasons and on most soil types some extra water will be required by the crop to ensure that the necessary

PLATE 6.5 Sprinkler irrigation on beds of young hawthorn transplants aids growth and maintains the activity of herbicides.

growth and quality of the finished plants are achieved each year (Plate 6.5).

The MAFF provides a classification of all farmland in the United Kingdom, which places soils into four grades according to their structure, water-holding capacity and their versatility of use. The lower the number the more versatile the soil. Grade 3 and 4 soils may be suitable for permanent pasture, but not for the production and winter harvesting of seedlings and transplants. For this the soil must be Grade 1 or 2.

Light land, which falls into Grade 2 classification, can be regarded as being of Grade 1 value if adequate irrigation is readily available, even in the driest seasons. Grade 1 land, such as the loam and peat soils of the Fens, will grow high-yielding crops with minimal need for irrigation. The addition of further irrigation and allied inputs (fertilisers etc.) results in exceptional yields by responsive crops such as potatoes and sugar beet.

Tree and shrub production does not need such high quality land. One starts out with a single plant and no amount of expense can convert it into two plants. Good Grade 2 and some Grade 3 land is suitable, given an adequate water supply.

Recent dry summers, coupled with an increased demand by farmers and the community at large, has led to a depletion of underground water reserves. Farmers and growers have to pay the

National Rivers Authority for the water they extract from streams and rivers. All are subject to the quota stated upon their licence to extract water. Quotas can rarely be increased.

Most growers with a licence to extract water would like to be able to use more, but a combination of restrictions on use and a conscience over the way they use their quota has led to a reassessment of water use.

A plant's need for water is related to its growth stage, its ability to draw water from the soil and the prevailing weather conditions. Irrigation 'scheduling' follows the development of a crop through the season, monitoring its requirement for water to sustain the increasing overall bulk of its aerial and root growth. This need will fluctuate day by day and has to be measured accordingly.

A farmer wishing to remove the guesswork from irrigation decisions can employ a soil analyst to examine the physical properties of the soils on his farm to a depth of at least 60 cm (2 ft) in order to calculate the 'available water capacity', which is the amount of water which each soil type can retain for uptake by plant roots.

Knowledge of the available water capacity of a soil allows the grower to calculate when he will need to irrigate. This will be related to the crop's growth stage, its weekly water uptake at that stage and the amount of rain which has fallen during the week.

From this information he can prepare a 'balance sheet' showing the soil's available water and rainfall on the 'credit' side and the week's transpiration and use by the crop on the 'debit' side.

Example of a manual water balance sheet

Assume that the plant has used all of the available soil water in mid-July. During the week, 15 mm of rain falls onto the crop, but the weather has been hot and sunny for most of the week. Calculate the total daily water loss attributed to evaporation from both the soil and plant leaf surfaces from tables available from ADAS or MAFF, which cover grid areas across the whole country. Tables 6.1 and 6.2 are for the area within which the author's farm is situated.

Six clear, sunny days in July will account for 30 mm of evaporation. Deduct the 15 mm of rain which fell on the one cloudy wet day of the week, and one is left with a water requirement of 15 mm for the week, which should be applied if no further rain is imminent. If there is a likelihood of rain, delay irrigation for a day or so, to take account of the possibility of adequate rain to make up the week's deficit.

For professional irrigation scheduling, neutron probe tubes are sunk into the area of the fields with low available water capacity. Throughout the growing season, a soil analyst visits the farm at

**Soil Moisture Deficit (* for Area 31 North)
Simplified Calculation System**

Table 6.1 Daily Water Loss Values for 15 to 75% Crop Cover

	Overcast virtually all day	*Mainly cloudy*	*Mainly sunny*	*Blue skies virtually all day*
	mm	mm	mm	mm
April	0.7	1.2	1.9	2.5
May	0.9	1.7	2.8	3.6
June	1.0	1.9	3.2	4.1
July	1.0	1.9	3.2	4.1
August	0.8	1.6	2.7	3.4
September	0.5	1.0	1.7	2.1

Table 6.2 Daily Water Loss Values for 75% Crop Cover Onwards

	Overcast virtually all day	*Mainly cloudy*	*Mainly sunny*	Blue skies virtually all day
	mm	mm	mm	mm
April	0.8	1.4	2.3	3.0
May	1.1	2.0	3.4	4.3
June	1.2	2.3	3.9	5.0
July	1.2	2.3	3.9	5.0
August	1.0	1.9	3.2	4.1
September	0.6	1.2	2.0	2.5

* Area 31 North is contained within a boundary running around Oxford, Thame, Reading, Hungerford, Swindon and back to Oxford.

regular intervals and takes accurate soil moisture readings in the tubes, using a neutron probe. These figures are allied to rainfall and weather records taken on the farm each day to provide a forecast sheet of crop needs. The crop's stage of growth plays an important part in the forecast. A seedling crop has a lower water requirement than a fully leafed crop of transplants reaching maturity in mid-summer.

The professional advice available is accurate, due to both the value of the neutron probe assessments and access to MAFF regional weather data, which combine to provide the grower with the most cost-effective irrigation recommendation on a weekly basis.

For the production of transplants from seedlings or for those establishing hedges from seedlings, there are three definite response periods when applied irrigation will be of value:

- When establishing the newly planted stock (April–June)
- When producing growth on established stock (May–July)
- When lifting in a dry autumn (September–October).

SUMMER OPERATIONS

As the summer progresses carry out pruning of tree species to keep them growing as straight as possible.

The most important single operation is to walk the rows, cutting off any branch which competes with the leading shoot, or cutting off selected side shoots to ensure that one will become a straight leader if none were present prior to pruning.

All the shrub species which had been given a degree of pruning prior to planting should produce good bushy growth as required for strong hedgerow transplants.

The large numbers and the low value of hedgerow transplants will place a question mark against time spent on pruning. Few growers can justify the work suggested in the face of current low market prices.

AUTUMN LIFTING

Well-grown and disease-free transplants will retain their leaves later into the autumn than their wild hedgerow companions. Lifting should not commence before the plants lose at least one-seventh of their leaves.

Leaf drop can be hastened by undercutting the beds of plants in September, but such an operation must be followed by some irrigation if conditions are dry at the time, otherwise some species will suffer from die-back as a result of such shock treatment so early in the autumn.

The transplants should only be lifted from their beds as they are required for sale. In many cases growers will lift the stock in bulk before the onset of severe winter conditions and move the plants into cold storage or extensive heeling-in lines to await grading and despatch according to demand.

Bare-rooted transplants should spend the minimum of time exposed to the open air. Once lifted, graded and bundled (Plate 6.6),

PLATE 6.6 Well-rooted and vigorous transplants. Hawthorn (left) *and blackthorn* (right).

PLATE 6.7 Trimmed transplants with good fibrous root systems. Hawthorn (left) *and blackthorn* (right).

they should be held under cover to await despatch or use.

Those plants, whether they be seedlings or transplants, which are being used for hedge planting, should be placed in robust plastic bags upon lifting, be correctly labelled and remain in the bags until they are needed for planting out.

Good transplants will benefit from trimming back before planting into a hedge (Plate 6.7), to help the plants establish and to encourage bushy growth. Trimming is best carried out soon after lifting to reduce bulk before the plants are placed in bags to await the planting gangs.

HARVEST CONSIDERATIONS

The most common tractor-mounted 'lifter' consists of an elongated, U-shaped undercutting blade, to the rear of which is fitted a shaker mechanism. The shaker consists of a row of steel fingers which vibrate up and down to remove all the soil from the plants' roots, leaving them lying on top of the soil ready for grading and bundling.

The undercutter/shaker will require considerable tractor horsepower when working under a bed 1.5 m (60 in) wide and at a depth of 0.25–0.3 m (10–12 in).

The wider the undercutter the greater the volume of soil moved and shaken, so more horsepower is needed; thus the narrower the undercutting machine the better. On a four-row bed with tractor wheel centres set 1.5 m (60 in) apart the actual area occupied by the four rows of plants is only just over 1 m (39 in). The width of the undercutter need only be the width of four rows, plus a margin on the outside of the first and fourth rows to ensure those rows are lifted with all their roots intact. A 1.3 m (51 in) width blade will suffice, and minimise the horsepower needed to lift the plants in adverse winter conditions. It is worth recalling the desirability of growing the crop on light, free-draining soils. If the plants are to be freshly lifted throughout the winter months according to demand, easy working soil conditions are of paramount importance.

If the crop is grown on a clay soil, which could be impossible to work in wet winter conditions, the whole crop will have to be lifted in the early autumn and the plants held in cold storage to await demand. In such instances the nursery has to absorb the heavy extra capital outlay to build and maintain a cold store.

Many large wholesale nurseries own substantial cold storage facilities to ensure winter deliveries of stock are not curtailed by bad weather. If the crop can be grown on a light sandy loam, with adequate irrigation to hand, then time lost during winter months due to hard, frosty conditions is not normally a serious problem in southern and central England. It is more likely to be a contributory factor to the use of cold storage in northern England and Scotland.

REFERENCES AND FURTHER READING

Bailey, Roger (1990), *Irrigated Crops and their Management* (Farming Press).
Ivens, G. W. (1991), *The UK Pesticide Guide – 1992* (CAB International and British Crop Protection Council).

Chapter 7

Preparation and Planting of Hedges

To everything there is a season, and
a time to every purpose under the heaven.
A time to be born and a time to die,
a time to plant . . .
ECCLESIASTES 3:1 THE HOLY BIBLE

Grants are available from the Countryside Commission or MAFF for the provision, replacement or improvement of hedges (grown on the flat), hedgerow trees and hedgebanks (grown on a bank). In addition, the necessary protective fencing and associated gates, stiles and other fittings are included within the schemes.

It is important to obtain the necessary grant scheme booklets before starting work, and to prepare a detailed plan with a summary of expenditure to be incurred.

All current grant details are listed in Appendix 2 on page 258.

PLANNING – CHOICE AND SUPPLY OF PLANTING MATERIAL

Upon deciding to plant a hedge and the reason why, make a list of the shrub species suitable, according to the soil type and local conditions, adding any species which are personal favourites.

Contact the local Agricultural Development and Advisory Service (ADAS) or Farming and Wildlife Advisory Group (FWAG) office to help in the choice of a suitable nursery capable of supplying the plants. The Yellow Pages directory or the local National Farmers Union may also help.

It is important to see the stock growing before committing oneself to purchase. To see the size and quality of the plants available provides the assurance that one's money will be well spent.

British Standards Number BS3936 (Table 7.1) sets out tree and

Table 7.1 Dimensions of Trees and Shrubs (British Standards)

Relevant British Standard	*Designation*		*Circumference of stem measured 1 m from ground level*	*Height from ground level*	*Clear stem height from ground level to lowest branch*
BS3936 Part 4. Specification for Forest Trees		Age (years)*			
	Seedling	(1+0)	Does not apply	15–30 cm	Does not apply
	Seedling	(2+0)		30–45 cm	
	Undercut seedling	(1u1)		45–60 cm	
	Undercut seedling	(1u2)		60–90 cm	
	Transplant	(1+1)		90–120 cm	
	Transplant	(1+2)			
BS3936 Nursery stock Part 1. Specifiction for Trees & Shrubs	Whip (Shall have been previously transplanted at least once in its life, shall not necessarily be staked, and shall be without significant feather growth and without head.)		Does not apply	1.2–1.8 m 1.5–1.8 m 1.8–2.1 m 2.1–2.5 m	Does not apply
	Feathered (Shall have been previously transplanted at least once in its life, shall have a defined reasonably straight upright central leader, and a stem furnished with evenly spread and balanced lateral shoots down to near ground level, according to its species.)		Does not apply	1.5–1.8 m 1.8–2.1 m 2.1–2.5 m 2.5–3.0 m 3.0–3.5 m	Does not apply

* Key to age abbreviations:

Seedling A small plant, under 1 year old, grown from seed, usually 15–30 cm (6–12 in) tall.
1+0 One season in the seedbed, grown from seed.
2+0 Two seasons in the seedbed without undercutting.
1u1 One season in the seedbed, then undercut, followed by another season in the seedbed.
1u2 One season in the seedbed, then undercut, followed by two further seasons in the same seedbed.
1+1 A one-year-old-seedling which is lifted and replanted to be grown on for another season to become a transplant.
1+2 A one-year-old-seedling which is lifted and replanted to be grown on for a further two years.

Prepared by the Committee on Plant Supply and Establishment (CPSE).

shrub designation and size requirements for commercial growers. Knowledge of the age and sizes of plants available will help in the decision regarding the style of hedge to plant, which must be made at an early stage to allow an accurate calculation of the number of plants required.

The planting calculator (Table 7.2) will help calculate the number of plants required for a length of hedge.

GROUND PREPARATION

There are a number of methods of preparing the ground for a hedge, depending on site and soil conditions, and budget restrictions.

The best course of action is to plan ahead to fallow the site for the year prior to planting. Plough and cultivate the planting strip to provide a good tilth free of both annual and, particularly, perennial weeds.

The site may be an existing arable field edge with the planting strip for the hedge being incorporated into a cereal crop in that same field. Prepare and drill the field, including the hedge site, with an autumn-sown crop of winter barley, wheat or oats. Later in the winter hand or machine plant the new hedge into the young cereal crop, which will grow up to nurse and protect the young hedge in the following spring and summer during extremes of heat, drought and wind. In some exposed regions hail or heavy rain can cause damage to young shoot growth.

It may not be possible to carry out fallowing or cultivations to provide the ideal planting conditions. The site may be too close to other physical barriers to allow access for machinery. Do as much advance cleaning of the site as possible. If there is rank grass or weed growth, cut this down well ahead of planting to allow a follow-up spray of herbicide to control the regrowth of grass and weeds. Glyphosate (Roundup) in the summer or autumn prior to planting will give good control of all regrowth.

Where heavy soil conditions discourage prior cultivations, ensure a clean site by mowing and/or the use of herbicides. It will then be possible to put down an artificial mulch of wood chippings, rotten straw or farmyard manure, to smother any possible weed regrowth as well as provide some humus to be incorporated at planting time.

Alternatively on wet or heavy land plough along the proposed planting line in the summer before planting. Thereafter, use glyphosate (Roundup) or paraquat (Gramoxone) to keep the ploughed land clean. In the following months the ploughed furrow

Table 7.2 Planting Calculator*

Distance between plants in row	Length of hedge in metres 1	2	3	4	5	6	7	8	9	10	20	30	40	50	60	70	80	90	100	200	300	400	500	600	700	800	900	1 km
15 cm (6 in)	6	13	20	26	33	40	46	53	60	66	133	200	266	333	400	466	533	600	666	1333	2000	2666	3333	4000	4666	5333	6000	6666
30 cm (12 in)	3	6	10	13	16	20	23	26	30	33	66	100	133	166	200	233	266	300	333	666	1000	1333	1666	2000	2333	2666	3000	3333
45 cm (18 in)	2	4	6	8	11	12	15	17	18	22	44	66	88	111	133	155	177	200	222	444	666	888	1111	1333	1555	1777	2000	2222
60 cm (24 in)	1	3	5	6	8	10	11	13	15	16	33	50	66	83	100	116	133	150	166	333	500	666	833	1000	1666	1333	1500	1666
75 cm (30 in)	1	2	4	5	6	8	9	10	12	13	26	40	53	66	80	93	106	120	133	266	400	533	666	800	933	1066	1200	1333
90 cm (36 in)	1	2	3	4	5	6	7	8	10	11	22	33	44	55	66	77	88	100	111	222	333	444	555	666	777	999	1000	1111

* To calculate the number of plants required for a length of hedge, simply take the length units and add together:

For example, 655 m of hedge with plants spaced 30 cm (12 in) apart:

600 m = 2000 plants
50 m = 166 plants
5 m = 16 plants

Thus, 2,182 plants are required for 655 m of hedge.

ridges will become friable with the action of drought and, later, winter frosts, to produce a fine planting tilth.

A black polythene 'mulch' strip (laid along the planting line) can be used, whether or not the land has been cultivated. After weeds have been tightly mown or strimmed, lay a black polythene sheet (200 gauge) to cover the width required for planting a single or double line hedge. The sheet must be wide enough to give an adequate 'tuck-in' to hold it in position for its lifetime.

At planting, simply cut a slot through the covering sheet at each required planting station and dig a deep notch into the soil for simple slit planting, preferably using either 20/40 cm (8/16 in) seedlings (1+0) or small transplants (1+1) of 30/45 cm (12/18 in).

The black polythene covering has many features to recommend its use, although the initial cost to buy and lay the film is higher, and it is a slower process to plant carefully through the smallest possible slit holes. The polythene acts as a 'mulch' to: prevent weed growth; retain soil moisture by preventing surface moisture loss; raise soil temperature; reduce nutrient leaching from the soil; prevent soil erosion or cracking in dry summer conditions.

An effective method of using black polythene film for a hawthorn-only hedge is to plough and rotovate the hedge strip. Plant strong thorn transplants. Spray an overall herbicide (simazine); then cut off top growth down to 15 cm (6 in) above the ground. Lay the black polythene film over the plants, burying the edges either by using a polythene laying machine or digging in with a spade. Finally walk the line, pushing the stems of the plants through the polythene. This ensures that a minimum of the underlying soil is exposed to light, preventing weed growth.

Cutting back a good 45/60 cm (18/24 in) transplant to a 15 cm (6 in) 'stump' may seem very severe, but it is the method proven by the planters of 19th century enclosure hedges as being the best way to obtain strong, vigorous and upright growth in the first year after planting. They developed the technique to obtain the best results in the shortest possible time, which must surely be an enduring intent!

PLANTING TIME AND CONDITIONS

The season for planting hedges begins in early November, as soon as the required stock has lost most of its leaf.

Planting can continue throughout the winter months, in suitable conditions, until early April, when the sap will begin to rise and buds break from their dormancy.

Suitable conditions for planting will not occur every day in winter. Do not plant during frost (below 0°C/32°F) nor on wet or windy days. Wet ground will puddle when you firm up around the plants, compacting the soil, damaging its structure and causing anaerobic conditions in which the roots cannot 'breathe' or grow properly.

In windy conditions there is a risk of desiccating the bare-rooted planting stock before it goes into the ground, particularly if the plants are laid out in advance of planting. It is best to keep them in the plastic planting bags until the moment each is required.

Evergreens, such as holly, should be planted either in the autumn (September/October) or left until March/April to minimise damage from frost.

HEDGE POSITION

In deciding where to plant a new hedge, adequate space must be allowed to account for its final, mature size. A mature hedge will spread to cover a width of approximately 2 m (6 ft 6 in) for single

PLATE 7.1 A newly planted hedge at Peasemore Farm, Oxfordshire, 1992. The first line of transplants is set well back from the road edge and the second row is well spaced from the first to allow adequate room for proposed untrimmed growth.

line planting, or as much as 3 m (10 ft) for a double line hedge.

A reasonable verge width beside a road or lane for the safe passage of normal road traffic and large harvesting machinery must be considered before siting the hedge (Plate 7.1).

Leave a wide access for entrances into fields and adequate vehicle 'sight lines' for drivers exiting, and do likewise from a farm lane onto a public road.

Hedges must not be planted close to an adjacent wall, fence, verge or roadway, where later growth could damage foundations, become entangled, or obscure the vision of road users.

When planting a boundary hedge, notify your neighbours of your plans. It may not be a legal requirement, but it is the best policy to keep them informed and do consider carefully any views they may express about the future maintenance of their side of the hedge.

MARKING OUT

If the planting line has been cultivated, the edge of the cultivated or ploughed strip will provide a line to work from.

Naturally, planting into a ploughed trench will need no marker, on the assumption that the ploughman has drawn out a straight furrow! The same principle applies for tine cultivator preparation.

For planting directly into a desiccated grass sward, it may be possible to mark the planting line by driving a tractor to straddle the line, using the two wheel impressions as a guide.

If these simple measures do not suffice, there is no alternative but to lay out a string line, stretched tight and straight and held in place, at regular intervals, by canes hooked into the line. It will need two people to lay the line straight – one to sight from one end to the other, while the other places the smaller, intermediate canes as directed.

CARE OF PLANTS PRIOR TO PLANTING

Choose a delivery date for the plants close to the actual day you intend to commence planting.

Check the stock upon arrival, to ensure that you have been sent the right items of the right size and in good, fresh condition.

If the roots have dried in transit, give them a good soaking immediately in a water trough or with a fine hose, and place them into strong plastic bags. *Clean* fertiliser bags are acceptable, but thick, black plastic planting bags are preferable.

Tie the neck of each bag tight to prevent the roots drying out and store them away in a dark, cool, frost-free room ready for early planting, in February or March.

If any delay of more than 2–3 days in planting is anticipated, dig a heeling-in trench and line out the bundles of stock, with their roots well covered with soil against any possible frost risk.

Do not accept or allow delivery of planting stock in frosty weather.

William Cobbett, writing in 1825, recommended the practice of pruning plants prior to planting (Figure 7.1). Pruning both the top and the roots is still recommended as the best way to stimulate vigorous growth. Remove at least a quarter of the total root and cut the top back by a third to encourage the formation of fresh young roots and good top growth in the following year.

Top and root pruning is still practised by many nurserymen lining out seedlings or transplant shrubs for growing-on to form stronger plants (Plate 7.2). We should never be too proud to look back on the good tree planting practices of the late 18th and early 19th centuries. A large proportion of our remaining hedgerows date from those times and the hedges continue to testify to the quality of the work.

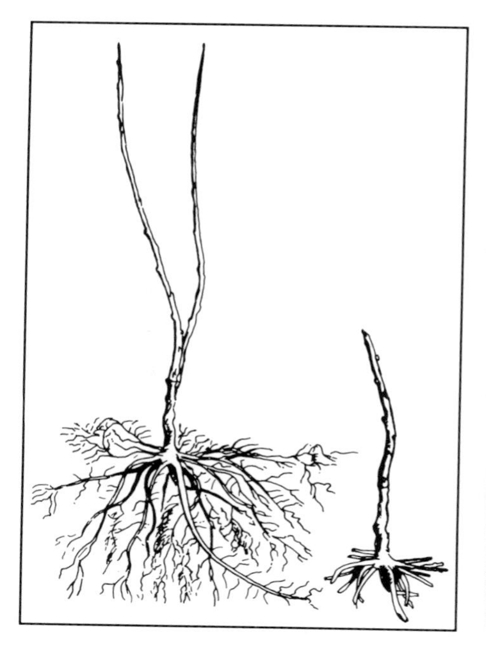

FIGURE 7.1 William Cobbett's method of plant pruning (1825). (Left) *A young tree lifted from a nursery, and* (right) *pruned ready for planting.*

PLATE 7.2 Bundles of crab apple (left) *and common dogwood* (right). *Note the bulky, fibrous roots of dogwood.*

SINGLE ROW HAND PLANTING

Hand Planting into Cultivated Soil

Most of the traditional hawthorn enclosure hedges were planted closely in single rows. Single row planting is still an acceptable practice.

A strip of ground at least 1 m (3 ft) wide should be prepared, to a depth of 0.5 m (18 in) to give friable, weed-free soil for good, easy planting. Strong two-year-old transplants should be lined out at 15–25 cm (6–10 in) intervals and, after planting, the hawthorn cut back to 45 cm (18 in) above the ground.

Ploughed Trench

If space, time or local conditions do not allow the full preparation of seedbed conditions for planting a closely spaced single row, an alternative is to plough out a single furrow, lining the plants along the furrow wall and simply replacing the soil and firming up the plants well (Plate 7.3).

PLATE 7.3 A ploughed trench. The plants are lined against the furrow wall and fresh ploughed earth is used to cover them.

Ploughed Ridge

For areas with limited topsoil depth, poor drainage or adverse soil conditions, it may be worth trying the ploughed ridge or crown method of planting.

In the summer prior to planting the hedge, mow down all grass and weeds before using a plough to make a traditional plough opening and return pass to form a 'crown' or a 'soil cairn' as it is termed in North Wales. Keep this ploughed strip clear of weeds with herbicides until planting a closely spaced 20–30 cm (8–12 in) line of plants into the ridge cap in the autumn before wet winter weather.

The inverted and rotting turf will provide better planting and drainage conditions, in heavy or wet soils. Ensure that the ploughed ridge is kept completely free of weeds prior to autumn planting, to help maintain weed-free conditions after planting and to encourage the exposed soil to dry and weather to become more friable for easy digging.

Slit (or Notch) Planting

Slit planting is cheaper than other methods of planting. Use smaller (1+0) 20/40 cm (8/16 in) seedlings and notch or slit plant 22 cm (9 in)

PLATE 7.4 Slit, or notch, planting. A wide slit is opened by working the spade back and forth, placing the plant in the space created behind the spade.

apart. Insert a narrow-bladed forester's or garden spade into the soil to its full blade length, and move vigorously backwards and forwards to open a slit. Insert the plant, spreading out its roots, and heel up firmly (Plate 7.4).

A single line hedge must be closely planted to allow for any gaps from dead or slow growing plants to be partly filled by extra growth from adjacent plants.

The single line should be planted with vigorous and bushy species to ensure adequate growth to provide the necessary density – use hawthorn, blackthorn, wild plum, hazel or field maple.

A minimum of 60% of the plants should be either hawthorn and/or blackthorn, with other species intermixed for variety. As a suggestion, use 50% hawthorn, 20% blackthorn, 10% wild plum, 10% hazel and 10% field maple

DOUBLE ROW HAND PLANTING

Cultivated Strip

As with single row planting, the best results will be achieved by ploughing and/or rotovating to produce a well prepared and weed-free seedbed. This ensures that the roots of each plant are placed into the optimum cultivated conditions for good root development.

Ploughed Trench

If time, money, inclination etc. do not allow such good preparations, ploughing the two planting lines is a practical alternative, except that there will be more soil to replace to refill the trench between plants in each row. The plants in a two row hedge will be at a wider spacing in each row.

Pit (or Spit) Planting

Using a clean, sharp garden spade fitted with foot treads, dig a hole to approximately the depth of the blade and the blade's width square.

Loosen the soil in the bottom of the hole. Place the plant in the prepared hole, spreading out its roots fully (Plate 7.5). Replace friable soil around the roots, gently shaking the plant up and down in short strokes to ensure that the soil percolates in amongst the roots. Then replace the rest of the soil and firm by treading around the stem.

PLATE 7.5 Pit planting. An adequate hole is dug with the earth piled close by. The tractor wheelings and ring roller marks can be used as a planting line.

If the soil dug from the hole is of inferior quality, or lacking in nutrients, it may be possible to dig a spade full of good nutrient-rich topsoil from the edge of the adjacent cropping field.

The use of a special planting compost is not recommended, unless the soil is very poor, of a heavy quality, or in the absence of any good adjacent topsoil.

Tine or Subsoiler Slot Planting

A fixed tine cultivator, subsoiler or better still a 'shakerator' can be drawn through the cleared area for the hedge to open out and loosen the soil along the planting lines. Two passes in opposite directions, with the minimum of tines fitted, returning along the exact line of the first tine pull, will provide the marked lines. The resulting slot will need only a little extra opening up with a treaded spade to a satisfactory width to be able to slide in the plants, spreading out their roots and firmly treading around each plant and along the full length of the tine channels to firm the soil down again. This will ensure that there are no air pockets, which could prevent the roots from growing properly.

Slit (or Notch) Planting

This method, whilst widely used for planting fresh seedlings, is not recommended unless the ground has been well prepared, making it easy to open out a wide slit (or notch) to insert the plant into good, friable conditions.

The three main dangers with slit planting are: the slit may not be big enough to take the roots properly spread out; the sides of the slit may be smeared or compacted on opening, making it difficult for the young roots to penetrate, particularly in clay or heavier loam soils; a slit opened in a heavy loam soil may not close up properly around the root, leaving an air pocket which can either kill or stunt the development of new root tissue.

Whether a contractor, farmer or conservation group, all will wish to get the work done as quickly as possible. However, speed should not be allowed to become the reason for doing a job badly. It is a false economy to slit plant a new hedge to get the work done quickly if it results in the plants either dying or being severely stunted. If the plants die the work will have to be done again the following year. If they are severely stunted the hedge may be overtaken by weeds, so taking much longer to become established.

For slit or notch planting, the area should have been at least ploughed or deep rotovated, to ensure adequate soil conditions. It is no good notch planting into a compacted grass sward, even if it has been desiccated with herbicide prior to planting. It is unlikely to present adequate growing conditions.

'The Hedge With Two Faces'

A dairy or stock farmer, with an eye for the conservation value of a new hedge, could consider planting a double line hedge with a difference.

The inner line of the hedge facing the stock field could be planted with hawthorn, lined out closely at 20–30 cm (8–12 in) spacings, to

FIGURE 7.2 'The hedge with two faces.'

give a good stockproof hedge which can be trimmed.

The outer (second) line of the hedge could be spaced about 2 m (7 ft) away and planted with a variety of other species, and allowed to grow with less formal trimming to provide a better habitat for wildlife (Figure 7.2).

This 'hedge with two faces' is an ideal option for a stock field beside a road, lane, or on a boundary not bordered by another stock field.

It will provide the farmer with a tight stock fence to keep his animals in the field. Also it will provide a good sanctuary for wildlife, with a higher conservation value for the pleasure of passers-by.

MACHINE PLANTING

A vegetable transplant machine can be used for planting hedgerow seedlings or small transplants. They are widely used by most commercial tree growers for lining out small tree and shrub seedlings, transplants and larger plants over 1.2 m (4 ft) in height.

Handfed machines speed up the work rate, improve the quality of planting, regulate spacing and maintain straight line working, without recourse to markers or string lines.

In Chapter 6, three types of machine planter are described in detail for lining out one-year-old seedlings up to 45 cm (18 in) high. A further description of bare root transplanters and module transplanters is given on pages 150–153 of *Machinery for Horticulture*, a comprehensive book for growers, published by Farming Press Ltd.

Hand planting remains a common and very acceptable way to

plant hedges. However, those engaged in commercial hedgerow planting or committed to a longer term programme of farm or estate hedge planting should borrow or purchase a transplanter to speed up the work rates and save costs.

It may be possible to hire a suitable machine from a local nurseryman or vegetable grower, who would not be using the machine regularly during the winter months. It may also be possible to buy a good second-hand single or two row transplanter, avoiding the higher expenditure of a new machine for limited winter use.

Where the position of a new hedge and ground conditions allow for tractor access, it is strongly recommended that the plants are machine planted. Look at the examples of work rates shown in Chapter 15. The author's experiences of both hand and machine planting tell their own tale, particularly if long stretches of new hedges are to be planted on a regular annual basis.

If a transplant machine is used for planting a single line hawthorn hedge only, two people will be required: the tractor driver and one operator placing the plants into the opened furrow. For a conservation hedge using a mix of 50% hawthorn and 10% each of five other shrub species, one extra person will be required to hand the changing sequence of plants to the planter, to ensure that he can keep up a good speed and not lose track of the correct sequence as he concentrates on placing each plant correctly into the open share (Plate 7.6).

SPACING

Whichever form of planting is chosen for a double line hedge, the two lines must be stagger-planted, to give the necessary even distribution of plants along the mature hedge line.

Spacing within each line may vary between 22 and 45 cm (9 and 18 in), according to the style of hedge required.

For a stockproof fence a high proportion of hawthorn and/or blackthorn at a close spacing of 22 cm (9 in) should be used. For a conservation hedge which will be allowed to grow more freely, a mixture of species should be used, with adequate hawthorn or blackthorn spaced at 45 cm (18 in). The distance between each of the two lines will vary according to the proposed use or value of the hedge.

A stockproof hedge for cattle or sheep should have the two lines placed closer together than for the more mixed species conservation hedge. 0.5 m (19 in) between the two lines is ideal for a stockproof hedge, increasing to 0.6/1 m (2/3 ft) for a conservation hedge.

PLATE 7.6 Tractor driver and machine operator aided by two assistants handing the correct plants in turn. A third man checks the completed work. The new hedge contains a mixture of six species.

REGIONAL DIFFERENCES IN THE CHOICE OF SPECIES

Oxfordshire/Berkshire

An arable area, but with some dairy, stock and sheep farms.

The planting of a double row hedge is recommended, with the two rows 60–90 cm (24–36 in) apart and with plants spaced 22–30 cm (9–12 in) apart along each row and staggered in relation to the first row planted.

Hawthorn is the main species (at least 50%), with a percentage of field maple, hazel, blackthorn, spindle, wild plum and other species to add greater emphasis to the conservation value.

Somerset

A dairy and stock farming county, with exposed hill fields and some need for amenity and conservation areas in the unspoilt landscape, parts of which attract many summer tourists.

For inexpensive stockproof hedges, the mix of species includes mainly hawthorn and blackthorn, with some field maple, hazel and holly. Amenity hedges, planted at wider spacing, can include common dogwood, spindle, common buckthorn, wild rose, wayfaring tree and guelder rose.

Devon and Cornwall

Two dairy and stock-rearing counties which also feature arable and early horticultural crops. The exposed coastlines present special requirements for the provision of shelter and the need for plants that will tolerate salt-laden winds.

Hawthorn and blackthorn are prerequisites for stockproofing of hedges and hedgebanks, with sea buckthorn and privet recommended for exposed coastal sites. For other inland hedgerows and banks, field maple, hornbeam, hazel and common beech are used in both counties.

Avon and Gloucestershire

Both counties feature lowland and hill areas, each requiring differing treatments according to the topography and changes in soil type.

Hawthorn and blackthorn are found, with field maple, hornbeam and beech, in addition to a wider use of species such as alder and common blackthorn, wayfaring tree and guelder rose.

East Anglia (Norwich area)

A mainly arable area, with some horticultural cropping.

Once again, hawthorn and blackthorn are the main choice, together with field maple, common dogwood, hazel and spindle. Occasionally less common species, such as hornbeam and the buckthorns, are used.

There is a wide variety of plant mixes, according to the site and objectives of the owner.

Essex

A largely arable area, with a coastal fringe to the east and the London environs reaching in from the west.

Hawthorn, blackthorn and field maple are the three main hedgerow constituents, accounting for 90%. Other species which typically contribute to the remaining 10% include hazel, dogwood, dog rose and spindle.

Hampshire

Most hedges are planted on the flat in this largely arable county, with open downland, the New Forest and a gentle coastline.

Hawthorn is the most widely used hedge species, with the addition of blackthorn, field maple and hazel.

Herefordshire and Shropshire

Two counties with enduring mixed farming traditions.

With good land and good husbandry stockproof hedges are found of hawthorn and blackthorn, together with a mixture of field maple, common dogwood, hazel, spindle, wild rose, the wayfaring tree and guelder rose.

South Wales

Dairy, early potatoes, stock and sheep farming, with some arable. Like Devon and Cornwall, an area of smaller fields, hedged and wall-banked for shelter and early cropping.

Hawthorn, hazel and blackthorn are the most commonly seen hedgebank shrub species, together with some wild rose and field maple.

North Wales

Largely a dairy, sheep and stock area, with exposed coastal and mountain regions.

Many fields are bordered with earth-banked hedges, with hawthorn, blackthorn, hazel and holly the most common species. Blackthorn and hawthorn can withstand exposed conditions better than most other hedgerow species.

Lancashire

A good arable and mixed farming area. Moving north does not change the main ingredients of a good hedge – hawthorn, blackthorn, field maple, hazel and guelder rose are all recommended for double row hedges.

Earth-banked hedges are recommended for improving the chances of growth of a new hedge planted on reclaimed land, such as coal pit sites and tips etc.

Cumbria

A mainly livestock area, with fencing required for sheep and cattle, in addition to good hedges.

There are some earth-bank and flat-land hedges though stone walls are much more common. For new hedges, there is a choice of hawthorn, field maple, hazel, spindle and blackthorn. Both the buckthorns, wild rose and guelder rose are recommended for greater variety within the hedge.

Fencing of new hedges is highly recommended, in view of the importance of stock control.

Yorkshire

An arable and stock area.

Hawthorn and blackthorn are required as the mainstays, together with a wider selection of other species according to local conditions. Sea buckthorn is used in coastal regions, otherwise the choice is open – field maple, common dogwood, hazel, the two buckthorns, wild rose and the guelder rose, all helping to form good conservation hedges.

Encouragement is also given to the establishment of a perennial grass sward at the hedge bottom, to discourage annual weeds and provide nesting cover.

Dumfriesshire and Galloway

Moving across the border into the rolling hills and dales of the Scottish lowlands, hawthorn is the most common hedge species, with beech used for some estate hedges. Other minor species include blackthorn, wild rose and guelder rose.

The traditional Galloway style 'hedge' is the combination of a stone wall with the hedge planted to grow out from the wall's base. This style is not being reinstated, because of the high cost of new wall-building.

Fencing around new hedges is encouraged to prevent damage from sheep and rabbits. There is also a keen interest in the management of field margins to provide rough grass 'corridors' for barn owls to hunt along.

In addition, game conservancy headlands are recommended where appropriate. The Scottish Agricultural Council at Auchincruive, Ayr, are looking into the management of field margins and suitable cutting techniques.

CARE AFTER PLANTING

Weed control

After planting, apply an appropriate herbicide to control existing weeds, or to prevent their establishment. Chapter 11 gives full details of the options and the chemicals available for use according to site conditions. ADAS or FWAG offer good advice and have the latest information on the range of chemicals which have been cleared for use on hedgerows.

If the new hedge has been planted into an old sward or herbage, some of this will regrow following winter weed control measures.

Desiccate the weeds with a contact herbicide using a guarded spray jet around the hedge plants, or trim back regrowth with a strimmer or scythe to prevent competition with the young plants.

Watering

At some stage in the spring or summer during the first two years' growth, there will be periods of hot, dry weather, which will affect the establishment of the plants if they are left unwatered.

There are several ways to effectively apply water to the plants:

- A water bowser – which a farm may possess for watering stock.
- A crop sprayer – which can be used to apply water either by gravity feed or by a hose taken from a boom outlet.
- An open water tank with buckets, mounted onto a trailer or trolley.

PROTECTIVE CLOTHING

Little or no research has been carried out to develop protective clothing for those working in outdoor conditions, handling some of nature's less friendly plants.

Protective clothing for operators handling a range of trees and shrubs outdoors in all weathers is required to ensure the wearer is:

- dry in wet weather
- warm in cold weather
- cool in mild weather
- free from perspiration when protected against the weather or plants
- given the maximum freedom of movement
- not burdened with weighty clothing
- provided with clothing that will withstand wear and tear
- able to wash or clean off dirt from the surface of the clothing.

All these requirements can be met to a high degree with the following range of garments:

A one-piece polyester/cotton boiler suit

Universal wear for many outdoor manual operations, polyester/cotton is hard wearing, it will give good protection against dirt and is easy to wash. The fabric breathes well, minimising the effects of perspiration. A wide range of boiler suits is available to suit most personal preferences for pockets and styling.

A pair of good quality leather boots

Dr Martens Air Wair boots have cushioned soles and provide comfort and freedom of movement. The sole is strong enough to withstand spade work. Regular cleaning and treatment with dubbin will keep the leather uppers flexible and waterproof, except in severe wet weather, when the operator should resort to . . .

A high-quality pair of rubber wellington boots

There are many brands and styles to choose from. Beware of the cheaper lightweight plastic types; they do not withstand hard digging and the thinner material is vulnerable to punctures from thorns and the edge of the spade.

A pair of strong yet supple gloves

These are to deter thorns and give protection against both cold and wet conditions. Thin, cheap, cotton gloves are suitable for digging, but are too thin to resist thorns. Leather gloves give greater protection, yet are liable to become hard when dried following use in wet conditions. The higher quality, quilted, leather gloves feel warm and remain waterproof longer, but the quilted lining restricts the movement of fingers, particularly when gripping a spade or secateurs for long periods, which can lead to cramp or strain in the hands.

An ADAS work study of the author's team while harvesting, grading and bundling transplant trees noted the effects of thick gloves on both the dexterity and speed of handling. This led to the design of special gloves, which met most of the requirements for all-weather use.

'Gortex' fabric was used for the body of the glove, a material which is light, hardwearing and waterproof. It has the ability to 'breathe', allowing any localised perspiration to escape. The finger backs are sewn up as individual strips to ensure maximum dexterity. An elasticated band seals the glove at the wrist. A two-piece soft leather palm is sewn onto the Gortex base, the thumb part shaped and sewn on individually to ensure maximum freedom of movement. The soft leather palm also covers the underside of the four fingers and extends to cover the complete first finger. A moon-shaped piece of soft leather is sewn onto the inner side of the wrist to give added protection against thorn scratches.

The gloves performed very well in all but severe cold conditions, where the breathing Gortex fabric was allowing too much heat to ventilate from the back of the hand. A thin cotton lining on the back of future gloves should resolve this without losing freedom of movement (Plate 7.7).

A pair of forearm protectors

These should be made from a close weave fustian or thin canvas, tapered from the elbow to the wrist with elasticated ends – a strong

PLATE 7.7 A selection of gloves. (Left to right)*: Industrial all-leather glove; cheap, thin cotton glove; Gortex-backed and leather-palmed glove; Gristle glove (a thin cotton glove dipped in a latex rubber solution). All are suitable for handling thorny plants apart from the thin cotton glove which is only useful for pruning or spade work.*

outdoor version of the casino croupier's black sleeve! These will keep the boiler suit arms clean, dry and free of thorn snags and will allow the user to work without the restriction of movement from wearing a long-sleeved jacket.

A sleeveless, waxed cotton, lined body warmer

This ensures the maximum freedom of movement, body warmth, protection from wind, light rain and cold conditions.

A set of plasticised canvas leggings

Hung from a waist belt, these provide protection from thorns, wet and cold conditions and give maximum movement and the minimum of inconvenience, when compared with the restrictions from wearing plastic trouser leggings as part of a two-piece anorak suit, which will not give the wearer the required ease of quick movement necessary for sustained outdoor work.

A hat

A hat, to suit the wearer, is essential. At least 15% of body heat can be lost from the head, which may be desirable if working in warm autumn or spring conditions. Most planting will be during colder winter conditions, so a hat will keep the wearer warm.

A little thought given to the clothing worn to undertake specific manual tasks will be rewarded with extra ease of movement and the retention of generated body heat, which are important factors when working in outdoor conditions (Plate 7.8).

PLATE 7.8 The author dressed for handling hawthorn. Leggings, forearm protectors and a body warmer keep out the cold as well as the thorns.

Chapter 8

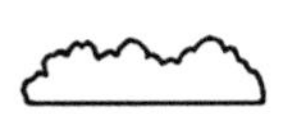 Alternative and Regional Hedges

[Strawberry Hill] is set in enamelled meadows, with filigree hedges.

TO CONWAY, 8 JUNE 1747 HORACE WALPOLE

Hedges grown on level ground are common throughout England, but regional variations have evolved to suit different conditions. For instance, the Cotswold and Mendip hill fields are bordered with stone walls, as are many other lowland fields in Gloucestershire, Oxfordshire and Somerset. Devon, Cornwall, much of Wales and some of the adjoining counties feature stone-faced or turf-banked hedges, often built because of poor soil conditions or to provide a better level of protection in exposed southern and western areas. Devon, Cornwall and Wales are continuing to use local hedgebanks wherever new roadworks or road widening schemes have affected old existing banks.

In the early 1970s the concern of conservationists at the loss of hedgebanks during road improvement schemes led to the development of a new form of hedgebank. Len Wade, a county council surveyor at South Molton in North Devon, devised a simple and much cheaper way to build hedgebanks.

He took a section of galvanised, heavy-duty, wire mesh, of the type used in the prevention of coastal erosion, and formed it into a narrow-necked U-shaped basket framework. The inner face was lined with turfs and the rest of the basket filled with earth and some small stones, all of which would normally be available on the site of a road improvement scheme. The mesh framework provided both the shape and stability at a cheaper price than building the hedgebank in the traditional manner.

His idea has led to the widespread use of 'the Devonwade hedgebank' (Plate 8.1) throughout the Southwest and in many areas

PLATE 8.1 A new Devonwade hedgebank at Newport, Dyfed, showing the galvanised wire mesh skeleton in place to form a banked gateway recess.

of Wales, wherever road realignment or widening schemes require the reinstatement of an original hedgebank.

THE DEVONWADE HEDGEBANK

The only requirements for the foundations of the hedgebank are firm and level soil conditions. No preparatory footings are necessary (Plate 8.2). Galvanised 'weldmesh' (BRC No. 3610) or a similar approved fabric with a mesh size of 150 mm × 75 mm × 10 mm SWG in sheets 3,750 mm wide are bent to form an open top, tapered neck, U-shape with a base width of 1,350 mm and sides 1,200 mm high.

A length of the basket cage is made up along the line of the proposed hedgebank. Two large metal plate formers are fixed on the outside of the mesh cage to hold the floppy mesh in position, like a couple of book ends, while the section is filled. Turfs are placed on the inner face of the cage, with the grass side facing outwards to provide a 'living' lining which will retain all the loose soil and small stone core material (Plate 8.3). The core soil is placed into the cage by a digger bucket as the turfs are placed up the sides.

PLATE 8.2 The weldmesh basket framework in place ahead of the bank former plates, laid onto a level earth base.

PLATE 8.3 Building a Devonwade hedgebank. The steel former plates hold the bank shape while the section is lined with turfs and earth-filled. A barrowful of turfs in the foreground awaits use.

Three galvanised wire ties of 8 SWG wire are fitted horizontally across the cage at regular close intervals along the cage line to hold the filled basket in its correct shape once the former plates are removed and fitted to the next section (Plate 8.4).

It requires a four-man team to build the bank at a reasonable speed; one man on each side of the cage line fitting the turfs up the inner wall faces, the digger driver filling the core with earth and the fourth man working either inside or at the open end of the cage to ensure the earth is evenly compacted, and inserting the wire ties as the filling progresses.

PLATE 8.4 A view into the basket frame showing the three wire ties across the earth fill to hold the sides in and together, at the correct angle.

The open top of the cage is not turfed, but filled a little proud of the cage lip with good soil (Plate 8.5), into which the young hedge will be planted.

PLATE 8.5 The filled Devonwade hedgebank basket, topped up with good topsoil.

The newly built hedgebank is left to settle for a year before the seedlings are planted. Any compaction sinkage of the soil will require topping up with good topsoil before the plants are lined out at the rate of 10 per m, at staggered centres. This is equivalent to one plant every 20 cm (8 in).

If good quality meadow turfs are used, within one year the bank will have become naturalised and the mesh will be overgrown and almost invisible (Plate 8.6).

Grants are available for the repair (Plate 8.7) and restoration of turf hedgebanks. See Appendix 2 for current rates and conditions.

PLATE 8.6 The same hedgebank a year later. Grass has covered the basket frame and hawthorn, though not visible, has been planted on the crown.

PLATE 8.7 Severe erosion on the sides of a relatively new Devonwade hedgebank, probably because no turfs were used to line the inner face of the weldmesh framework. The weldmesh appears to be too vertical; it should be angled inwards more to form a gentler bank slope to reduce erosion.

THE PEMBROKE HEDGEBANK

In many parts of Cornwall, Devon and Wales turf banks give way to stone-faced or Pembroke hedgebanks; quite often the wall banks do not have a hedge on the top.

In Wales, Dyfed County Council continue to use the Pembroke hedgebank where road improvements require the resiting of an existing wall-bank, or where suitable stone can be found locally at a reasonable cost.

The wall bank takes longer to build and requires extra skills to achieve the necessary quality.

The only preparation necessary is to strip away the topsoil to a depth of 100 mm (4 in), so that the large base stones can be set into firm and level ground, to prevent them slipping outwards with the weight of the subsequent stone courses. No other footings are necessary.

The Pembroke stone bank has a wider base than the Devonwade turf bank, starting at 180 cm (6 ft) wide and tapering to 60 cm (2 ft) at the top. The height of the wall is the same as the turf bank, at 120 cm (4 ft) (Plate 8.8). Often, another 20–30 cm (8–12 in) of earth is heaped

PLATE 8.8 End view of a Pembroke hedgebank showing the graded stone layers with their turf bedding and the earth core. The wall is capped with a layer of earth and turf.

PLATE 8.9 A new Pembroke stone and turf hedgebank, near Haverfordwest, Dyfed.

on top to form a domed cap, which will sink a little in subsequent months as the earth core compacts.

Once the first course of large stones have been laid, topsoil is placed into the core centre. 60 mm (2½ in) thick turves are laid on top of the first course of stones, with the edge of the turf sticking out slightly from the leading edge, to act as a bedding (like mortar) to accept the next layer of stones, which are smaller in size than the base stones. Again the centre is filled with topsoil before another turf bedding is placed on top of the stone layer, so the wall progresses to a height of four stone courses.

The building stone faces of the wall should be between 300 and 450 mm thick (12 and 18 in) and angled inwards at 45° to the vertical. This, combined with the topsoil core and turf bedding layers between the stone courses, builds up a strong and durable wall (Plate 8.9).

Within a year the turfs will have grown to partly cover the stone face, and their rooting into the earth core will help bind the whole wall together.

A year after building, a double line of hawthorn transplants are planted into the topsoil cap of the wall at the rate of 10 plants per metre (3 ft), at staggered centres; the two lines of plants being 100 mm (4 in) either side of the centre line, 200 mm (8 in) apart.

Dyfed County Council requests the wall builders to reuse all soil saved from the former old wall, if the new wall is a reinstatement.

This ensures that some of the insect population of the old wall is reinstated into the new wall. Otherwise, good quality topsoil is required to fill the core of the wall to aid the establishment and growth of both the turf bedding layers between each stone course and the hedge planted on the crown of the wall bank.

Within three to four years the new wall will have become overgrown and lost its fresh-built look, blending into the surrounding scenery as though it had been there for scores of years (Plate 8.10).

It is very heartening to know that county councils, such as Devon and Dyfed, take great care to retain and foster traditional regional styles.

PLATE 8.10 A mature Pembroke hedgebank, now well overgrown from the turf bedding between the stone layers. The closely planted hedge was trimmed two to three years ago to improve its density.

Grants are available for the repair and restoration of wall hedgebanks. See Appendix 2 for current rates and conditions.

WILLOW OSIER HEDGES

The bushy-topped pollarded willows, which line many miles of river and stream bank throughout the country, are a familiar sight; other traditional uses for willow are a less common sight.

The reduction in demand for basket-making material has led to a decline in the need for osiers – the long thin shoots (or 'wands') which the stools of *Salix triandra* (the almond-leaved or French willow) and *S. viminalis* (the common willow) produce in a one-to-two-year cycle of cutting.

Willow is one of the fastest growing plants with a potential for hedge use. The vigorous growth of a wide range of willows makes them ideal for planting as a windbreak hedge in moist or reasonable loam soil. They will not grow so fast in dry, sandy soils.

The open landscape of the East Anglian Fens could benefit both visually and practically from the wider use of hedges. The willow, with its attractive stem colours, could break up the monotony of fenland fields, as well as offer protection to the adjacent crops and a variety of useful by-products from regular cutting. The large fields could be divided in half, or at least bordered, by willow hedges.

Planting

Willow 'sets' consist of one-year shoots cut into 20–30 cm (8–12 in) lengths (Plate 8.11) and simply pushed into the ground in late winter (February–March) to a depth of 15 cm (6 in). An overall weed control spray of 2½ kg simazine plus 2½ kg propyzamide (Kerb) per hectare (or 1 lb simazine plus 1 lb Kerb per acre) will control weed growth during the early season. A further application six to eight weeks later should ensure weed-free conditions for most of the first growing season. The same weed control measures can be repeated the following year to keep the plant lines clean until they are well established.

Willow sets should be planted at 0.5 m (19 in) intervals as two staggered lines 1 m (3 ft) apart. This allows adequate room for each set to produce a good growth of shoots and the space between the two rows will allow the landowner to cut down one row a year, thus retaining good wind protection and the visual appearance of the hedge. The cutting-down of alternate rows can continue in rotation to maintain vigorous growth and control the overall hedge size.

PLATE 8.11 A tray of prepared willow cuttings. The base of each cutting has been dipped in hormone rooting powder.

Colour

If the hedge is to be planted for both crop protection and appearance, choose varieties with attractive winter bark colours such as *Salix vitellina* (a striking golden-yellow) and *Salix britzensis* (a rich orange-scarlet).

Where wind protection is the sole aim, plant the taller and more vigorous cultivars of *Salix purpurea* and *Salix viminalis*. It may be preferable to leave the rows uncut and maintain a taller, dense hedge by trimming according to growth with a flail hedge trimmer.

Osier Production

There is no reason why the hedge cannot earn money as well as providing shelter and visual appeal. The use of *Salix triandra* or *Salix viminalis* for both lines of the hedge allows rotational cutting of the long shoots (or 'wands') for sale to basket-makers, once they have reached a height of 2–3 m (6–10 ft). In good conditions this should be achieved in *one* growing season (Plate 8.12).

Before planting a hedge with a view to producing osiers, find an outlet for the shoots. Grow the correct variety of willow required for the type of basket-making being undertaken and cut the crop to suit the basket-maker's needs. Cut the shoots by hand or possibly a heavy-duty cutter-bar mower.

PLATE 8.12 One year's growth from an annually cut willow stool bed. It shows the potential for a good hedge or screen on light soil.

Biomass Production

Biomass is defined as the gross weight of living material produced in a defined area – a situation where the producer is concerned only with the production of a total quantity of bulk matter.

The rapid and bulky growth of certain willow varieties makes them ideal for the quick production of woody matter, which can be harvested as chippings to be used as a mulch material or compressed and dried into fuel briquettes.

Both these uses are finding wider acceptance because the energy source, the living willow plant, is renewable. Their use is not contributing to the rapid decline of peat or coal reserves, so the greater use of such materials should be encouraged.

Research work carried out by Ken Stott at Long Ashton Research Station and G. H. McElroy with M. Dawson at the Horticultural Centre, Loughgall in Northern Ireland, between 1976 and 1982, recommended *Salix 'aquatica' gigantea* (now known as *S. burjatica*) for producing the highest yield of dry matter. To achieve maximum output, the trials indicated that dry matter yields increased with the harvesting cycle. The yield from *one* three-year-old crop was greater than that taken from *three* one-year-old crops.

Trials at both sites confirmed the value of certain varieties which had been under observation for between five and seven years. *Salix viminalis* and its Bowles hybrid × *dasyclados*, and clones of *Salix burjatica* have all produced good yields of dry matter.

Current research at Long Ashton is being led by Dr J. R. Porter.

Yields of 12 tonnes (oven dry) per hectare (5 tonnes per acre) per year can be sustained from a crop grown on a three-year cutting cycle.

Productivity can be seriously affected by the Melampsora Rust fungus. Present research is being directed towards understanding how the fungus affects growth and the principles underlying willow growth and development. Estimates have shown that yields could be increased by 30–50%.

Further information can be obtained by joining the Institute of Arable Crops Research, at Long Ashton Research Station, Bristol.

HOLLY HEDGES

The advantages of holly for hedging are that it is evergreen, stock-proof and produces dense growth if trimmed regularly (Plate 8.12).

The disadvantages are that it is slow-growing and needs protection from deer, hares and rabbits. These animals will make straight for the holly planted in young hedge lines, to browse on its foliage and succulent green bark. Holly needs some form of guard to protect its early years of growth. It grows well in tree shelters, but mice and voles can present a problem during winter months, so seal the bottom of the shelter well.

The case for growing holly hedges in the countryside rests on a decision to line them out to produce a tall hedge which will yield branches for the Christmas decoration and wreath trade.

PLATE 8.13 Holly hedges for providing cuttings as well as for the Christmas decoration trade.

Most Christmas holly is taken from individual woodland or wayside trees, quantities being sold by gypsies. There are a few commercial holly growers in the United Kingdom, producing berried holly from orchards of wider spaced trees.

There is a potential for combining the commercial yield of saleable branches and providing an evergreen shelter hedge or field boundary, in addition to woodland and hedgerow planting of individual trees.

Male and Female Plants

Most holly cultivars are either male or female. Only female varieties bear berry crops, so the ratio of male to female plants should be one to ten to ensure adequate pollination.

It is possible to graft or bud scions from male cultivars onto branches of the female trees, so removing the need to have any non-berried male trees present.

The increasing popularity of variegated leaf varieties could reduce the trade's insistence on good berried stems. The variegated margins, usually a white or cream colour, are more attractive than the normal, plain, glossy, green leaves, overshadowing the impact and necessity for the blood-red berries.

If a selection of green and variegated holly cultivars are planted to form a close windbreak hedge, space individual plants 5 m (16 ft) apart in the line with male cultivars introduced at a ratio of one to eight female plants to ensure good pollination along a straight line. This spacing will seem very wide in the early years of growth, but the plants will spread in direct proportion to their height to fill the gap, allowing a little room for pruning access around each bush.

Choice of Varieties

A wide choice of cultivars is available. The following are cultivars which the author has grown and found to produce the bush shape and vigour suitable for commercial cutting of Christmas foliage.

Female cultivars

Amber A vigorous, pyramidal habit. Bark green or purplish, with open branches. Dark green foliage. Undulating spiny leaves of lanceolate shape. Large bronze-yellow fruits.

Argenta marginata A strong-growing, compact, pyramidal shape. Bark of young plants green. Leaves broad and ovate, with slightly mottled disc (centre part of holly leaf). An irregular, narrow, silvery to pale cream leaf margin with an undulating and spiny edge. Regarded as one of the best silver variegated varieties.

Belgica aurea A fine, vigorous and pyramidal form with compact growth. Young bark green. Leaves ovate to oblong-ovate, flat, with a dark green disc with a thin silver margin. Few spines. A severe frost can discolour the silver margin, turning it partially pale brown.

Camelliaefolia A very vigorous, tall, bushy plant. Bark of young wood green. Leaves oblong, large, dark olive-green and very glossy. The margin smooth, flat and spineless, except for a sharp pointed tip to the leaf. A handsome and ornamental form which bears bright red berries.

Madam Briot A vigorous and compact pyramidal form. Young bark purple to green. Leaves broad, oblong to ovate, with a dark green disc. The leaf margin is silver to cream, steeply undulating with pronounced long spines. A very attractive leaf.

Pyramidalis A vigorous, compact, conical form. Bark light green when young. Leaves long, narrow, lanceolate and glossy green. The margin is flat, smooth and spineless, except for the occasional short spine near the leaf tip.

J.C. Van Tol Recommended for its heavy crop of red berries. Leaves dark green, glossy and smooth, margins spineless and somewhat convex. Excellent for the Christmas wreath-making trade.

The author has no experience of this cultivar, but it has been highly recommended to him for the above reason.

Male cultivars for pollination

Argenta regina (silver queen) This cultivar with a female name is a male form! A very attractive, compact, pyramidal shape. Green bark on young wood. Leaves broad and lanceolate with a dark green disc. A cream to pale yellow margin with gentle undulations and irregular short spines.

Ferox (hedgehog holly) A bushy, low and slower-growing form. Bark dark green when young. Leaves dark, glossy green and curled. The unusual feature of this holly is the leaf shape. Small, closely spaced, stiff leaves are ovate to oblong, with short sharp spines on the upper edge of the partly rolled leaves.

There are two variegated forms of *Ferox*. One is *Ferox argentea*, with white margins and numerous spines, and the other is *Ferox aurea*, with a yellow leaf centre, green margins and also very spiny. Both variegated forms have the distinctive lightly curled leaf.

All forms of *Ferox* are slow-growing and do not produce adequate growth for cutting, nor are its branches suited to the Christmas and wreath trade. Very much a garden ornamental cultivar.

THE FALSE ACACIA (OR BLACK LOCUST) *(ROBINEA PSEUDOACACIA)*

A native of the eastern United States, which has been cultivated throughout Europe and become naturalised in south-west Europe. In China it is commonly grown as a windbreak.

In North America it is grown for the durability and strength of its timber, which is used for fencing stakes and other outdoor applications. Its attractive light to dark brown wood is highly valued for many aspects of house-building. It has the lowest shrinkage value of United States domestic timbers.

The tree is perfectly hardy in most parts of Britain, particularly in central and southern England where it can grow vigorously.

It grows remarkably well on light sandy soil. In the author's nursery conditions, a 30 cm (1 ft) high seedling will grow up to 2 m (6 ft) in one season; far in excess of the growth attained by other seedlings of common tree or shrub species grown under the same conditions. The false acacia will grow rapidly upwards in its early years to form a good straight stem, before it spreads outwards with age to form more horizontal branches.

The young branches have short, sharp, hooked spines, which are not seen on older wood. This feature will aid its survival in the face

PLATE 8.14 The false acacia growing in an urban setting, its most common use today.

of adjacent grazing livestock.

It is a very attractive tree in summer, with a mass of pale green, lush foliage and fragrant, pendulous clusters of white flowers, which bloom in June. The false acacia is one of the latest trees to flower and is attractive to honeybees – particularly at a time when there is little other blossom left for them to feed upon.

The false acacia is more widely grown as an ornamental tree in gardens and parks. This should not detract from its potential use in the countryside.

It is worthy to be grown as a closely planted hedge, which could be coppiced for hard and durable fencing stakes, once the necessary girth has been acquired. Its ability to sucker should ensure a steady supply of shoots, which would replace those coppiced, as well as retaining the shelter value of a hedge.

Its other great asset is its ability to fix nitrogen, which makes it a worthy contender for planting on degraded sites.

J. L. Beddall put the case for the acacia very well in his comment, 'There is no reason why we should not have more variety in our hedgerow trees. An uncommon tree is always interesting and becomes a source of pride for the owner. So whatever you plant, be it oak, ash or acacia, it adds value to your land and will become something worthwhile to hand down to future generations, just as we now reap the harvest planted by our forefathers. We must not fail in this, for the future beauty of the countryside is one of our foremost responsibilities.'

REFERENCES AND FURTHER READING

The American Horticultural Magazine (1970), *Handbook of Hollies* (Fall Issue/Volume 49/No. 4, a special issue on ILEX).

Beddall, J.L. (1950), *Hedges for Farm and Garden* (Faber & Faber Ltd, London).

Brown, James (1982), *The Forester* (William Blackwood & Sons).

Cobbett, William (1825), *The Woodlands* (William Cobbett, London).

Hume, H.H. (1953), *Hollies* (The Macmillan Company, New York).

Institute of Arable Crops Research (1989), *Willow Biomass (as a Source of Fuel) (1984)* (University of Bristol).

Nitrogen Fixing Tree Association Highlights (July 1991), *A Publication of the Nitrogen Fixing Tree Association* (Waimanalo, USA).

Porter, Valerie (1990), *Small Woods and Hedgerows* (Pulham Books by Stephen Greene Press, London).

Stott, K.G. (1971), *Willows for Amenity, Windbreaks and Other Uses (Reprinted from the Report of Long Ashton Research Station, University of Bristol 1971).*

Chapter 9

The Use of Trees in Hedgerows

I think that I shall never see
A poem as lovely as a tree
Poems are made by fools like me
But only God can make a tree

TREES 1914 ALFRED JOYCE KILMER

Dutch elm disease killed nearly all the elms in hedgerows during the devastating epidemic of the mid 1970s. Until that time we had accepted the presence of trees within the hedgerow as being a traditional part of the landscape of lowland Britain.

Cereal farmers will confirm that the demise of the elm was no bad thing. However attractive it may have looked to the passer-by, the reality was one of severely reduced crop yields within the shadow of the tree, together with its extensive suckers and intrusive root system.

We associate the English countryside with fields bordered by hedges, leafy lanes and trees dotted across the landscape, all knitted together with parcels of woodland to form a rich patchwork – 'England's green and pleasant land'.

With all the elms now cleared away, the hedgerow tree has become a lonely figure. The odd ageing oak, ash or beech looks almost out-of-place where many others once stood in a richer mixed company.

William Pontey, writing in 1805, was clearly against an abundance of trees within a hedgerow. He offered reasons which are as valid today as when he set out his views in his treatise *The Forest Pruner*.

> In hedgerows, dividing fields, where grain etc. is cultivated, the matter is of still worse consequence; as there the shade alone, beyond the limits of the drip [of rain], frequently does more harm than the drip itself. Shade prevents the grain filling and ripening sufficiently, and also, has a direct tendency to promote the mildew; an evil, under which the country is, at this moment [1805] suffering severely.

> When a timber owner occupies the land himself, the loss falls into its proper place, but not so when, as is much more common, it is let to a tenant, who must pay both rent and taxes. By him these inmates [the trees] may be considered as 'soldiers at free quarters', who will be served first, regardless whether anything is left behind; while the tenant is put upon doing, what human nature, in its present imperfect state, can scarcely be supposed capable of; namely standing by as an unconcerned spectator of the ruin of his hedges and the spoiling of his corn.
>
> It is not said, that it would be desirable entirely to discontinue the growing of trees in hedgerows, even where grain is grown; for a few may be permitted, under a good system of management. Among grass fields, it is the excess, and abuse, in the practice, which are principally complained of. Certainly, so far as appearances are concerned, a few are abundantly preferable to many.
>
> To such as have hedges to make, it may be suggested, that the *policy* of planting many trees in them is essentially bad; as, independent of the damage they do, such are in the very worst situation for making a profitable return, if left to themselves; and, if otherwise, they would require three times the attention, of the same quantity of timber in a *Wood* or *Plantation*. Their form too, must be of the worst sort to yield any beneficial degree of shelter. Everything may be good or bad in certain situations; the *shade* we are condemning in one place, is easily converted into *shelter* in another. When we come to treat of plantations, its beneficial effects will have due consideration.

Farming today is no longer in a position to support the production of hedgerow timber which once would have been an important added source of income to the landowner. Such timber was used in the construction of buildings, machinery and many other facets of rural life.

Today, the wood merchant is very wary of accepting timber from hedgerows because of the likely presence of pieces of barbed or plain wire and generations of fencing staples, which render the wood only fit for the log fire.

The loss of the elms and the current problems with ash die-back have focused attention on the need to replace some of these heavy losses. Pontey readily accepts that some trees along a hedge are an attractive addition to the scenery and they do provide shelter for stock on a hot summer's day or during cold winter weather.

Awareness of the needs of other animals in the countryside now enters the equation. Trees provide song posts for some birds, nest and vantage points for others. Rodents live and forage within their shade, all part of nature's life cycle in the fields. A mixed habitat of trees, hedges and field margins will ensure that a wide selection of animal life can live and thrive.

The Forestry Commission undertook trials to find the best methods of establishing trees in both existing and new hedges. Their research information *Note 195* describes the problems new trees face in competing with both adjacent plants in the existing hedge and the thick weed cover likely to be present. The use of a black polythene sheet mulch to suppress weed competition and to conserve soil moisture proved more effective than chemical weed control.

Planting a new hedge at the same time as planting individual trees into the new hedge is much easier to carry out. Both will be planted simultaneously, so they will compete and grow on equal terms.

SUITABLE TREES FOR USE IN NEW HEDGES

The species most commonly found growing in existing hedges today are oaks, ash and beech and to a lesser extent, alder, horse chestnut, sycamore, white willow, goat willow and sallow (*Salix alba* and *S. caprea*). Oak and ash still remain excellent first choice species, but other less common hedgerow trees also merit consideration, in addition to those mentioned.

It is worth looking for suitable trees of a smaller and more compact stature, to minimise shading and roots poaching into the adjacent crop.

Smaller trees

Field maple (Acer campestre) (Plate 9.1)
A native of Britain and Europe which is common as a hedgerow shrub. Like the crab, it can be encouraged to grow into a small, slightly spreading tree. It rarely grows beyond 10–15 m (33–50 ft). Field maple is attractive for its ribbed bark and the beautiful tints to its autumn leaves as they turn from green to golden-yellow and flame-red.

Hornbeam (Carpinus betulus) (Plate 9.2)
Usually found growing as a hedge plant, but will form a fine broad to conical head. A slow-growing tree which does not attain great age (100–150 years) and rarely more than 18 m (59 ft) high. It is often mistaken for a beech, having similar bright green foliage and smooth bark when young. An attractive tree which forms winged seeds that hang in a cluster like a chinese lantern.

PLATE 9.1 A mature field maple growing in an old hedge. A compact, attractive tree.

PLATE 9.2 Slender branches and a conical form distinguish the hornbeam in a roadside hedgerow.

Wild crab or crab apple (Malus silvestris) (Plate 9.3)
A native of Britain and Europe and commonly found in hedgerows. It can be encouraged to grow up from the hedge to produce a small 8–10 m (26–33 ft) high bushy tree, which will produce a profusion of pink-white flowers in May to yield an abundance of small crab apples in the late summer, highly recommended for the making of crab apple jelly.

PLATE 9.3 *Two crab apple trees laden with fruit in late summer.*

Wild cherry or gean (Prunus avium) (Figure 9.1)
A quick-growing, broad-headed tree, which can reach a height of 18 m (59 ft). Its white spring flowers become welcome fruits for autumn-feeding birds.

Bird cherry (Prunus padus) (Plate 9.4 and Figure 9.2)
A native of Europe and Britain. A hedgerow plant which will grow into a small tree up to 15 m (50 ft) in height. A mass of small, creamy-white flowers can result in a heavy crop of cherry-like fruits in late summer. Its bark and pale green leaves are smooth, giving the tree a somewhat unnatural appearance in a countryside setting.

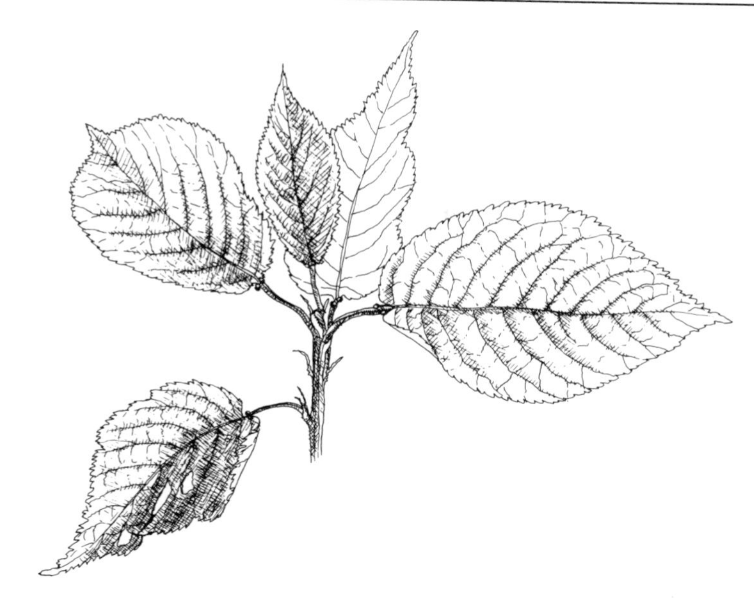

FIGURE 9.1 Wild cherry.

PLATE 9.4 The compact and upright growth of bird cherry planted in a new mixed species, and untrimmed, hedgerow.

FIGURE 9.2 Bird cherry.

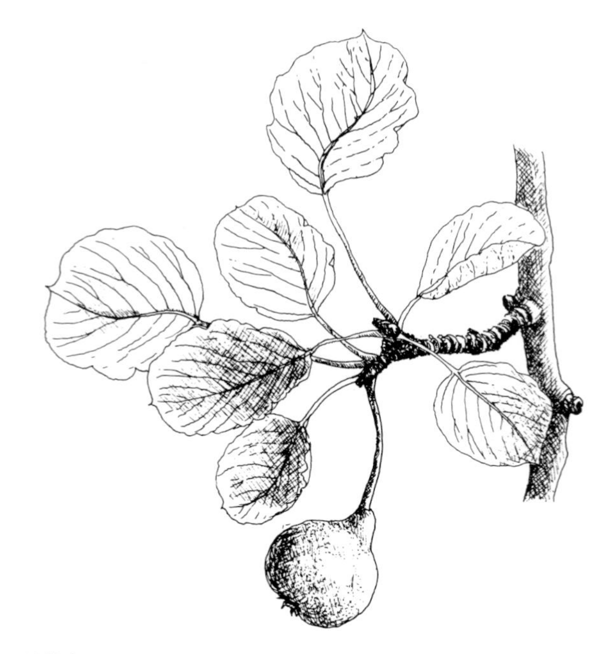

FIGURE 9.3 Wild pear.

PLATE 9.5 The distinctive columnar form of the wild pear in full flower. An uncommon tree worthy of wider use in the hedgerow.

Wild pear (Pyrus communis) (Plate 9.5 and Figure 9.3)
A somewhat rare, yet native tree which is worthy of further cultivation. Its upright, compact bearing and distinctive fissured bark and shiny green foliage are features which make it an interesting and attractive tree for use in new hedges. Its profusion of white summer blossom is often transformed into a heavy crop of small, hard pear fruits, which often form with no viable seed present.

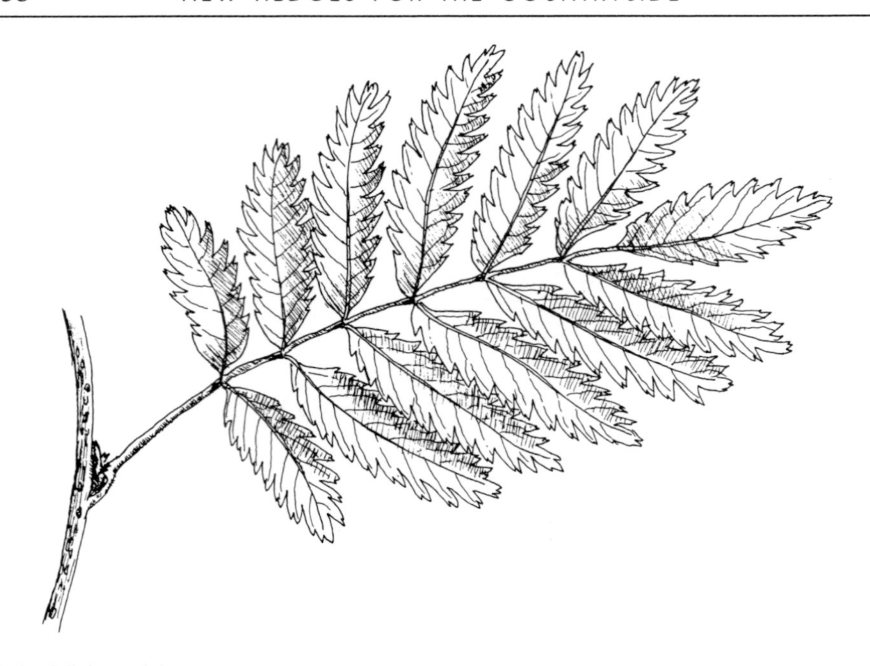

FIGURE 9.4 Mountain ash.

Mountain ash or rowan (Sorbus aucuparia) (Figure 9.4)
A small, slow-growing, compact tree, with a conical crown, rarely growing above 15 m (50 ft). A native tree of southern Europe, but increasingly common in Britain, where it will grow on a wide range of soil types but does not like thin chalk soils. Its berries are very popular with blackbirds and thrushes.

Returning to the main contenders for use in new hedges, the following points may give some indication of their long-standing popularity and the reasons why they remain widely used.

English oak (Quercus robur) (Plate 9.6 and Figure 9.5)
Synonymous with all that is traditional in the English countryside. A stout short trunk supports a broad-spreading and domed crown.

It produces valuable timber if felled in its prime. Whilst it produces a broad crown, it does not prevent the hedge from growing properly within its shade. Neither does it rob the adjacent ground of moisture and nutrients, because of its tendency to produce deep tap roots early in its life, which help stability and, according to soil type, the ability to draw its moisture needs from deeper in the soil.

PLATE 9.6 The familiar spreading dome of the English oak, still widely planted.

FIGURE 9.5 English oak.

The oak thrives on most soils, but the best shaped and sized specimens are found growing on the deep heavier loams. It can stand quite exposed sites, growing well but forming a more squat, flat-topped shape. In the present awareness of conservation considerations, the oak earns high marks. T. R. E. Southwood's research, as outlined in *Hedges* (Pollard, Hooper and Moore), indicates that as many as 284 species of invertebrates feed or live on a mature oak. Squirrels, mice and other rodents are attracted by a good acorn crop, which in turn attract owls hunting for such prey at night.

Taller trees

Common ash (Fraxinus excelsior) (Plate 9.7) (Figure 9.6)
The demise of the elm has focused attention on the ash as the most common hedgerow tree. Many are savagely kept in check with the routine flail cutting of hedges.

The ash will grow to form a tall, rather than spreading, form capable of reaching a height of 40 m (131 ft).

It is one of the last deciduous trees to come into leaf in the spring and one of the first to lose its leaves in the autumn.

PLATE 9.7 The ragged form of an ageing ash contrasts with the younger ash trees on the right-hand side of the road.

FIGURE 9.6 Common ash.

It produces a light, smooth-grained, hardwearing and strong wood, which is highly valued for the manufacture of furniture, coachwork, implement handles and for interior use in house-building.

Where a mature tree has been felled in a hedgerow and a number of new shoots have risen from the stump of the old tree, these can be allowed to grow to be coppiced for firewood or for tool handles.

The ash will grow on a wide variety of soils but produces the best timber when grown on a good deep loam. It is rarely seen growing well in exposed sites or on a thin, poor soil. Like the oak, it will live to a great age; up to 200-year-old specimens have been known.

TREES FOR WET SITES

Common alder (Alnus glutinosa) (Plate 9.8) (Figure 9.7)

The alder is a true native tree. It is found growing alongside streams, ditches and damp sites in general and is even capable of growing in areas too wet for poplars or willows.

PLATE 9.8 A line of mature common alders, somewhat bare-stemmed with sparse tops, forming a field margin on low-lying land.

FIGURE 9.7 Common alder.

It will grow on any soil type where moisture levels are adequate, to form a small, short-stemmed tree 15 m (50 ft) high at the most with an untidy crown. It does not live to a great age. Its timber has little use beyond firewood.

Alder bears attractive catkins in the spring, and seed 'cones' in autumn. Its roots have the ability to fix nitrogen in the soil, so it will not rob any adjacent crop of nutrients.

COMMON TREES NOT RECOMMENDED FOR HEDGEROW PLANTING

Beech and sweet and horse chestnuts are large spreading trees not recommended for hedgerows. They are more commonly grown for their woodland and ornamental value. They spread widely from lower down on the main stem to give good shade for cattle grazing in a parkland setting, where competition with adjacent cropping is not a problem.

Avoid planting trees which are liable to sucker freely, such as the small-leafed lime (*Tilia cordata*), elm (Plate 9.9) and aspen (*Populus*

*PLATE 9.9 The problem with elms. A forest of suckers have sprung up from the stump of one Jersey elm (*Ulmus minor var. sarniensis*) that died in 1976.*

tremula). The small-leafed lime is also not recommended, together with the broad-leafed lime (*Tilia platyphyllos*), because they are both capable of growing to a great height – over 30 m (99 ft) – and can reach 40 m (131 ft) earning the distinction of being the tallest deciduous trees in Britain. They can cause maintenance problems as they mature, if growing near buildings or power lines.

PLANTING

As stated earlier, the establishment of trees in a new hedge line is relatively easy, all the plants growing together from an equal start. It is recommended that the trees are given their own plastic sheet or mat mulch and are provided with a tubular tree shelter to encourage stem growth to get them growing ahead of the surrounding hedge and so minimise the risk of their being cut off by the hedge trimmer. If 45–60 cm (18–24 in) transplants are used for the hedge planting, then a larger size of tree or 'feathered whip' is suggested at 90–120 cm (3–4 ft) to give the tree a head start from the hedge, which will help to ensure that it is noticed should the hedge line be mechanically trimmed early in its life.

Regardless of whether the new hedge is machine or hand planted, the young feathered whip trees should be planted into a large hole, dug out with a spade to accommodate their full root area properly. Dig the hole at least 30 cm (1 ft) square and to the depth of the spade's blade, loosening the earth in the bottom of the hole to aid penetration of new root growth. Spread the tree's roots out evenly and replace the soil, firming up with the feet.

If the soil dug out of the hole is either impoverished, weed-infested or poor quality, it is often possible to dig up some cleaner and nutrient-rich soil from the adjacent cultivated field to place immediately around the roots and refill the hole.

Once planted, stake the trees and enclose them with a spiral guard or tubular tree shelter for protection and, in the latter instance, to stimulate growth. Tree shelters and trainers provide the young sapling tree with its own microclimate. This will encourage early establishment and more vigorous growth, free from cold winds, rodent damage etc. Ensure that the tree shelter tube is pushed firmly into the soil to discourage rodents from getting inside the tube and nesting in the warm sheltered conditions. Mice and voles within the tubes will often eat the bark at the base of the tree, killing it quickly.

If planting into a mature hedge, tag each tree to prevent it being trimmed by the hedge cutter (Plate 9.10).

PLATE 9.10 How not to treat trees planted into an existing hedge. The oak is still alive, but should have been tagged to prevent trimming damage.

SPACING

The position of trees in a hedge should be according to both personal preference and the eventual size of the crown of the maturing tree.

A spacing of 20–30 m (66–99 ft) apart is a good rule of thumb. It is better to space them at random to give a natural appearance. If spaced along a hedge at even intervals, it gives the impression of an estate avenue, which in some instances may be the effect desired. In most cases the trees will look better if they are dotted at random. Physical or natural features on the site may dictate their own influence on spacing to provide a desired effect. There are no hard and fast rules, except not to plant them so close that they eventually crowd each other out and stunt the growth of the hedge beneath their spreading canopy.

Take care to keep clear of electric or telephone pylons as well as buildings, walls and roadways. Try to envisage the area that the tree could occupy once it has grown to its mature size, to minimise the problems of maintenance.

The full benefit of hedges can soon be realised, but trees take longer to grow to a size where they can be appreciated. We now enjoy the beauty of mature trees which were planted in Victorian times, so it is fitting that each generation plants trees to maintain the continuity of mature trees and the pleasure of their presence around us.

Figure 9.8 shows the tree and its parts, the benefits it bestows upon man and wildlife alike, together with its life cycle.

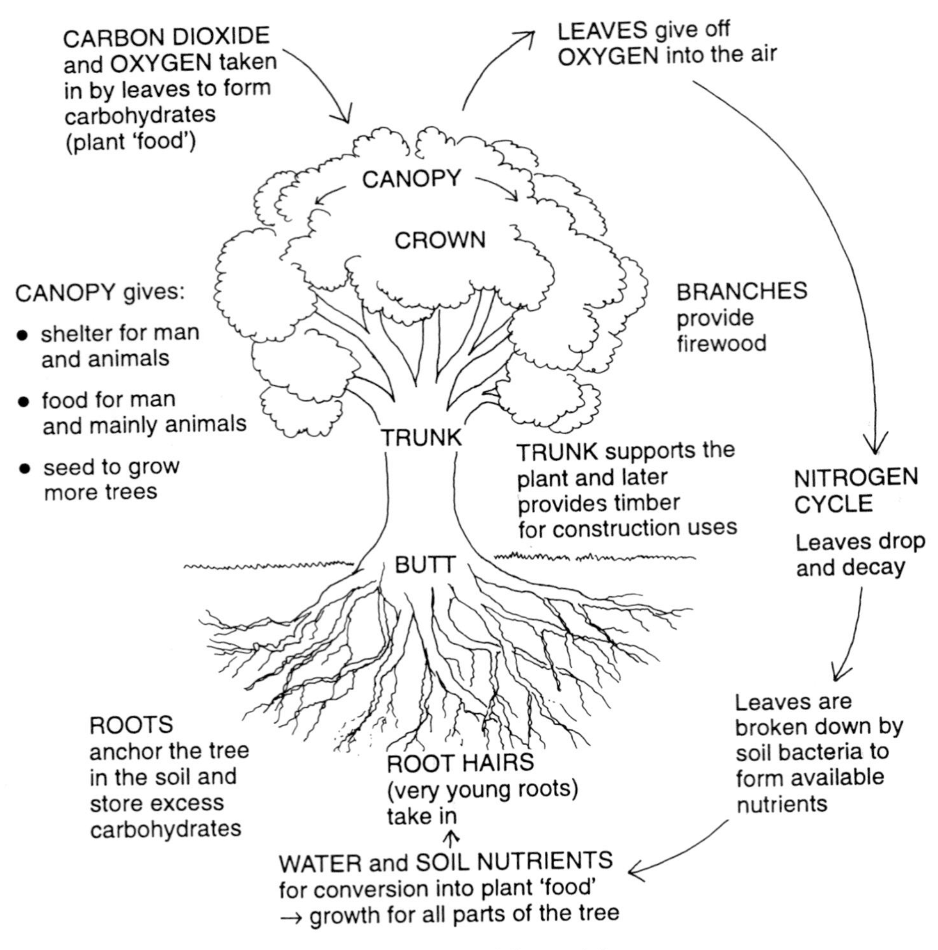

FIGURE 9.8 The tree: its parts and what it provides.

REFERENCES AND FURTHER READING

Brown, James (1982), *The Forester* (William Blackwood and Sons).

Narz, Kurt (1980), *Trees and Shrubs – Chatto Nature Guides* (Chatto and Windus Ltd.).

Phillips, Roger (1978), *Trees in Britain* (Pan Books Ltd., London).

Pollard, E., Hooper, M.D. and Moore, N.W. (1974), *Hedges* (William Collins Sons & Co. Ltd.).

Trees

Not all man's seed will raise fine sons
Nor will all acorns become fine oaks.
Yet, once born, they both will grow
Upwards, fast and free.
The child from youth will reach
To harness knowledge with wisdom
And take the reins of manhood.
So plant sound roots into strong soil
And the spreading branch will climb
To sift the sun and catch the rain.

Beware the evils of greed and envy,
Like knots in a straight grain
They spoil the quality of the wood.
Be not as brittle as the Ash,
Bend with the Willow in the wind.
Give your support to others,
Like the Hazel to the gardener's beans.
Be as charitable as the Chestnut
Distributing conkers to children.
Do your duty as does the Lime
Standing sentinel beside many a lane.
Copy not the Mistletoe -
A parasite living on others.
Be prepared, to stand alone
Like the Moorland Pine.
In a crowded world, sow but a little seed,
Never as freely as the Sycamore.
There is as much virtue in the hard beauty of Walnut
As in the scented softness of the Poplar –
Each has a value for differing needs.

Always remember the tree,
Rooted in youth to a single spot,
It strives to reach the clouds,
But can only give shade and shelter
To those who to it come.
You can travel freely over land and sea,
Fly above the clouds and yet return.
Use your gift of freedom
That other men and other trees
May also live and grow.

Murray Maclean

Chapter 10

Field Margins

You shall see them on a beautiful quarto page
where a neat rivulet of text shall meander
through a meadow of margin

RICHARD BRINSLEY SHERIDAN

As the value of arable crops declines at a time of excess production throughout much of western Europe, the importance of restoring the former beauty of our countryside becomes both feasible and relevant to current trends in the area of land required for future food needs. Unified grants for the establishment and maintenance of hedges and field margins around arable cropping land bear witness to this.

The main point of this book is to engender an interest in reviving the English hedgerow and to describe the important part it must play in maintaining the conservation of wildlife and the unique visual appeal of our landscape, part of which is the flora and fauna associated with hedgerow and woodland margins.

The drive for increased food production encouraged farmers to cultivate as much of every field as possible including the margins. However, the current cultural techniques of spraying or rotovating a 1–2 m (3–6 ft) strip between the crop and field edge to contain the spread of sterile brome, cleavers, nettles and other misplaced plants, indicates that farmers are prepared to sacrifice some land to ensure greater crop cleanliness and yield across the rest of the field. Encouraging farmers to treat all or part of this strip of 'no-man's-land' as a wildlife corridor and habitat should be only one painless step forward. This could transform the value of hedges in their role as conservators of wildlife.

Farmers will be quick to point out that leaving an unsprayed strip could lead to an explosive influx of noxious weeds from the hedgerow. Many of the problem weeds emanating from hedgerows thrive on fertiliser spun into the hedge bottom or because this area has been sprayed or disturbed by cultivations. Where hedge verges

PLATE 10.1 'Salt Way', an old Gloucestershire drove road with a wide verge, or margin, and old hedges. This exemplifies the desired qualities of field margins.

are kept free of fertiliser, sprays and cultivations, it does not take long to restore the balance of vegetation in favour of less aggressive annual and perennial broad-leaved plants (Plate 10.1).

The provision of a 2 m (6 ft 6 in) margin allows room for the farmer to incorporate a sterile strip around the field crop to prevent any unwelcome weed in the conservation margin from attempting to spread into the adjacent crop. FWAG (in their booklet *Farming and Field Margins*) concede the option of a 1 m (3 ft) sterile strip between the margin and crop as a compromise between the conflicting elements of necessity for the farmer to run a viable business and a desire to do the most he can to foster wildlife on the farm (Plate 10.2).

A field margin also has a worthwhile value to the farmer. It will play host to many insects (e.g. hoverflies) which predate upon pests in the adjacent crops.

CREATING AN ARABLE FIELD MARGIN

Crops growing close to a hedge will yield 10–15% less than the rest of the field; thus if a margin is left adjacent to the field edge, there is less to lose, as well as a reduction in the crop's growing costs.

It is recommended that a strip around the field be left uncropped and every effort made to ensure that no fertilisers and sprays are applied to this area.

PLATE 10.2 A narrow field margin separated from the field crop by a 1 m (3 ft) sterile strip, to protect the crop from intruding plants and the margin from crop sprays etc.

The width of the uncultivated strip is a matter of personal choice. Anything is better than nothing and the wider the better! A convenient width would be that of the mower intended to trim the strip.

The area involved can be marked out easily when ploughing or cultivating the field prior to cropping. The uncultivated strip should be mown to control vigorous weed species and help convert the range of plants from aggressive problem weeds to a better balance of flowering plants and grasses, which will begin to re-establish themselves as the fertility of the soil in the strip declines in the absence of inorganic fertilisers and no sprays are applied.

Currently, MAFF are paying grants for set-aside field margins. Contact your MAFF Regional Service Centre for full details.

NATURAL REGENERATION

Natural regeneration is more likely to give better results on lighter than on heavy soils.

A sward will only result if there are suitable seed sources in adjacent hedge bottoms or on nearby ditch banks.

The changes in the composition of the sward will be most rapid in the first two years, after which the rate of change slows down. The dominance of annual plants is most noticeable in the first season. Thereafter, perennials begin to establish a dense sward which makes it increasingly difficult for annuals to become established. The dominant perennials are those species able to make the best use of the high nutrient levels remaining in the soil from earlier cropping.

For those who wish to see a more diverse mix of wild flowers and grasses, it is possible to sow both in mixtures to suit conditions.

A SOWN SWARD

The sowing of wild grass or a farm grass ley (Plate 10.3) will help control weeds, where localised seed sources for regeneration are poor. Sowing is also the sure way to establish an attractive mixture that will enhance the conservation value of the margin. ADAS, FWAG and other local conservation bodies will be pleased to help choose a suitable mix according to soil type.

The preparation for sowing of margins with grass or wild flower mixtures needs to be as thorough as that undertaken for adjacent field crops.

PLATE 10.3 A sown margin of cocksfoot grass between other trial sections at the University Farm, Oxford, winter 1991.

THE TIMING OF MOWINGS

Large-scale experiments were established at the University Farm, Wytham, Oxford in 1987, funded by the Nature Conservancy Council with additional commercial support, to investigate the effects, timing and frequency of mowing on the development of both sown swards and natural regenerated field margins (Plate 10.4).

Changes on the fallowed crop margins of the experiment followed a similar pattern to that recorded on abandoned arable fields in North America during times of farming depression. A large number of plant species colonised at an early stage, with both annuals and perennials establishing together. But by the end of the second season, a dense perennial cover effectively excluded any further re-establishment of annual plants. Perennials were more adept at colonising any remaining small gaps in the sward.

The use of sown grass ley mixes proved advantageous over natural regeneration. For both sown and regenerated swards, management by mowing at specific times was necessary to prevent the spread of noxious and rhizomatous perennial weeds.

The inclusion of oxeye daisy in seed mixes gave a quick and dramatic visual effect, but it will become less dominant if subjected to spring mowing. All grasses included in the seed mixes established

PLATE 10.4 Field margin sward trials at the University Farm, Oxford. The field margin is 8 m (26 ft) wide either side of the hedgerow.

PLATE 10.5 Collins Farm field margins managed as tracks around each field. Less frequent cutting of the grass in summer would encourage the return of a wider variety of plants from adjacent hedges.

well, but crested dog's tail declined quickly if the margins were left uncut. Scabious and knapweed established readily. Cowslips required three years of growth before flowering. They germinated either when freshly sown in summer or following a cold winter.

The problem weeds – brome, blackgrass and wild oats – which flower in that order, required cutting at specific times to control their spread. Brome had to be cut in early growth before it bolted. Growth in blackgrass and wild oats was reduced by a summer cut and both declined within two years under this regime. Couch was similarly weakened by summer cutting. Consult your ADAS or FWAG advisor for more precise details of cutting times related to the mixture of flowers and grasses present in your own margins. Poorly timed cutting can be ineffective and may be detrimental to achieving the desired effect (Plate 10.5).

ENCOURAGING BUTTERFLIES

Many species of butterfly do not move far from their established habitat. If one is keen on their successful establishment, take note of their habitat requirements and ensure that the necessary plants are available – and in flower – at the times needed by particular butterflies. Many butterflies will remain within one field area for their whole life and hedgerows are an invaluable shelter for them. The combination of a hedgerow and its adjacent field margin can provide the butterfly, among many other insects and mammals, with the ingredients for a good habitat.

It is important to realise that butterflies need different foods for their larval and adult stages. In addition, different butterflies feed on different plants: small tortoiseshell live and feed around short nettles, such as the regrowth after summer mowing. Peacocks feed on tall nettles in south-facing, sunny positions. Meadow browns gather on the oxeye daisy for its rich source of nectar.

EXCLUSION OF FERTILISER AND SPRAYS

Great care must be taken with both the application of fertiliser and sprays to ensure that none are applied to the margin or the sterile strip.

Fertiliser spinners can be fitted with a blanking plate to prevent spread on one side for the first bout round the field edge. Similarly, the end nozzle of the sprayer can be fitted with a stop tap to prevent chemical drift or direct application to the field margin. Both controls should become standard practice around the edge of all crops to prevent wastage of expensive chemicals and fertiliser, so reducing variable costs.

REFERENCE AND FURTHER READING

FWAG (1991), *Farming and Field Margins* (a booklet printed by Monsanto Agricultural Company).

Smith, H. and MacDonald, D.W. (1989), *Brighton Crop Protection Conference Report (Weeds Section).*

Chapter 11

Weed Control

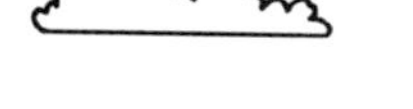

What is a weed?
A plant whose virtues have not been discovered
FORTUNE OF THE REPUBLIC   RALPH WALDO EMERSON

Complete control of competition between weeds and the hedgerow plants is essential to ensure good growth in the early years of the hedge (Plate 11.1). Once established, the hedge will be able to compete with weeds on equal terms.

PLATE 11.1 Good weed control through the growing season helps ensure vigorous growth. These 90–120 cm (3–4 ft) wild cherry transplants are grown from 25 cm (10 in) seedlings in one year.

Grass and broadleaved weeds allowed to grow around young trees and shrubs will compete with them for moisture and nutrients; they also harbour pests which may harm the young stock.

The large number of plants required for establishing a hedge encourages the use of herbicides in preference to some of the control methods adopted with wider spaced individual trees in a woodland setting, e.g. plastic or felt mats placed around each plant would be uneconomic for hedges.

ORGANIC MULCHES

The use of an organic mulch or compost can be expensive and time-consuming to spread. It may provide a home for damaging rodents such as mice, voles and rats which are capable of gnawing the plant stems in dry weather and during adverse winter conditions; they may use the mulch as a place to hibernate or nest.

If straw is readily available on the farm or from a local farm supplier, it may be cheap to purchase and spread around the plants to provide a thick mulch, which will suppress weed growth.

Bark chippings or other chipped crop waste, such as fruit tree prunings, can provide a mulch with a better structure and length of life than straw and with a reduction in the risk of rodent 'squatters' moving in.

Farmyard manure has long been used as a mulch for controlling weeds and providing organic nutrients to garden rose beds. If available, it can work just as well for a young hedge.

Where straw, bark chippings or any other organic form of mulch is used, it is recommended that some nitrogen fertiliser is spread upon the mulch to assist with its decomposition and to provide nutrients for the young hedge.

Application of a soil-acting herbicide to the ground before laying an organic mulch will enhance weed control over a longer period.

The Forestry Commission has undertaken trials to assess the comparative effectiveness and longevity of a black polythene mulch versus herbicides. Both greatly enhanced the survival rate and growth of plants.

POLYTHENE SHEET MULCH

In the trials poor quality trees survived and grew when protected with a polythene mulch, but died when planted without a mulch into adjacent weedy ground.

The trials highlighted the necessity of the polythene sheet mulch covering at least an area of 1.25 m^2 around each plant. When applying the principle to a hedgerow it means that the sheet must be continuous, with the trees and shrubs planted through holes made in the sheet.

The main benefits from using a polythene mulch are: the complete suppression of weeds, which will compete with the plants for moisture; a substantial reduction in soil moisture loss from the soil's surface by evaporation; and the retention in the topsoil of nutrients, which combine with the soil moisture to make themselves more readily available for further fresh root growth. The soil will also warm up earlier in the spring and maintain a higher average temperature throughout the summer. The resulting improvement in root growth will in turn enable the individual plants to grow stronger and taller.

The only potential problem is that a polythene mulch may encourage shallow rooting, stimulated by the warm, moist topsoil. This could render the plants vulnerable to moisture stress should the polythene sheet be removed prior to full establishment. For optimum benefit a polythene mulch should be kept in position for at least two to three years.

Hedges have been established by planting through a continuous polythene sheet, which has been mechanically laid and its edges buried. Use of a sheet laying machine requires cultivated ground along the length of the proposed hedge line. This may not always be physically possible if the hedge is to be planted close to a road, wall or an existing fence.

The most common and cost-effective way of controlling grass and weed growth is to use herbicides (the collective term used to describe chemicals developed to kill plants).

THE USE OF HERBICIDES

In recent years there has been a steady increase in the amount of legislation governing the use of all herbicides.

Pressure from conservation groups, allied to emerging and growing problems of chemical residues in the soil, which are now affecting the quality of ground water supplies, has combined to enhance public awareness.

Since the end of the Second World War, the chemical control

of weeds has advanced at a stunning rate, allowing farmers and growers to greatly increase the growth, yield and quality of crops. It has enabled a major reduction in manpower to be achieved in the face of static, or falling, prices. The use of the hoe for weeding arable and vegetable crops has been largely eliminated. Gone are the gangs of workers weeding and singling sugar beet and vegetable crops across southern and eastern England.

Pressures upon the farming community to produce crops at lower market prices have forced the pace of development in herbicide use to reduce labour requirements on the land.

Recent legislation to curb the misuse of many chemicals has led to growing restrictions, which are reflected in the recommendations for controlling weeds in a newly planted hedge.

The Food and Environment Protection Act (FEPA) 1985 was introduced to provide mandatory powers for the control and use of pesticides on the land; to protect animal, human and plant life in the environment. A pesticide is a substance, usually chemical, which destroys pests. Pests include animals, plants and other organisms. This Act was followed by the Control of Pesticides Regulations 1986. Most of the chemicals available for the control of weeds, pests and diseases were already on the market and being used in accordance with the MAFF approval scheme which defines the use of each chemical for specific approved applications.

The introduction of the new Regulations has led to many previously approved uses now being withdrawn until clearance for their continued use has been sought and approved. Some uses for specific chemicals have been granted an 'off-label' approval, whereby their use for stated purposes can be continued, but entirely at the user's risk.

In 1989 the Control of Substances Hazardous to Health Regulations (COSHH) came into force, to add to the regulatory powers governing the use of pesticides. It is important that any person not familiar with these Regulations becomes fully conversant with their implications and requirements, before using any chemicals for the control of weeds, pests and diseases on new hedges.

The complex and ever-changing legal requirements for pesticide use are so extensive that this book cannot cover the subject adequately and so will not attempt to do so.

The chemicals listed for controlling grass and weed growth in new hedges have obtained full approval under current legislation, *except where otherwise stated*.

As with all legislation, there are anomalies in interpretation. Chemicals cleared for use in hedges and in woodland appear under the heading of 'Forestry', but the *production* of most trees and shrubs is classified under 'Hardy Ornamental Nursery Stock'. A limited range of chemicals are cleared for 'Forest' use, yet if the same plants are grown in an ornamental setting for ornamental use, there is a much wider selection of chemicals available.

Chemical recommendations do not cover rate of application, water volume, addition of wetting agents or compatibility with other chemicals. These factors vary according to soil type, weather conditions, crop growth stage and the selection of plants used.

Commercial contractors, growers and farmers will have the available information to make a correct assessment of these variable factors, or have access to professional advice to make a correct decision.

For those wishing to undertake chemical weed control along a new hedge and who do not have the experience of using herbicides, it is recommended that they contact the local officers of one of the following bodies: the Agricultural Development and Advisory Service (ADAS), the Ministry of Agriculture, Fisheries and Food (MAFF), the Agricultural Training Board (ATB), the National Farmers' Union (NFU). Their addresses are in the local telephone directory and, if they are not able to help, they will be able to direct the enquiry to the most appropriate local organisation.

Suppliers of pesticides to farmers now employ their own agronomists to advise upon crop protection chemicals. They will be conversant with current legislation and approved chemicals for use in woodland and hedgerow planting.

The following details provide a basis for choosing suitable herbicides. Consult the manufacturer's product label for full instructions on correct use.

Herbicides fall into four main categories. The first three categories have both advantages and limitations, but a range of chemicals in each category is available for use on young trees and shrubs, giving the grower a selection of options according to the weeds present, their size and severity.

Contact

The herbicide kills weed plants by contact with the leaves. It will only desiccate existing foliage, so weeds with large roots, e.g. perennials, may soon regrow after treatment. Contact chemicals are best suited to the control of seedlings and small weeds, which are killed more readily.

Translocated (systemic)

The herbicide is absorbed through the plant's leaves into its translocation system. Translocated herbicides kill plants in differing ways according to the chemical composition. They may stimulate the treated plant to grow at an excessive and fatal rate, or destroy certain tissues or metabolic systems within the plant.

Residual
The herbicide is sprayed onto the surface of the soil and acts upon the developing roots or hypocotyl of weeds, sometimes killing those present, but also killing them as they germinate. The chemical binds onto the soil particles and normally remains active in the top few inches of the soil surface for weeks or months. It can be compared to the effect of paint in preventing metal from rusting – so long as the cover remains complete no 'rust' can form; disturb the surface layer and the 'rust' will flourish on exposed areas.

Selective
The herbicide's action is selective, with the ability to eradicate one particular plant type within a crop of closely related species. For example flamprop-M-isopropyl (Shell's Commando), a translocated post-emergence herbicide, will eradicate only wild oats in most growing cereal crops (except oats).

The herbicide's mode of action will normally be that of one of the three preceding groups, i.e. contact, translocated or residual.

Weed Control Prior to Planting

It is always best to plant a new hedge into weed-free ground. The ground may be cultivated, to remove the weeds present and to work the soil into an open texture for ease of planting.

In the autumn, prior to preparing the ground, kill off existing vegetation with one of the following herbicides:

Paraquat (Gramoxone or Scythe)
A contact herbicide which will desiccate (dry out) the aerial parts of grasses and broadleaved annual weeds, but some grasses (e.g. annual meadow grass) and deeper-rooted perennial weeds will recover.

Paraquat is more commonly used as a guarded spray around plants in the growing season to reduce weed competition. Great care should be taken to avoid spray application or drift onto the bark of young plants, which can be damaged.

It is poisonous and subject to the Poisons Rules 1982. It is toxic if swallowed.

Paraquat can be used as a pre-emergence spray on tree and shrub seedbeds, but must be applied at least three days before the seedlings are due to emerge.

To achieve the best results, spray the weeds when they are growing actively, in spring and early summer, during cool conditions. Do not spray in hot weather or when rain is imminent, as both will reduce the effective uptake of the chemical by the weeds, resulting in only a partial kill of their aerial parts. The chemical is quickly deactivated on contact with the soil, allowing planting to be carried out three days after spraying.

Paraquat/diquat (Parable/Farmon PDQ)

A non-residual, contact herbicide and crop desiccant. It acts quickly to kill the green leaf tissue of plants by contact.

The addition of a non-ionic wetter can improve the contact action and allow good weed kill at a lower dose rate. The chemical is deactivated quickly on contact with the soil and is active within minutes of drying on the leaf surface.

It is best applied to small weeds which are growing actively. Its speed of action and overall efficiency will be reduced in cold conditions.

Paraquat/diquat must only be applied as a directed spray to weeds growing around the plants in a hedgerow line, using a shielded spray boom to prevent spray drift.

As with paraquat (alone), any contact with the bark of young trees should be avoided. It will also cause damage if sprayed onto the green parts of plants.

The chemical is toxic and subject to the Poisons Rules 1982. Like straight paraquat, it is only available to professional contractors, farmers and growers.

Glyphosate (Roundup)

A translocated, non-residual herbicide which will kill the aerial and root parts of most weeds. Grasses (such as couch) must have an adequate area of leaf which is growing actively to ensure a good uptake of the chemical to kill all roots present. The same applies to the more persistent perennial weeds such as thistles and docks, which are best sprayed when in flower.

The chemical takes longer to achieve complete control of weed growth than desiccants, so should be applied early in the autumn and spring.

To obtain best results, do not spray in dry, hot weather, when rain is imminent or if frost is predicted.

The chemical is rapidly deactivated upon contact with the soil; allow at least 14 days before cultivating the sprayed weeds to ensure full uptake and activity within the weed tissue.

Trifluralin (Treflan)
A soil-incorporated residual herbicide which will not control existing weed growth. It acts upon germinating weeds and must be worked into the prepared ground soon after applying. It will control a wide range of annual weeds well into the growing season.

Best results are achieved by spraying onto well-cultivated ground which has been prepared as a fine, level, clod-free seedbed. The chemical must be harrowed or lightly rotovated into the top 8–10 cm (3–4 in) of the soil within half-an-hour of application.

The use of this chemical has been approved for a wide range of edible crops and for use on ornamentals and nursery fruit trees and bushes. Treflan currently has no specific clearance for use on trees and shrubs. It can be used under plant nursery conditions. It is recommended that transplants are hardened-off before planting into treated soil.

Weed Control After Planting

Simazine (Gesatop)
A soil-acting, residual herbicide and member of the triazine group. It is safe to spray over most plants in the hedge line for the maintenance of weed-free conditions.

The chemical is root-absorbed and acts by interrupting photosynthesis. It is best applied to a fine, moist soil which must be free of weeds. Regular applications of small amounts of water – 30 mm (1 in) per hectare (12 mm (½ in) per acre) – applied every ten days will retain topsoil moisture levels, keeping the herbicide active as well as helping the early establishment of the young plants in the hedge line or nursery.

In dry weather the herbicide's uptake and effect is reduced. Light irrigation will reactivate the chemical in the soil; excessive irrigation or heavy rain – especially on light soils – can wash the chemical down the soil profile and increase the risk of uptake by and damage to sensitive species such as ash, hornbeam and *Prunus* species.

When the herbicide is used at the low rates recommended by the manufacturer for spraying over transplanted trees and shrubs, its activity is reduced within eight to ten weeks, according to soil type, due to breakdown by soil organisms. One further low-rate top-up application is necessary during the summer to maintain full control of seedling weeds.

Most translocated and residual herbicides have limitations in the range of weeds which they control. Simazine will not prevent the germination of cleaver, speedwell and willowherb, and repeated use has led to resistant strains of groundsel and annual meadow grass developing in many areas.

Atrazine (Gesaprim)

Another triazine herbicide for the pre- and post-emergence control of a wide range of weeds. It is most commonly used for weed control in maize and sweetcorn. It has received full clearance for use in coniferous forests and around field boundaries, where it may be used in the year prior to hedge planting, to maintain a weed-free strip ready for planting the following spring. It should not be used for the control of weeds in a growing hedge.

Atrazine has both foliar- and soil-acting capabilities. It is absorbed by the leaves of emerging weeds and through their roots, killing them slowly. It is best applied to clean ground in spring or early summer. It will maintain weed-free conditions all summer, but the ground should be ploughed or cultivated in the following autumn to ensure full dispersal of any residues prior to planting the hedge.

Propyzamide (Kerb)

A soil-acting, residual herbicide for use on a wide range of agricultural crops (oilseed rape, sugar beet, field beans and lucerne) and horticultural crops (brassicas, lettuce and fruit crops). It is an excellent chemical for maintaining weed-free conditions, as well as having some activity on various existing seedling weeds.

It can be effective for the suppression of many established grasses.

Kerb can be sprayed at appropriate rates on young nursery beds and over the planted hedge; it is safe to spray over the hedge during the growing season. The low rate recommended allows a further application to be made eight to ten weeks after the initial post-planting spray. The low application rate recommended may not fully control fumitory, shepherd's purse, dead-nettle and scarlet pimpernel. Charlock, field pansy, mayweed and sow-thistle are not controlled by propyzamide but can be when mixed with simazine or other approved residual herbicides. It will maintain its residual activity through the main summer period of weed germination and active growth. Best results are obtained by spraying onto clean, clod-free, moist soil in late winter, following planting. Soils with a high organic content reduce the activity of the chemical more quickly than sandy loams.

Diphenamid (Enide)

A safe, soil-acting, pre-emergence, residual herbicide with a short active life. It can be used to control a limited range of weeds in young trees and shrubs.

The chemical must be applied to a fine, moist and weed-free soil, prior to the germination of weed seedlings. Do not use on soils with more than a 10% organic matter content. Adequate moisture is essential to ensure good uptake of the chemical and light applications of water will be necessary to maintain Diphenamid's activity in dry conditions. The herbicide is absorbed by the roots of weeds as they germinate.

Use at the rates recommended for ornamentals. A further top-up spray can be applied six to eight weeks later to maintain weed-free conditions over an extended period well into summer. This technique will control the germination of most weed seeds past their normal active growth stages. Weeds not normally controlled by diphenamid include black bindweed, dead-nettle, field pansy, black nightshade and sow-thistle.

Chlorthan-dimethyl (Dacthal)

A residual herbicide for the control of annual dicotyledons (two-leafed plants) in soft fruit, vegetable and ornamental crops.

It must be applied to fine, clod- and weed-free soil with adequate rainfall or irrigation following application to ensure good results.

Check the manufacturer's product label for the list of ornamental plants over which Dacthal can be sprayed safely.

Dacthal and Enide mixed in equal volumes provide a broader weed-control activity than the two chemicals used independently. The mixture is recommended for use on hardy ornamental nursery stock and gives the added control of fat-hen, dead-nettle, field pansy and sow-thistle, plus some control of black bindweed and black nightshade.

Oxadiazon (Ronstar Liquid)

A very effective, soil-acting, residual herbicide, with some contact action for use on woody ornamental trees and shrubs.

The dictionary definition of 'ornamental' is 'a plant grown for its beauty'. Thus, if a hedge is planted for commercial and farming use, this herbicide may NOT be used. If the hedge is to be planted for the ornamental value (beauty) of the chosen trees and shrubs, then

Ronstar may be used for the control of weeds around the plants.

It should only be applied as an overall spray in late winter/early spring, immediately after planting and before weeds have begun to emerge. It must be applied before buds have begun to break on any of the species planted to prevent scorch damage to the emerging young leaves. Once the leaves have broken bud, it will only be possible to use the herbicide as a directed spray to the soil around each plant. This chemical must not be used over a growing crop. It will control a wide range of seedling weeds, including groundsel (simazine-resistant) and willowherb. The control of perennials (e.g. bindweed) is enhanced if they are just emerging when the chemical is applied.

Chickweed and volunteer cereals become resistant after emergence. Oxadiazon mixed with simazine or propyzamide helps to control them.

Consult your local ADAS adviser or chemical supplier before use.

Metazachlor (Butisan S)

A soil-acting, residual herbicide for use on a range of vegetable crops and hardy ornamental nursery stock. It is best applied after planting to weed-free conditions as an overall spray, prior to bud-break.

The chemical has some ability to control or suppress emerged seedling weeds which have not developed beyond the two to four true leaf stage. Its main action is to inhibit weed seed germination through root uptake.

Metazachlor can be mixed with other approved herbicides to give better control of a wider range of weeds. It will give good control of groundsel, which is resistant to the triazine herbicides simazine and atrazine.

Lower application rates should be used on sandy or light soils. For these soils it is recommended that a low rate pre-emergence spray is followed by a second, post-emergence treatment at the same rate, 10–12 weeks later, at the *first* sight of fresh weed seedling emergence. A maximum of three applications may be made in one year.

Damage to the growing plants can occur if heavy rain or excessive watering occurs soon after spraying. It is important to ensure that the soil after planting is left moist, firm and free of any clods. This will ensure that the chemical remains fully active in the soil surface and is not leached lower to cause damage to new root growth.

The top-up (second) spray, later in the summer, should not be applied during prolonged hot weather or during the heat of the day. To avoid short-term scorch damage, apply the herbicide in cool morning or evening conditions.

Pendimethalin (Stomp)

A residual herbicide for the control of annual grasses, blackgrass, wild oats, cleaver and speedwell in winter wheat, barley and rye. It is also approved for use in both top and soft fruit crops. The addition of metazachlor (Butisan S) for summer use increases the range of weeds effectively controlled.

It must be applied to fine, moist and weed-free soil and soil moisture levels must be maintained for optimum chemical activity.

It can be used during the dormant season (November–March inclusive) as an overall spray prior to bud-break. Thereafter it must be used as a directed spray. 'Stomp' has approval for use as a pre-emergence herbicide in farm coppice and woodland during the dormant season, on both conifer and broadleaved trees and shrubs.

Consult the manufacturer's product label for the correct rates of use according to the time of year.

Alloxydim-sodium (Clout)

A translocated herbicide for the post-emergence suppression of most grass weeds except annual meadow grass on woody ornamental trees and shrubs.

Note: This chemical has only been approved for use on *woody ornamentals* in addition to a wide range of vegetable crops and strawberries.

Couch and other grass weeds are often a major problem in establishing hedges, particularly beside roads, paths and on the edge of fields. This herbicide will stunt the growth of couch and restrict its competition with young trees and shrubs. Other weeds suppressed include wild oats, blackgrass, rye-grass (at the seedling stage), sterile brome and volunteer cereals.

Before using any of the approved chemicals described, it is essential that the manufacturer's label instructions are studied carefully, or the correct advice obtained, to ensure that the application and dilution rates are suitable for the site and prevailing weather conditions.

The performance of all soil-acting, residual herbicides will vary considerably according to the soil type and its organic matter content and moisture.

The application rate for use on or around hedgerow plants will be lower than the recommendation for other approved crop applications.

Tables 11.1 and 11.2 set out the susceptibility of a wide range of common weeds to herbicides applied as both pre- and post-emergence sprays over planted hedges.

Table 11.1 Pre-Emergence Weed Control

Weed	*Butisan S*	*Enide*	*Kerb*	*Simazine*	*Dacthal*	*Ronstar*	*Flexidor*
Bents	–	–	S	–	–	–	–
Bent – creeping	–	–	S	–	–	–	–
Bittersweet	–	–	S	–	–	–	–
Black bindweed	MS	R	S	MS	MS	S	MS
Blackgrass	S	–	S	–	–	–	–
Black nightshade	–	R	S	S	MS	S	S
Brome – barren	MS	–	S	–	–	–	–
– soft	–	–	S	–	–	–	–
Buttercup – creeping	–	–	S	–	–	–	–
Camomile – corn	–	–	–	S	–	–	–
– stinking	–	–	–	S	–	–	–
Charlock	–	–	–	S	R	S	S
Chickweed – common	S	S	S	S	S	R	S
– mouse-eared	S	S	S	S	S	R	S
Cleavers	MS	R	S	R	R	S	MS
Cocksfoot	–	–	S	–	–	–	–
Common couch	–	–	S	–	–	–	–

Symbols: S = susceptible; MS = moderately susceptible; R = resistant

Table 11.1 (*contd.*) Pre-Emergence Weed Control

Weed	*Butisan S*	*Enide*	*Kerb*	*Simazine*	*Dacthal*	*Ronstar*	*Flexidor*
Cranesbill – cut-leaved	S	R	R	R	R	–	–
– meadow	S	–	–	–	–	–	–
Creeping soft grass	–	–	S	–	–	–	–
Cress – hairy bitter	–	S	–	–	–	S	S
Crested dog's-tail	–	–	S	–	–	–	–
Dead-nettle – red	S	R	R	S	MS	S	S
– white	–	R	R	S	MS	S	S
Dock – broadleaved	–	–	S	–	–	–	–
False oat grass	–	–	S	–	–	–	–
Fat-hen	MS	MS	S	S	S	S	S
Fescues	–	–	S	–	–	–	–
Fescue – meadow	–	–	S	–	–	–	–
Field horsetail	–	–	MS (at high dose rate only)	–	–	–	–
Flebane – Canadian	S	–	–	R	–	MS	S
Fool's-parsley	–	–	–	MS	–	–	–
Forget-me-not	S	–	MS	S	–	–	–

Weed	*Butisan S*	*Enide*	*Kerb*	*Simazine*	*Dacthal*	*Ronstar*	*Flexidor*
Fumitory – common	R	R	MS	S	R	S	S
Gromwell – Field	S	–	–	–	–	–	–
Groundsel	S	S	R	MS (at high dose rate only)	R	S	MS (at high dose rate only)
Hemp nettle – common	R	–	–	S	–	–	–
Henbit	–	–	–	S	–	–	–
Knotgrass	R	MS	S	R	S	S	S
Marigold – common	S	–	–	S	–	S	–
Mat grass	–	–	S	–	–	–	–
Mayweed – scented	S	S	R	S	R	S	S
– scentless	S	S	R	S	R	S	S
Meadow foxtail	–	–	S	–	–	–	–
Meadow grass – annual	S	S	S	S	MS	S	R
– rough & smooth	–	–	S	–	–	–	–
Mustard – black	–	S	–	S	–	–	–
– white	–	S	–	S	–	–	–
Nettle – annual	MS	S	S	S	S	S	S

Table 11.1 (*contd.*) Pre-Emergence Weed Control

Weed	*Butisan S*	*Enide*	*Kerb*	*Simazine*	*Dacthal*	*Ronstar*	*Flexidor*
Nightshade – black	R	R	S	S	MS	S	S
Onion couch	–	MS	–	–	–	–	–
Orache – common	S	MS	–	MS	–	S	S
Oxalis	–	–	–	–	–	S	–
Pansy – field	R	R	R	MS	S	R	S
– wild	R	R	R	MS	S	R	S
Parsley – piert	S	–	–	S	–	–	–
Pearlwort – procumbent	R	S	MS	–	–	R	MS
Penny-cress – field	R	S	S	S	R	–	S
Pimpernel – scarlet	–	–	R	S	–	–	S
Pineapple weed	S	–	–	S	–	–	–
Plantain – broadleaved	–	–	–	–	–	–	S
Poppy – common	S	–	–	S	–	–	–
Purple moor grass	–	–	S	–	–	–	–
Radish – wild	–	–	–	S	–	S	–
Redshank	MS	MS	S	MS	MS	S	S
Rye-grasses	–	S	S	–	–	–	–

Weed	Butisan S	Enide	Kerb	Simazine	Dacthal	Ronstar	Flexidor
Sedges	–	–	MS	–	–	–	–
Sheep's sorrel	–	S	S	–	–	–	–
Shepherd's-purse	S	S	S	S	R	S	S
Smooth sow-thistle	R	–	R	S	–	S	R
Speedwells	S	S	S	R	S	S	S
Speedwell – ivy-leaved	S	S	S	R	R	S	S
Spurrey	MS	S	S	S	–	S	S
Sweet vernal grass	–	–	S	–	–	–	–
Timothy	–	–	S	–	–	–	–
Tufted hair grass	–	–	S	–	–	–	–
Volunteer cereals	R	S	S	S	R	R	R
Wavy hair grass	–	–	S	–	–	–	–
Wild oat	R	S	S	S	R	R	R
Willowherb – American	R	S	MS	R	R	S	R

Table 11.2 Post-Emergence Weed Control

Weed	*Butisan S*	*Kerb*	*Ronstar*	*Dacthal*	*Clout*	*Flexidor*
Bents	–	S	–	–	S	–
Bent – creeping	–	S	–	–	MS	–
Bindweed – black	–	S (at seedling stage)	–	–	–	–
– perennial	–	–	MS (at high dose rate only)	–	–	–
Blackgrass	S (up to 2 leaf stage)	S	–	–	–	–
Black nightshade	–	S (at seedling stage)	–	–	–	–
Brome – barren	–	S	–	–	S	–
Buttercup – creeping	–	MS (at full dose rate) (winter application)	– –	–	–	–
Chickweed – common	S (up to 4 leaf stage)	S (as seedling or established plant)	– –	–	–	–
Cleavers	–	S (at seedling stage)	–	–	–	–
Cocksfoot	–	MS	–	–	MS	–
Couch	–	MS	–	–	MS	–
Creeping soft grass	–	S	–	–	S	–
Cress – creeping bitter	–	–	–	–	–	S
– hairy bitter	–	–	–	–	–	S

Symbols: S = susceptible; MS = moderately susceptible; R = resistant

Weed	*Butisan S*	*Kerb*	*Ronstar*	*Dacthal*	*Clout*	*Flexidor*
Crested dog's-tail	–	S	–	–	–	–
Dock – broadleaved	–	S (at high dose rate on seedlings)	–	–	–	–
– curled	–		–	–	–	–
False oat grass	–	S	–	–	S	–
Fat-hen	–	S (at seedling stage)	–	–	–	–
Fescues	–	S	–	–	R	–
Fescues – meadow	–	S	–	–	R	–
Fleabane – Canadian	S (as small plant)	–	–	–	–	S (as small plant)
Forget-me-not	S (up to 2 true leaf stage)	–	–	–	–	–
Knotgrass	–	S (at seedling stage)	–	–	–	–
Marigold – common	S (up to 2 true leaf stage)	–	–	–	–	–
Mat grass	–	S	–	–	S	–
Mayweed – scented	S (up to 4 true leaf stage)	–	–	–	–	–
– scentless			–	–	–	–
Meadow foxtail	–	S	–	–	S	–
Meadow grass – annual	–	S	–	–	R	–
– rough & smooth	–	S	–	–	S	–
Penny-cress – field	–	–	–	–	–	S (as small plant)

Table 11.2 (*contd.*) Post-Emergence Weed Control

Weed	*Butisan S*	*Kerb*	*Ronstar*	*Dacthal*	*Clout*	*Flexidor*
Purple moor grass	–	S	–	–	–	–
Redshank	–	S (at seedling stage)	–	–	–	–
Rye-grasses	–	S	–	–	R	–
Sedges	–	MS (at high dose rate only)	–	–	–	–
Shepherd's-purse	–	–	–	–	–	S (as small plant)
Speedwells	S (up to 2 true leaf stage)	S (at seedling stage)	–	S (at seedling to small plant stage)	–	–
Speedwell – ivy-leaved	S (up to 2 true leaf stage)	S (at seedling stage)	–	R	–	–
Sweet vernal grass	–	S	–	–	S	–
Timothy	–	S	–	–	S	–
Tufted hair grass	–	S	–	–	S	–
Volunteer cereals	–	S	–	–	S	–
Wavy hair grass	–	S	–	–	S	–
Wild oat	–	S	–	–	S	–

REFERENCES AND FURTHER READING

ADAS (1988), *Leaflet P3172 Weed Control in Field-grown Nursery Stock* (MAFF).

Forestry Commission, *Information Notes 171, 201 and 203 (1990–91).*

Fryer, J. and Makepeace, R. (1972), *Weed Control Handbook Volume II – Recommendations* (Blackwells Scientific Publications).

Ivens, G. W. (1992), *The UK Pesticide Guide 1992* (CAB International and British Crop Protection Council).

MAFF/ADAS (1985), *Chemical Weed Control in Field-grown Nursery Stock* (MAFF).

Chapter 12

Disease and Pest Control

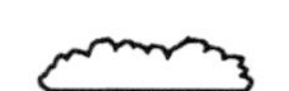

A desperate disease requires a dangerous remedy.
6 NOVEMBER 1605 GUY FAWKES

The nurseryman has to protect the emerging seedling in the seedbed to keep it free from attack by both diseases and pests. Throughout the growing season, from emergence and into the second year of growth to become a saleable transplant, preventative sprays are applied to control disease infection (Plate 12.1).

PLATE 12.1 *Two years' growth on a mixed species roadside hedge. The line of plants close to the field has grown more vigorously due to less localised weed competition and fertiliser and disease control sprays applied to the cereal crop.*

Attacks from aphid, caterpillar and weevil pests are controlled as they occur.

The professional grower is strictly regulated in the range and application of pesticides which he can employ, to maintain healthy and vigorous growth.

DISEASES

The two most important diseases of the hedgerow are fire blight and mildew.

Fire Blight

This was first observed in 1780 on apple and pear trees in the Hudson Valley, United States. By 1900 it had reached the Pacific coast. It was first reported outside the United States in New Zealand orchards in 1919. The disease initially occurred in England in 1957, when it was identified in a Kent pear orchard. Since then it has been recorded throughout Northern Europe and has spread beyond the boundaries of Kent into most counties of central and southern England.

The disease is of particular concern to apple and pear growers because an infection can cause severe die-back of fruiting branches, leading to the death of trees which are not treated in time.

Fire blight is caused by the bacterium *Erwinia amylovora,* which affects many members of the sub-family *Pomoideae.* It will attack other ornamental species such as *Crataegus, Cotoneaster* and *Sorbus. Prunus* and *Rosa* are not affected.

The bacterium lies dormant over winter, but during moist, warm weather in early summer (18°C (64°F)) it spreads rapidly. It can be spread by wind and rain as well as by pruning and saw cuts. Blossoms are susceptible to infection, and the disease spreads through cuts and other wounds to the bark, such as late hedge cutting in the spring.

The bacterial spore is capable of spreading over a distance of 200 m, but is more likely to be transferred over short distances from an infected tree to its immediate neighbours.

The first symptoms will be seen when clusters of blossoms die off prematurely. Later infections often start with young shoots becoming limp, wilting and hanging over like a 'crook'. The leaves then turn dark brown but do not readily fall off.

Scraping the bark of an infected branch or shoot will reveal reddish-brown stained tissue underneath. It can turn a dark green to brown colour as the infection spreads. Sometimes the infected wood produces a bacterial watery ooze. It is often necessary to scrape the bark back a substantial distance from the visibly infected area to reach fresh, uninfected tissue.

Once fire blight has been identified, it is important to cut off all infected branches. Felling complete bushes or trees may be necessary to ensure that all infected wood is removed. Immediately burn all the prunings and timber to prevent the spread of the infection.

If the disease breaks out in a nursery, dig up all the infected trees and burn them immediately. Then carry out regular inspections of the crop twice a week until there are no more symptoms of the bacterium spreading across the crop. An outbreak in one small patch can 'jump about' in the crop and reappear some distance away from the initial source of infection. Examine the whole area at each inspection and take every precaution to avoid damaging the plants in any way which may give the disease an easy access.

Where orchards or tree nurseries are surrounded by hawthorn hedges, it is a wise precaution to trim the hedges in late summer to reduce the amount of flower bud formation in the autumn, thus minimising the risk of spring blossom infection. For new orchard hedges, select alternative shrubs to hawthorn, or use trees such as Italian alder.

There is no chemical control for the disease, which can only be prevented from spreading by adopting the strict procedure mentioned and the disposal of all infected wood by burning. It is strongly recommended that secateurs and saws are cleaned in a disinfectant liquid after each cut.

Mildews

Hawthorn, the backbone of the English hedgerow, is the most susceptible species to mildew attack. The powdery mildew of hawthorn is caused by the fungus *Podosphaera clandestine,* which infects the leaves and young shoots, covering them with a white down of fungal mycelium. Severe leaf infection causes a purplish discoloration, leading to curling and shrivelling before the leaves fall. Plant growth can be severely stunted if no remedial action is taken in the early years.

Warm, dry, sunny days in spring and summer and dewy nights favour the development of the white mycelium, which produces abundant powdery spores. The spores are carried on summer breezes to spread the infection along the hedge.

The disease will overwinter as a mycelium on bark and young shoots and in the buds. It can be easily introduced into a new hedge via infected young planting stock.

Podosphaera clandestine is specific to hawthorn, but other hedgerow species suffer from mildew.

Crab apple, field maple, wild rose, blackthorn and wild plum are all vulnerable to infection by various strains of mildew. Crab apple can be severely infected and its growth stunted as a result, which could be serious if the crab is being encouraged to grow up as a hedgerow tree rather than as a shrub within the hedge mix.

Currently, no fungicide sprays have been approved for woodland and hedgerow use. However, commercial growers raising plants for garden and ornamental use are fortunate in having a range of approved chemicals. These chemicals, which have good mildew protective and eradication properties, could be used on hedgerow tree and shrub species.

Bupirimate + triforine (Nimrod-T)

A systemic protectant and eradicant fungicide for the control of black spot and mildew on ornamentals and rust on roses. The chemical is harmful to fish, so do not use near ditches, ponds and waterways.

Myclobutanil (Systane 6)

A systemic curative and protectant fungicide for the approved control of scab and mildew on apples, scab on pears and both mildew and black spot on roses.

Apply every two weeks from early June, or the first signs of disease infection, until the end of the summer.

The chemical is harmful to fish, so do not use near waterways etc.

Triadimefon (Bayleton)

A systemic fungicide with both curative and protectant abilities, for approved use on a wide range of cereals, vegetables, plus fruit crops and herbs. Currently, the chemical has no approval for hedgerow and woodland use.

It must be applied to the foliage at the first signs of mildew infection and thereafter every two weeks, to maintain both its protectant and curative action.

It is a 'kind' fungicide, which should have little difficulty in obtaining approval for use in woodland and hedgerow situations if a manufacturer felt potential sales could justify the cost of putting the chemical through the approval scheme.

Triforine (Saprol)

A leaf systemic fungicide with protectant and curative abilities, approved for use on barley mildew and net blotch, apple and hop mildew and powdery mildews of some soft fruits, flowers, roses and ornamental crops.

A 'harsher' chemical which can harden soft summer leaf growth. It should be applied every two weeks as a routine protectant spray for approved fruit use.

During hot, sunny weather, avoid spraying during the day; apply sprays in the coolest part of the day.

Sulphur (Solfa)

A yellow-coloured, non-metallic element. It has approved use as a broad-spectrum, inorganic fungicide on a wide range of crops. It can also be used as a foliar feed component.

It will control a wide range of diseases in cereals, vegetables, fruit crops, grapevines, hops and ornamental trees and shrubs. Certain apple and soft fruit varieties are sensitive to sulphur, so avoid use on these. Sulphur has no curative action, so needs to be sprayed onto a growing crop before a disease attack, and thereafter repeated according to weather conditions to maintain its protective action.

Under the 1986 Control of Pesticides Regulations, it is illegal to use any pesticide (chemical) except those approved for specific uses. The *UK Pesticide Guide*, published annually, covers all MAFF-approved uses, together with related manufacturers' instructions. Check the product label in all cases. This should be done prior to any spraying. For details of the latest edition of the *UK Pesticide Guide*, write to the CAB International, Wallingford, Oxon OX10 8DE.

Diseases Caused by Viruses

Viruses are very small, single-celled organisms (smaller than bacteria) which exist in the living cells of animal and plant tissue.

They are transmitted from one host to another by vectors (carriers) such as insects (e.g. aphids). Some are carried in pollen, others in seed and many are transmitted by vegetative propagation, particularly in woody ornamental plants.

They can spread across the union of a graft, allowing a diseased rootstock to infect healthy scions and vice versa.

Often the damaging effect of a virus is so negligible as to go undetected, and may only show up for a short period during the growing season. This makes it all the more difficult to isolate or avoid when selecting scion wood for ornamental grafting.

Seed collectors will be attracted to trees carrying regular heavy crops of seed, yet these may be the result of a virus infection or damage in the tree. It is important to keep a check on the subsequent growth and vigour of the young stock raised from seed to eliminate such seed sources which could contribute to the spread of a specific disease across the nursery. Unfortunately the best-looking, healthy trees often produce the least seed.

Nematodes in the soil can transmit viruses from one diseased crop to successive healthy crops, even when the susceptible crop is only one in a long rotation. Some viruses can remain active for many years. Even if a suitable host crop is not present, they will remain in a dormant stage on other crops in the farm rotation.

The control of soil-borne viruses and nematodes has been covered in Chapter 5, where the intensive production of seedlings requires complete control of soil-borne pests and diseases.

The planting of a new hedge does not merit such a high standard of ground conditions. In most cases the soil is unlikely to contain damaging levels of soil-borne diseases. The problem is to avoid the purchase of virus-infected stock. This can be achieved by purchasing planting material from reputable nurserymen who grow their own plants, which can be inspected during the growing season prior to the requirement. Avoid planting stock which has been imported direct from the continent without being grown-on under United Kingdom conditions.

PESTS

An initial infestation of a particular pest is able to spread more rapidly on a commercial nursery raising seedlings or transplants because the host plants are grown in larger, more concentrated batches; giving the pest a greater number of plants in a smaller area across which to spread. In a good mixed hedgerow an attack of aphids on wild cherry may not spread beyond the initial plant, because the aphid is only acclimatised to the leaves of the *Prunus* species.

In nursery conditions, the grower is always on guard during the growing season for the first appearance of any pest which could quickly build up to damaging proportions.

The concern is to prevent the multiplication and spread through a crop of plants, damaging the growing point or its shape, to render the plants either unsaleable or of a lower grade. Whilst many aphids, caterpillars, mites and weevils can be fairly indiscriminate in the subjects they choose to attack, most are very selective.

It is important to identify pests correctly before considering any control measures. In a hedgerow, chemical control of problem pests must be regarded as the last resort, if one is to avoid destroying the developing and fragile ecology. Only resort to spot treatment with a selective insecticide if the pest is unlikely to be controlled by other predators, or is one which could spread across differing species to severely restrict the growth of a young hedge in its formative years.

Table 12.1 lists the most common pests which attack the range of plants found in hedgerows. Those which cause serious damage are in bold; these must be controlled once spotted in any numbers.

Table 12.1 The most common pests which attack hedgerow plants.

Hedgerow plant	*Common pests (most serious in bold)*
Field maple	aphid, scale insect
Alder	winter moth, eriophyid (rust) mite
Birch	aphid, leaf weevil
Hornbeam	spider mite, tortrix and winter moth caterpillars
Dogwood	aphid, winter moth caterpillar
Hazel	eriophyid (rust) mite, leaf weevil, spider mite
Hawthorn	aphid, **hawthorn button-top midge**, webber and winter moth caterpillars
Spindle tree	aphid, willow scale insect
Common beech	woolly aphid, vine weevil
Ash	**eriophyid (rust) mite**, goat and leopard moths
Holly	aphid, leaf miner
Common privet	aphid, leaf miner, hawk and tortrix moths
Crab apple	aphid, leaf miner, red spider mite, leopard and winter moth caterpillars, woolly aphid, weevil
Wild cherry	aphid, spider mite, sawfly, tortrix and **winter moth caterpillars**
Blackthorn	weevil
Wild pear	aphid, eriophyid mite, **sawfly caterpillar**, scale insect
Wild plum	aphid, spider mite, sawfly, tortrix and **winter moth caterpillars**
Oak	leaf miner, midge larva, gall wasp
Wild roses	aphid, sawfly, tortrix and vapourer moths, weevil
Mountain ash	spider mite
Wayfaring tree	aphid, capsid bug
Guelder rose	aphid, capsid bug

All the hedgerow trees and shrubs mentioned are liable to attack from a wider range of pests than those listed. A good mixture of different species along the hedgerow creates a good environment for predators, which will minimise the spread of a particular pest attack. Allow predators a chance to eliminate any pest before resorting to the use of an insecticide.

Hedgerow pests fall into the following five categories, which enables one to choose an insecticide according to the insect's feeding habits, or to choose a contact control:

Aphids
Sap-sucking insects which have winged forms to enable their quick spread along the hedgerow.

Caterpillars
The larval stage in the life cycle of all butterflies and moths. Caterpillars usually eat the leaves of plants, but can bore into the bark, roots or seeds of some plants.

Beetles and weevils
They eat the leaves of plants. The larvae of some beetles and weevils eat roots.

Spider mites
They feed by sucking the sap from the leaves or young shoots.

Scale insects
They are sap-sucking creatures.

Control of Pests According to Chemical Selectivity

Contact
An insecticide which kills the pest upon contact, often non-selective and damaging to other insects and wildlife in the vicinity.

Stomach poison
The insecticide is sprayed onto the plant to be protected, so that any scale insect, caterpillar or weevil is killed on eating the 'poisoned' leaf. Generally, this group of chemicals is broad-spectrum and harmful to other insect life with the same feeding habits.

Systemic poisons
The chemical is absorbed into the plant tissues, remaining in the leaf cells so that any sap-sucking aphid or mite is poisoned by the toxin in the plant sap.

Pesticides Approved for 'Forestry' (i.e. Hedgerow and Woodland) Use and for Use in Hardy Nursery Stock Beds

Gamma HCH
A contact, ingested and fumigant insecticide for the control of aphids, adelgids and weevils. Toxic to mammals and dangerous to bees and fish. Do not use near hives, watercourses or ponds.

Deltamethrin
A contact and residual insecticide, based on pyrethrum for the control of aphids, beetles, scale and other insects. Dangerous to bees and fish. Do not use near hives, ponds or watercourses.

Diflubenzuron
A persistent, selective-contact and stomach-poison insecticide for the control of caterpillars, browntail and winter moths and pine hooper.

Pirimicarb
A selective contact and fumigant insecticide for the control of aphids on a wide range of agricultural and edible field crops, ornamentals and forest nurseries. It has little adverse effect on bees, ladybirds and other beneficial insects.

REFERENCES AND FURTHER READING

Ivens, G. W. (1992), *The UK Pesticide Guide 1992* (CAB International and British Crop Protection Council).
Konynenburg, J. Van and Lawfield, W. N. (1958), *The Encyclopaedia of Garden Pests and Diseases (W. H. & L. Collingridge Ltd.).*
MAFF/ADAS (1983), Leaflet *CL39 Fire blight* (MAFF).
MAFF/ADAS (1983), *Guide to Pest Control on Hardy Ornamental Trees and Shrubs* (MAFF).

Chapter 13

Hedge Maintenance and Trimming

Cut is the branch that might have grown straight
And burned is Apollo's laurel bough,
That sometime grew within this learned man.

CHRISTOPHER MARLOWE

Every hedge needs to be maintained, and should have a maintenance plan based upon its importance to the landowner.

Within the last decade there have arisen alternative uses for the land, other than the production of food. Increasing acres of land are being used for such diverse interests as horse and pony paddocks, riding schools, golf clubs, shooting syndicates, clay pigeon shooting, wildlife and farm parks, nature conservation areas, together with the broader preservation and re-establishment of ancient meadows and downland. These uses place a different emphasis on the original concept of the hedge as a stockproof boundary and field boundary, and each affect the management of hedges accordingly.

With a general decline in stock-rearing and something of a retreat of dairy herds to the higher rainfall areas, the need for stockproof hedges around every small field has been reduced.

In many cereal growing areas, hedges have been removed to produce larger fields for more efficient production, as well as to reduce the cost of hedgerow maintenance.

Mixed farms have retained more hedges, but have limited the management to an annual trim with a flail cutter. Many of these hedges are cut too low and, with time, have become gappy and bare-stemmed. They are of little value to wildlife and the landowner. But they still exist and it is better that they are retained in this form than not at all (Plate 13.1). They grow in an uncultivated and unmanaged strip between fields, which allows some wildlife to exist.

Landowners and tenants should maintain hedges according to

PLATE 13.1 A very 'tired' 18th century hawthorn enclosure hedge, beyond regeneration by laying. Allowing it to grow up untrimmed would improve its value for wildlife if allied to an adjacent field margin.

their requirements, but also they should be increasingly aware of the added need to conserve wildlife for the enjoyment of others and the wellbeing of the countryside.

There are four basic methods of controlling the growth of hedges:

- Laying
- Trimming (flail or cutter bar)
- Coppicing
- Brushing, or siding up.

Laying

A time-consuming, expensive and skilled method of rejuvenating overgrown hedges, which is described later in this chapter. Traditionally, hedges in stock-raising or dairy-producing areas were laid approximately every 10–15 years to keep them growing tight and compact enough to contain livestock, prior to the introduction of barbed wire (from America) in the late-19th century. It is still regarded as the only sure way of keeping a hedge impenetrable to cattle and sheep.

Trimming

With the continuing development and improvement of the mechanical flail hedge trimmer, most hedges are now kept closely cropped with an annual 'haircut'. Once into a regular routine of machine trimming, hawthorn- and blackthorn-based hedges respond well to this method of containment and produce good tight regrowth, but with a tendency for the bottom of the hedge to slowly become open.

Coppicing

A very severe, yet sometimes necessary, resort to control the growth of an overgrown hedge which has been neglected for many years. The complete hedge is cut down to ground level. In some cases, selected saplings are left in place to grow on into hedgerow trees. It is advisable to put up a notice when coppicing an old or overgrown hedge line to explain to local people or passers-by that it is part of a hedge maintenance and restoration plan. This will avoid accusations being made that the hedge is being grubbed out or that the owner does not want the problem of looking after the hedge.

Brushing, or Siding Up

New hedges which contain a wide selection of species and are more than 50% non-hawthorn or blackthorn, will not respond so well to mechanical trimming. They will contain a high proportion of slow-growing species (e.g. guelder rose and wayfaring tree) and some with brittle shoot growth (e.g. field maple and spindle).

Mixed species hedges should be allowed to grow up with less formal maintenance. A quick trim with a pair of loppers or a long-handled slasher will keep the branches from drooping too much. It may be necessary to thin out some larger stems from time to time to keep the hedge young and prevent it from growing up to become more like a miniature woodland strip.

Any species which becomes too dominant at the expense of its slower-growing neighbours will need more severe pruning or thinning to keep its growth in balance with the other hedgerow plants.

HEDGE LAYING

Whether the new hedge was planted in a closely spaced single line or a wider-spaced and staggered double line, both will need to be managed alike in the seven to ten years leading up to laying.

At the end of the first growing season, use clippers or secateurs to trim back the leaders of any vigorous shoots, but leave weak growing stems untouched. This gives a low, level top to the hedge. Trim off any excess side shoots to form a box shape, so keeping the hedge compact.

In the second and third years, repeat the process, which could be done with a flail trimmer if new growth has been sufficiently vigorous. This trimming will continue the process of maintaining compact growth.

Thereafter, do not cut the hedge but allow it to grow up untrimmed until the seventh to tenth year, according to its vigour. By that time the hedge should be at least 12 feet tall with stout stems and ready for laying.

Equipment Required for Hedge Laying

- A good first-aid kit is a priority for dealing with cuts, grazes and thorns, which will affect even the most competent hedgelayer. Hawthorn thorns are unpleasant, but the thorns of blackthorn can lead to a septic infection if not removed quickly. Rose and bramble barbs will also need to be removed promptly. Clean, disinfect and place a bandage, or plaster, over all cuts immediately.
- A 21 in bowsaw is necessary for cutting out unwanted stems and for part of the preparation of the pleachers (intertwined branches).
- A billhook of one's choice. At one time, most hedging counties would boast of the advantages of their own regional design. Today the range available (Plate 13.2) has been reduced to four basic styles:
  The Newtown (or Montgomeryshire) – a straight-bladed billhook.
  The Southern Counties (or Bristol) – a billhook with a pronounced hook to the end of the blade. This type is easier for the inexperienced person to use than the Newtown.
  The Midlands (or Leicestershire and Warwickshire) – a heavy, single-handed tool with a gently curved blade on one side and a shorter straight edge on the back.
  The Yorkshire – a heavier, longer-handled tool, which is better suited for two-handed use on thicker stemmed bushes.
- A canoe-shaped sharpening stone.
- A slasher, preferably with a long handle.
- A sickle (grass hook) for removing grass and weed growth from the hedge bottom.

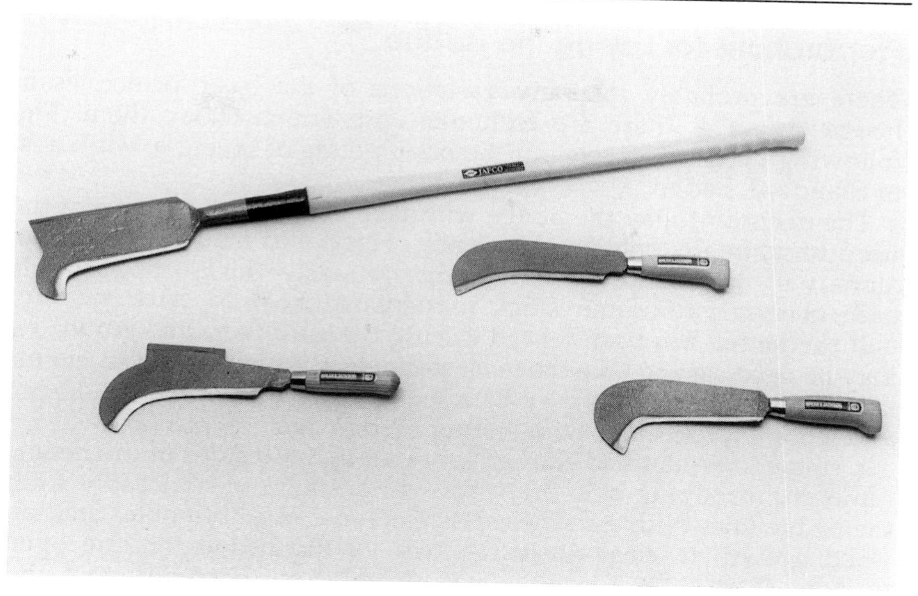

PLATE 13.2 Maintenance tools. (Top to bottom): *Yorkshire double-edged slasher with Nupla fibreglass handle* (Jafco Tools); *Newtown billhook* (Spear and Jackson); *Stafford billhook with double-edged blade* (Spear and Jackson); *Southern Counties billhook* (Spear and Jackson).

- A pair of limb loppers for tidier trimming of smaller brushwood at any stage.
- A pair of heavy-duty leather or thornproof gloves.
- A lightweight maul or sledge-hammer.
- A pitchfork.

If there is a fence to be lowered or removed, one will require:

- A claw-hammer.
- A pair of fencing pliers.
- A crowbar.
- A tin or box, to hold all removed nails and staples.

Before commencing work, ensure that all the tools are sharp and in sound condition. To sharpen the billhook and slasher, use the canoe-shaped stone, rubbing each side of the blade in a firm, small circular action at the correct angle to bring the blade to an even sharpness.

Always sharpen the blade away from one's body, holding the billhook in the forearm of the left hand.

For safety, lay all tools flat on the ground when not in use.

Preparations for Laying the Hedge

There are probably as many variations of the basic principles of hedge laying as there are billhooks with which to lay them. The following description sets out the basic points of laying a Midlands, or Standard, hedge.

The decision to lay the hedge will have been taken because of the need to maintain a stockproof 'fence'. Hand and machine trimming alone will not ensure that the hedge retains a thick, impenetrable base, necessary to contain stock, particularly sheep.

If the hedge has been fenced during the early years of growth, it may be necessary to take the fence down to allow adequate access for laying. However, there may be adequate space between the hedge and fence to proceed as with an unfenced hedge.

Using a long-handled slasher, work along both sides of the hedge, removing drooping side branches which stick out noticeably from the hedge line. With a slasher or sickle, remove all brambles and tall weed growth to clear away the base of the hedge for safe open working (Plate 13.3). Once the mature hedge has been tidied up and the base cleared of undergrowth, it is possible to see the true line of the hedge.

Proceed along the hedge, cutting out all dead wood and any elder which may have invaded the hedge line. Carry out a little more trimming of the lower part to leave selected and evenly spaced straight stems suitable to form the pleachers or laid stems.

Now start to prepare the pleachers for laying. Select straight stems with good bushy tops, at even spacings to provide the eventual uniform thickness along the laid hedge.

A golden rule of hedge laying is that the hedge must always be laid uphill. This ensures that the pleachers do not break at the cut when being laid down, which could happen if the angle was too wide. The ideal angle is about 40–60° from the horizontal.

Should there be a dry ditch on one side of the hedge, try working from that side. Standing in a ditch will require less bending to cut and trim the pleachers.

If you are right-handed, start cutting at the left-hand end of the hedge, as you face it, from the side you have chosen to work from. Cut the base of chosen pleachers on their right-hand side and lay them over to the left. Reverse the instructions if you are left-handed.

All straight, evenly spaced stems should be saved for laying as pleachers. Other thin, misplaced or misshapen stems should be cut out and disposed of. In many instances this could entail removing half the available shoots.

PLATE 13.3 Trimming the hedge prior to laying on an East Anglian farm.

Using the axe or bowsaw, cut three-quarters of the way through each pleacher stem at a point 10 cm (4 in) above ground level. Then, using a billhook, make downward chip cuts from a point 30 cm (12 in) above the saw cut to chop out a long wedge down to the cut, leaving the remaining stem very pliable at the cut point and easy to bend over to the required angle (45°) (Plate 13.4).

Bend the pleachers over in succession (like plates in a washing rack) to form the characteristic laid hedge, taking care not to break the thin, pliable 'hinge' of stem bark and tissue. Once a number of pleachers have been laid, staking can begin.

The stakes should be cut and selected beforehand. Choose straight 1.5 m (5 ft) stakes, 5–7 cm (2–3 in) thick of hazel, hawthorn or other

PLATE 13.4 Pleachers neatly cut and laid, using only the axe shown.

coppice clearings. Point up one end of each, using the billhook or a small axe on a chopping block.

Drive the stakes in at 60 cm (2 ft) intervals along the centre line of the hedge, weaving the pleachers and their bushy tops in between the stakes for mutual support.

Remove any excess twiggy shoots with the loppers or a billhook to give a compact, tight and tidy finish.

When a reasonable length of hedge has been laid and staked, use selected long, thin and very pliable shoots of willow, hazel or even briar, each 3 m (10 ft) long. Weave these along the top of the staked hedge to bind the stakes to each other in a basket-weave fashion. This is termed 'heathering' and completes the top of the laid edge (Plate 13.5).

It only remains to trim the stake tops level just above the top of the heathering, and remove any untidy twigs sticking out of the side of the laid hedge. Leave proportionally more bushy tops showing on the field side of the new line to discourage stock from browsing or trying to rub up against the new laid hedge. The ditch side can be tidied up in more detail to give a professional finish (Plate 13.6).

Those wishing to lay their own hedges or learn more about this traditional craft should purchase a copy of *Hedging*, an excellent book covering all aspects of hedge care, published by the British

PLATE 13.5 Prepared pleachers laid and interwoven.

PLATE 13.6 A newly laid hedge at Cokethorpe Park, Oxfordshire. Selected ash trees have been left to grow on while others have been cut back to act as growing stakes. These have begun to regrow.

Trust for Conservation Volunteers, 36 St Mary's Street, Wallingford, Oxfordshire OX10 0EV. Telephone 0491 39766.

HEDGE TRIMMNG

In the last ten years, hydraulically-operated flail trimmers have almost completely taken over from earlier cutter bar machines.

Sawhead trimmers are still used for coppicing a hedge or for cutting back an overgrown hedge which can then be flail trimmed.

New hedges containing a high proportion of hawthorn and/or blackthorn are suitable for regular flail cutting. The two species respond well to regular trimming, producing fresh bushy growth following each annual or biennial cut. Hedges containing a significant proportion of slow-growing species such as holly, wayfaring tree and guelder rose should NOT be flail trimmed regularly. The same applies to new hedges containing a quantity of stiff- and brittle-stemmed species (i.e. crab apple, field maple and spindle) all of which tend to produce straight vertical growth which will leave a ragged cut if trimmed hard.

Regular annual trimming, although carried out on most farms, is really only necessary on stock farms (to keep the new growth short and tight to give a good close appearance) or where the hedge has been allowed to grow up to the maximum height of the trimmer's reach as a windbreak for cash crops. Hedges on arable and cereal farms could be trimmed every other year. This reduces annual hedge maintenance costs and improves the habitat for wildlife.

Trimming should be carried out in the autumn to minimise the disturbance to nesting birds.

After planting hedges designed for stock control, trim off excess side and top growth each year. In the first two years it may be cheaper and easier to walk the hedgeline, cutting off any long side or top shoots with a pair of sharp hedge clippers or small loppers. If the growth has been vigorous it may pay to use a flail trimmer, but only if the growth is strong enough to be trimmed cleanly by the flail. If new growth is long and thin, it will be torn rather than cut by the flail, leaving a ragged and uneven finish which will not be conducive to good clean growth the following spring.

Once the hedge has begun to thicken up and produce stouter growth, in the third or fourth year after planting, trim each year with a flail cutter. Ensure that the operator does not drive quickly along the hedge, or cutting will be ragged, causing die-back and subsequent poor regrowth.

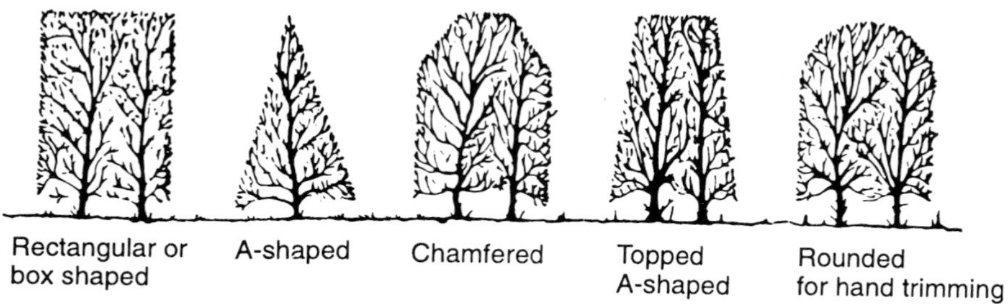

FIGURE 13.1 Hedge shapes.

Hedge Shapes (Figure 13.1)

Rectangular

The most common shape. It produces a thick hedge, if trimmed annually from early in the hedge's life. A flat top to a wide hedge can cause some problems with trimmings lodging in the top, dropping through to the bottom of the hedge's centre, and over the years building up as a mulch, which can affect growth in several ways. A build-up of trimmings in the early years is unlikely, but if the young hedge is trimmed tightly each year to keep it below 1.5 m (5 ft) high, any trimmings present may have some benefit in controlling weed growth in the hedge bottom.

As the hedge matures, there are conflicting opinions on the consequences of a build-up of an ever-thickening mulch in the hedge bottom. Some have expressed concern that this mulch will cause stem rotting and fungal infection if it remains constantly moist, particularly in higher rainfall areas. Others feel that the mulch will prevent weed growth, conserve moisture and eventually provide more nutrients as the mulch rots down, stimulating the hedge to grow stronger.

There is no denying that the accumulation of a thick mulch in the base of a tall, mature hedge deprives wildlife of a safe area to search for food. The mulch produces a sterile environment which may only harbour a few mice, rats and voles.

Chamfered

The chamfered top is a variation of the rectangular hedge, normally employed to give a tidier finish to a tall hedge, grown to the maximum reach of the hedge cutter. A tall hedge will attract more nesting birds, who can build their nests sufficiently high to avoid predators on the ground. This shape helps to deflect some of the trimmings away from the centre of the hedge.

The chamfered top will improve the flow of air over the hedge, reducing the vortex effect of the leeward side.

A-shape

The A-shape exposes both hedge faces to more sunlight, improves the fall-away of trimmings and the slip-off of snowfalls. It provides a thicker bottom (Plate 13.7) and better regrowth in the hedge generally, particularly if the hedge is aligned north to south. Hedges which align east to west have a shaded north side which does not grow so well, and a south side which produces good regrowth towards the sunlight. Care must be taken when trimming to keep the hedge in balance. The north (shaded) side should be trimmed lightly and the south (sunny) side trimmed harder; otherwise in time the hedge could slowly 'lean' towards the sunlight.

PLATE 13.7 A mixed species hedge, trimmed in a flat topped A-shape, to provide a thick, wide base, ideal for wildlife shelter.

Topped A-shape and Rounded

Topped A-shaped and rounded (Plate 13.8) forms have greater strength to resist the weight of snow and deflect deposits. Rounded older hedges are often seen growing down an awkward bank or across a wide steep ditch, making trimming access difficult. Both shapes help to retain a broad, thick base, ideal for good wildlife cover, but not for nesting birds, who will be exposed to predators on the ground and on the wing.

These two shapes are much better for keeping a hedge stockproof

PLATE 13.8 Dome shape trimming of a hedge beside a ditch.

than the tall rectangular or true A-shapes. Suckering shrubs, such as blackthorn, benefit from the broader-based shapes which do not restrict the spread of their suckers.

Both the A-shape and the topped A-shape will be more difficult to trim if they are growing behind a wire netting fence positioned close to the hedge. The flail head of the trimmer may not have adequate space to reach the ground if the base of the 'A' is close to the fence.

The FWAG booklet *Hedges & Field Boundaries* (1991) draws attention to areas where close trimming of the hedge can be relaxed to favour song birds. Junctions in hedges often occur in areas where there is less concern for their competition with the adjacent cropping field. These sections could be allowed to grow out to form a small, bushy thicket, with a tree in the corner to add a change in height, as well as more wildlife opportunities.

Mechanical Hedge Cutters

A combination of hydraulic motors, position rams and electric solenoid-operated controls gives the modern hedge trimmer such precise and versatile control that most new hedges will be machine trimmed for the foreseeable future. Bomford Turner Ltd has developed two machines, one for the farmer's use and one for heavier-duty contract use. These are not the only machines on the market, but they set standards which meet the changing needs of hedge trimming today (Plate 13.9).

Figure 13.2 shows the range of cutting positions possible with the Bomford Turner Mid-Position Flail Cutter. The machine can trim up the side of a hedge to almost 6 m (20 ft), ideal for tall hedges round hop gardens (Plate 13.10) or orchards. Its 1.25 m (4 ft) cutting head will deal with many hedge sides and hedge tops in one pass and allow a hedge to be grown up to 2 m (7 ft) high requiring two overlapping passes along each side and one top pass to complete the trim.

The sideways reach of 5.3 m (17 ft 4 in) (from the centre of the tractor) allows the operator to work across a wide ditch or to position the machine away from the work for better visibility.

The cutter head can be fitted with a choice of three flails to cover grass, wood up to 5 mm (2 in) diameter, and wood up to 10 mm (4 in) diameter. Thus the operator can fit the correct flails to suit the work – the professional approach to giving good results in a wide variety of conditions.

PLATE 13.9 A Bomford Turner B577L hedge trimmer shows its versatility reaching across a wide hedge.

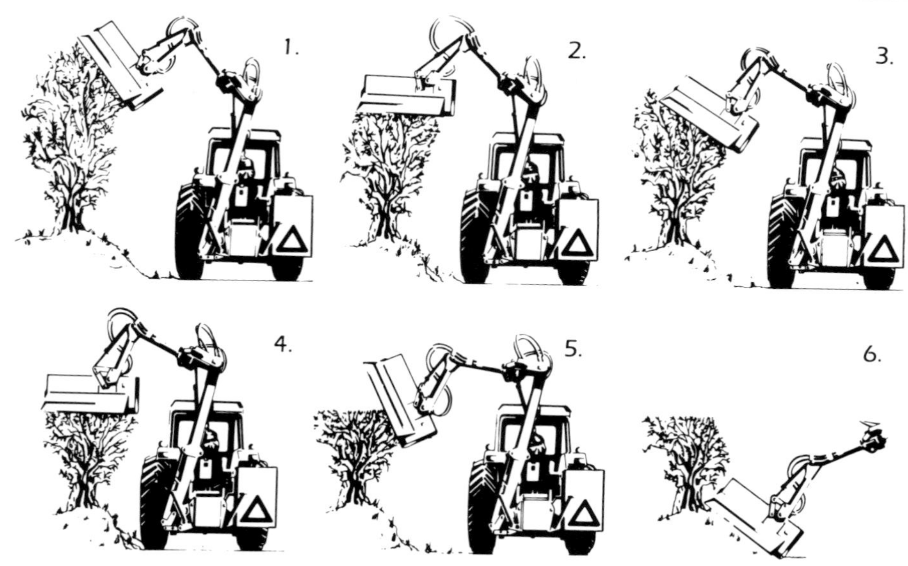

FIGURE 13.2 Series of cuts to reduce an overgrown hedge. Start from the top and work downwards. In this way cut material which has fallen will be further cut and mulched as the cutter head moves down the hedge. Cut off long material in a series of passes, taking off layers of approximately 450 mm (18 in) to leave short trimmings for rapid decomposition and to avoid overloading the hedge cutter.

PLATE 13.10 *A very tall hawthorn hedge protects the hop garden at Berkshire Hops, Southmoor, Oxfordshire. Regular annual trimming over many years has not resulted in the base of this hedge becoming bare.*

Time and Cost

The time and cost of trimming will be directly related to the number of passes required to do the work satisfactorily. Old enclosure hedges which still dominate the landscape are usually trimmed at 1.5 m (5 ft) high and are rarely wider than 1 m (3 ft), so the hedge trimmer will cut these hedges with two passes to each side and one pass over the top. More often than not a final pass will be made along the grass margin at the base of each side, to control tall weeds and brambles and to chop up further the fallen hedge trimmings to a smaller size.

A new hedge, whether it be for stock control or not, should be allowed to grow taller and wider than is currently the standard practice. Let the hedge grow to 2.5 m (8 ft) high, with a base 2.5 m (8 ft) wide, tapering to 1.5 m (5 ft) to form a flat-topped A-shape.

Figures 13.3 and 13.4 show the results of using a contractor's flail cutter, trimming a width of 1.2 m (4 ft) at each pass. Allowing the hedge to grow upwards and outwards to a height and base width of 2.5 m (8 ft) only increases the cost and time of trimming by 33% over the traditional enclosures hedge of 1.5 m (5 ft) high and 1 m (3 ft) wide. The latter has a sectional surface of 4 m (13 ft), which takes seven passes to trim. The bigger new hedge has a sectional surface of 7.5 m (24 ft) which will take nine passes to cut, only two more passes than its predecessor; a low price to pay for providing better shelter for stock and wildlife.

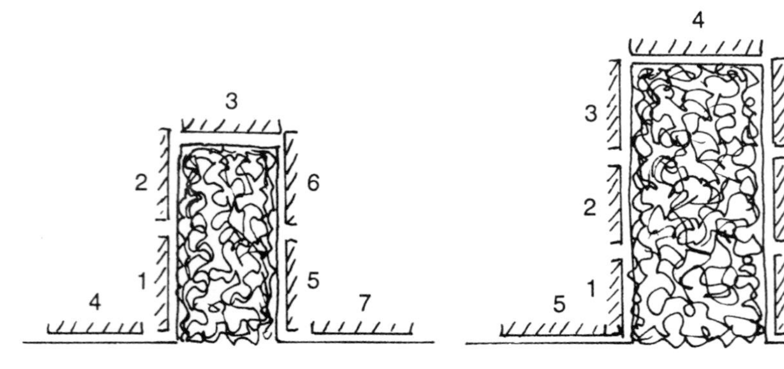

FIGURE 13.3 Seven cuts for a low hedge.

FIGURE 13.4 Nine cuts for a tall hedge.

Rotational Trimming

The extra cost of trimming can be more than offset if one adopts a policy of only cutting farm hedges every two years, on a rotational basis.

Trimming half the farm's hedges every year, combined with letting both old and new hedges grow from their current average height of 1.5 m (5 ft) to a height of 2.5 m (8 ft), will result in a lower hedge trimming cost than if all hedges and margins were trimmed each autumn.

Most farmers take great pride in the appearance of both their farmland and crops. In today's harsher economic climate, we may have to allow a few more weeds to raise their heads over the once pristine cornfields. In the same vein, rotational hedge trimming every two years may look somewhat untidy at first, but the knowledge that costs are being saved and depleted wildlife levels restored in the bargain, must make sense as an effective and progressive policy.

COPPICING

This will not apply to new hedges for many years. Coppicing of hedges entails cutting them down to ground level to start afresh. It is only recommended where a hedge has become so overgrown that the majority of the bush stems are too thick or bare for satisfactory laying. It is a severe remedy. Some sawn stems will not recover from the ordeal, but in most cases it will allow the hedge to rejuvenate and, in time, be managed by subsequent laying and/or trimming.

Hedge coppicing is done with a sawhead fitted to the hedge trimmer or by hand using a chainsaw. It is a slow, drastic measure but necessary for all overgrown hedges.

A considerable bulk of long brushwood will need collecting up and burning following coppicing.

On a mixed farm coppicing is carried out when the adjoining fields are turned over from grass to arable, allowing the subsequent regrowth to have formed the beginnings of a fresh hedge by the time that land is back to grass.

Before resorting to the severity of coppicing a hedge which has grown beyond the point of laying, it is worth trying to bring the hedge back to some semblance of shape using a heavy-duty flail cutter. The results will be extremely untidy for a year or two, but it is remarkable how hawthorn and blackthorn can recover quickly from visually devastating trimming (Plate 13.11). Figures 13.2, 13.3 and 13.4 show the sequence of cuts to reduce an overgrown hedge. It is not necessary to cut the hedge back to such a low level in one season.

PLATE 13.11 A badly trimmed roadside hedge. Often the scars heal quickly with vigorous regrowth.

REFERENCES AND FURTHER READING

Bomford & Evershed Ltd., *Hedges & Hedgerow Management* (Booklet).

The British Trust for Conservation Volunteers (1988), *Hedging – a Practical Handbook* (Wembley Press, Reading, Berks).

FWAG, *Hedges & Field Boundaries* (Booklet).

Chapter 14

Protection and Fencing

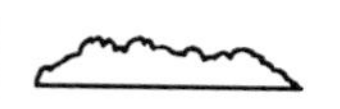

Protection is not a principle
but an expedient.

17 MARCH 1845 BENJAMIN DISRAELI

PROTECTION

The most common approaches to protection are the two extremes – either no protection is provided, or the complete hedge line is fenced in to keep out all predators. The author has planted a number of hedges over the past eight years and only one has been fenced.

Hedgerow plants are bushy objects, which do not fit easily into current proprietary guards. Protection of the young hedge presents a dilemma for the planter due to the high number of plants which are neither easy nor cheap to guard.

Spiral Guards

A flexible spiral guard (Plate 14.1) can be unwound and then wrapped around the more compact and upright-growing shrubs. A young, thin-stemmed hedge plant may need a cane to keep the plant and its guard upright.

Nurse Crop

The hedge lines are planted into a growing cereal crop usually (Plate 14.2), which grows ahead of the young plants during their first year; this provides shelter and acts as a nurse crop. In subsequent winters, damage by hares and deer usually only involves nibbling the plant tops down to the level of the remnants of the previous season's cereal crop, which continues to shelter, hide and discourage further serious damage.

PLATE 14.1 Hedge seedlings protected by spiral guards and a stout cane to support both guard and plant.

PLATE 14.2 A three-year-old hawthorn hedge planted into a growing cereal crop. Volunteer cereals are still providing protection and shelter for the young hedge.

However, such methods may not be suitable countrywide and further preventative measures may be necessary.

Repellant Sprays

To avoid incurring the considerable expenditure of a fence enclosure, spraying the shrubs with an organic bird and animal repellant, aluminium ammonium sulphate (Spere), is a short-term expedient. The chemical is mixed in the normal manner with water and sprayed over the crop or plants. The spray must dry fully onto the plants to provide a repellant coating which is distasteful to potential 'diners'. The addition of a sticker (coating agent) will prolong the protective activity.

Ziram (AA Protect) Paint

A dithiocarbonate-based repellant. Apply the *undiluted* chemical as a 'paint' to stems and lower branches of young trees and shrubs. Use as a diluted spray on thinner branches. This will not provide the same level of repellant as the undiluted application, which will deter deer, hares and rabbits. For the best results, the paint or spray applications should be allowed to dry for five hours to ensure a good lasting bond onto the stems and shoots.

Tree Shelters

A straight stem of a young tree can be protected in the early years of growth by a wide range of different shaped and sized guards, but all have the limitation that – sooner or later – the tree will grow out of the guard's protection to expose itself to the rigours of the climate and come within reach of larger predators, such as cattle or deer.

Young trees planted in the new hedge line should be protected with plastic tree shelters. These are made from corrugated plastic and come in the form of either an oblong box, triangle or a tube, which can be slid down over the planted tree.

The box- or triangle-shaped shelters need a stake to support them. Some come with the requisite length of stake and tie as a complete package. Tubex produce a range of sizes from 0.45 m to 1.8 m (18 in to 6 ft) in length. The base of their two smaller sizes, 0.45 m (1 ft 5 in) and 0.75 m (2 ft 5 in), is cut like a quill pen, hence their name Tubex Quill. This allows them to be pushed into the ground to prevent small rodents getting into the bottom of the shelter to nest or gnaw the tree stem in the warmer environment within the guard. Pushed well into the ground, these shorter guards do not need staking.

The other good features of all the Tubex guards is the fluted top edge, which improves rigidity and prevents the young stem of the emerging tree from rubbing on a straight-cut rim in windy conditions.

There is a wide range of tree shelters available; listed below are two well-known suppliers.

> Tubex Ltd., Tannery House, Tannery Lane, Send, Woking, Surrey G23 7HB. Makers of Tubex Quills in 0.45 m and 0.75 m lengths; Tubex Tree Shelters from 0.6 m long in stages up to 1.8 m; Tubex Thermat – a long-lasting mulch mat for weed suppression and moisture conservation; Gripper Pegs available for the retention of the mat.

> Geebro Ltd., South Road, Hailsham, East Sussex BN24 3DT. Suppliers of Rainbow Delta Shelter – tree shelters in lengths from 0.6 m to 1.5 m; Rainbow range of spiral tree guards; permanent and adjustable tree ties.

Tree shelters do more than protect young trees from being gnawed or eaten by voles, rabbits, hares, deer and farm livestock. The opaque, twin-walled, polypropylene tube provides a greenhouse environment for the young tree, encouraging early and vigorous growth. It protects the dormant plant from the extremes of cold, freeze drying, wind and severe frosty conditions. During the heat of the summer, the shelter prevents heat scorch and keeps the strimmer's blade from damaging the stem when cutting grass.

The Forestry Commission undertook trials in 1981 to assess the value of both tree guards and tube shelters for promoting growth in comparison with an unguarded control.

1+1 oak transplants, 22 cm (9 in) in height, grew unprotected to a height of 34 cm (13 in) within two years.

Similar (22 cm (9 in)) oak transplants fitted with a simple enclosed tree guard grew to a height of 53 cm (21 in) in the same two year trial period.

Using a polypropylene tube shelter, 22 cm (9 in) oaks grew to an impressive height of 132 cm (52 in) in two years.

Recent trials have confirmed the ability of the twin-wall, corrugated, polypropylene shelter to give a dramatic increase in growth to those healthy transplants or seedlings which have proved to respond well to such shelter.

Very good growth responses have been recorded using tree shelters around beech, hawthorn, lime, oak, sweet chestnut, crab apple, ash and sycamore. Variable or poor results have been noted when used around Italian alder, horse chestnut and whitebeam. Many other species have given good results on some sites, but not on others, so an element of caution should be taken in the widespread use of tree shelters with a mixture of species (Plate 14.3). Do not expect an equally good response from all of them.

PLATE 14.3 A young hedge of mixed species with individual trees protected within tree shelters.

FENCING

The only sure way to keep out hares and rabbits and deter most deer is to enclose the hedge line within a fence. This is an expensive measure which, like tree guarding, will probably cost more to erect than the total cost of planting the hedge itself, but it will ensure its survival.

If short-term protection is required for the start of the first growing season, it may be possible to borrow or hire electric sheep netting to place around the hedge, until the growth of fresh grass and other plants in the spring provides a more acceptable alternative food source for potential troublemakers.

A galvanised wire netting fence is adequate protection against hares and rabbits (Plate 14.4). 19 mm (0.7 in) gauge netting, made to BS 443 standards, with a 31 mm (1.25 in) to 38 mm (1.5 in) mesh size, can be purchased in 50 m (164 ft) rolls. The height should be 1,050 mm (41 in) to 1,200 mm (47 in), to allow for 200 mm (8 in) of netting to be buried to deter rabbits from burrowing under the fence.

Firstly, plough a 150 mm (6 in) deep single furrow trench at least 1 m (3 ft) away from the hedge line, to mark the fence line and for

PLATE 14.4 A new hedge on the Berkshire Downs well protected against deer and hares.

PLATE 14.5 A cattle fence positioned too close to the hedge, which is now growing through the netting.

burying the base of the netting. The space also allows for future growth of the hedge (Plate 14.5). Use stakes which are 1.7 m (5.5 in) long, 50–80 mm (2–3 in) wide at the top and pressure-treated for length of life, spaced at 5 m (16 ft) intervals and driven into the ground to a depth of 0.5 m (20 in) for good stability (Figure 14.1).

Choose 2.3 m (7.5 ft) long end posts of a minimum 100 mm (4 in) diameter, dug into the ground to a depth of 0.75 m (2 ft 6 in). Strengthen the end posts with a diagonal strut post 2 m (6.5 in) long and 80–100 mm (3–4 in) wide, braced in the ground with a large stone or wedge post. For long stretches of hedges, use intermediate strainer posts, with a strut on each side, every 50–100 m (55–109 yd) on average, or at any change in direction. All corners must be treated similarly.

Erect the end and corner posts as well as all intermediate stakes along the line of the ploughed furrow before attaching the netting.

Attach a single strand of barbed or plain wire just above the ground level and at the top of the proposed fence to hang the netting on and to give it adequate support.

Hang, tighten and fix the wire netting with staples, ensuring that 150–200 mm (6–8 in) of the netting is buried in the ground, with the

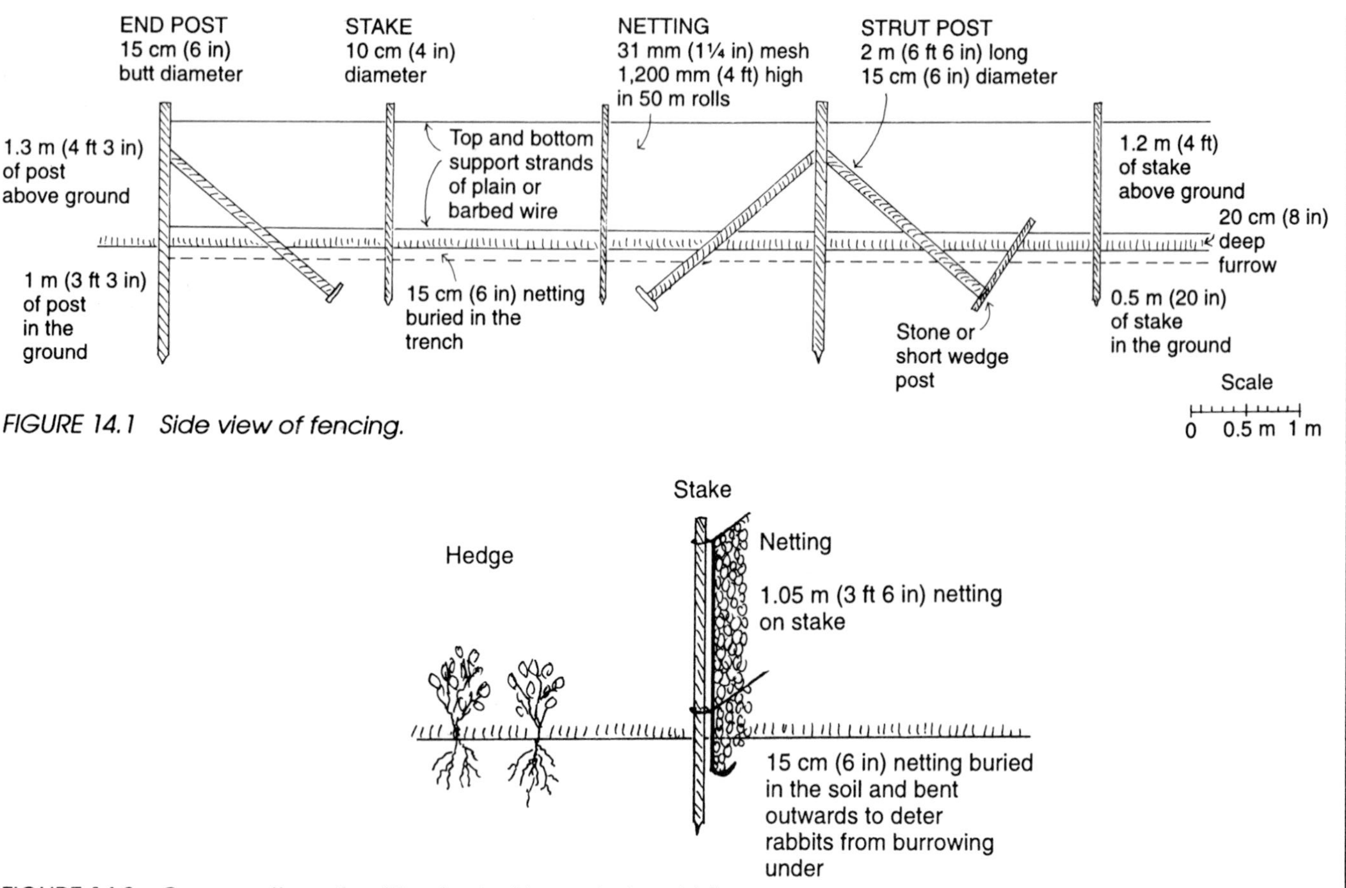

FIGURE 14.1 Side view of fencing.

FIGURE 14.2 Cross section of netting buried to exclude rabbits.

bottom bent over in an L-shape facing outwards (Figure 14.2). Replace the soil or turf in the furrow once the netting has been fixed to the posts.

Such work can be done easily by one's own staff assuming suitable tools are to hand (Plate 14.6), but a fencing contractor may be able to do the work as cheaply, because of his ability to buy the materials at advantageous prices. Also, his skills should ensure the work is done both quickly and to a higher standard.

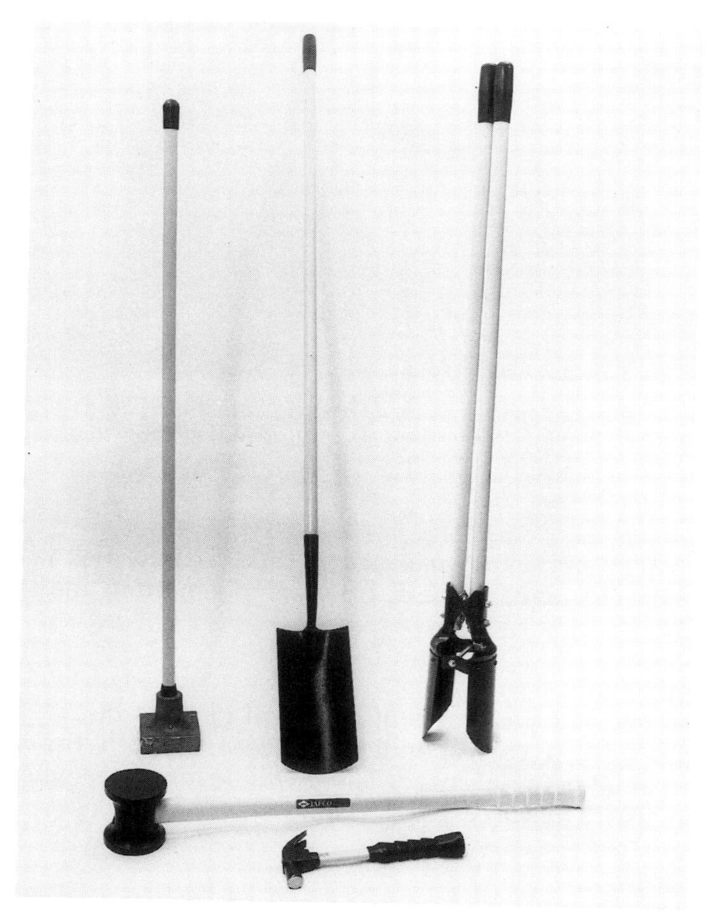

PLATE 14.6 Fencing tools. (Left to right and top to bottom)*: Earth rammer, square-headed; other patterns available* (Jafco Tools)*; grafting tool* (Jafco Tools)*; post hole digger* (Jafco Tools)*; fencing maul* (Jafco Tools)*; claw hammer. All these fencing tools have Nupla fibreglass handles for strength, lightness and long life.*

PLATE 14.7 A mixed species roadside hedge, planted in 1984, protected on the field side by cattle fencing. Note the close spacing of the stakes to give a stronger fence.

Stock control

In areas where stock are present, but there is little risk of damage from rabbits etc., square mesh cattle or pig netting may be used (Plate 14.7).

Deer control

Fencing to prevent the access of deer will need to be 2.3–3 m (7.5–10 ft) high, with a corresponding increase in both the size and dimension of all materials used. There will be few cases where a new hedge can justify this level of preventative protection.

Badger gates

Badgers make well worn tracks along their regular foraging routes and it is likely that one would notice the track, should it cross the line of a proposed or newly planted hedge. If the hedge is to be fenced, to protect it from vermin or adjacent stock, please fit a small badger flap gate at the point (or points) where the track meets the new fence.

Simply attach a wooden frame about 30 cm (12 in) square to the netting and peg it into the soil. Cut out the piece of netting within the main/outer frame and mount this onto a smaller 'door' frame to fit into the outer support frame. The netting door can be fitted to the top of the outer frame with a piece of thick plastic and nailed on to hang down as a hinged flap, like a domestic cat flap, and to be free to swing both in and out according to the direction of the badger's passage. Upon approaching the gate the badger will put its nose under the lower lip of the door and push its way through.

Those wishing to fence their own hedges or learn more about this craft should purchase a copy of *Fencing*, an excellent book covering all aspects of fencing, published by the British Trust for Conservation Volunteers, 36 St Mary's Street, Wallingford, Oxfordshire OX10 0EV. Telephone 0491 39766.

Footpath stiles or gates

Should the new hedge cross the line of an existing public, or private footpath, do not forget to instal either a simple stile, made from planks and posts, or a gate, should this be required by law or those who normally enjoy a right of free passage.

A decision on the need to fence may be related to grant aid conditions; check carefully at the outset with ADAS or FWAG on any such necessity and the merits of fencing related to local conditions or known vermin problems.

REFERENCES AND FURTHER READING

Blyth, J., Evans, J., Mutch, W. E. S., Sidwell, C. (1991), *Farm Woodland Management* (Farming Press Books, Ipswich, Suffolk).

Jacksons Fencing (1991), *The Good Fencing Guide* (Jacksons Fencing, Stowting Common, Ashford, Kent).

Porter, Valerie (1991), *Small Woods and Hedgerow* (Pelham Books, Stephen Greene Press, London W8 5T).

Chapter 15

Costings

A man who knows the price of everything
and the value of nothing.
DEFINITION OF A CYNIC   OSCAR WILDE

Many new hedges continue to be planted by hand, so the fixed costs for planting are limited to one good treaded spade for each person involved (Plate 15.1).

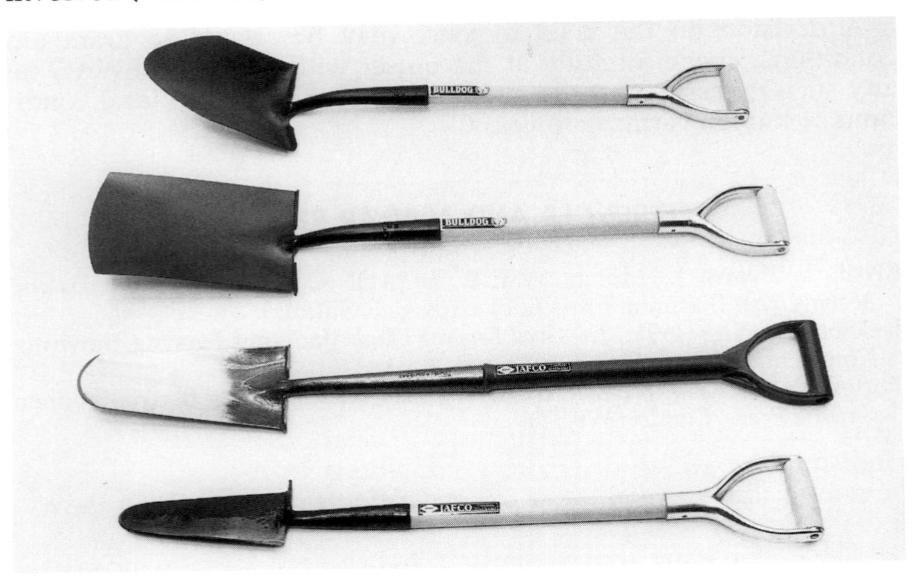

PLATE 15.1 *Planting tools.* (Top to bottom): *General service shovel, forward tread* (Bulldog Tools); *garden spade, treaded* (Bulldog Tools); *planting spade* (Jafco Tools); *planting spear – for cell-grown or seedling stock* (Jafco Tools). *This photograph illustrates two different types of Nupla fibreglass handle; all four patterns are available with both handle types from Jafco Tools.*

The cost of the work will be determined by the soil type and density of planting.

The price of the plants will vary according to the mixture of species chosen and their size; in addition, nurserymen have differing price scales.

Table 15.1 sets out the range of prices currently charged by three southern counties nurseries.

The cheapest species for volume (bulk) purchase is hawthorn, being the most widely used hedgerow plant. This is closely followed by other common plants, i.e. blackthorn, field maple and dog rose.

Table 15.1 Price Guide for Hedgerow Transplants (1+1)*

	Nursery Site		
	Sussex	*Oxfordshire*	*Gloucestershire*
Field maple	22p	20p	22p
Hornbeam	42p	25p	24p
Dogwood	37p	25p	26p
Hazel	34p	30p	30p
Hawthorn	22p	20p	22p
Spindle	42p	25p	25p
Beech	45p	N/A	33p (1+2)
Sea buckthorn	42p	35p	N/A
Holly (pot grown)	£2.70	N/A	N/A
Privet	40p	N/A	33p (1+0)
Crab apple	N/A	25p	23p
Blackthorn	26p	25p	24p
Common buckthorn	45p	N/A	25p
Dog rose	36p	N/A	22p
Wayfaring tree	43p	N/A	29p
Guelder rose	43p	N/A	33p (1+2)

* 45/60 cm (18/24 in) high purchased in a batch of 1,000 plants

It is easy to be critical of the variations in prices shown. They are indicative of differing growing conditions in the three areas, the relative importance of the production of certain species and the ease of growing those species on the individual nursery sites.

The Oxfordshire nursery is on a light sandy loam, which is unsuitable for slower growing species such as beech, wayfaring tree and guelder rose. Thus the nursery does not attempt to produce such species.

The Sussex nursery has the most comprehensive selection and also produces a wide range of forest and woodland seedlings and transplants. The hedging plants do not command quite the same level of importance to such a nursery as they do to the Oxfordshire nursery.

The Gloucestershire nursery provides a wide and competitively priced range of plants, grown mainly for the trade and farm woodland planting. Better soil conditions allow this nursery to provide the full range of plants, including slow growing species, to a high standard and within the necessary timescale for a 1+1 transplant (a one-year seedling which is lifted and grown-on for a second year to produce a taller, bushy and well-rooted transplant).

J. L. Beddall, in his book *Hedges for Farm & Garden* (published in 1950 but now unfortunately out of print), did not give prices for different hedgerow plants; instead he used a chart showing how long a stretch of hedge could be bought for £1.50 (30/–), using a range of different species. The visual simplicity of his chart was defeated by the fact that each of the species shown had its own plant spacing, which often differed from hawthorn. Table 15.2 shows how individual plant prices have changed over the past 40 years. (Figures from Beddall's chart have been converted into decimal currency.)

Table 15.2 Average Prices for Hedgerow Transplants (1+1)* Throughout the United Kingdom

	1950	*1991*
Field maple	2p	21p
Hornbeam	2p	30p
Hazel	2p	32p
Hawthorn	1p	21p
Beech	2½p	39p
Holly	8¼p	£2.50
Privet	1¾p	36p
Crab apple	2½p	24p
Wild plum	2p	25p
Blackthorn	2½p	25p
Gorse	1½p	(N/A)

* 45/60 cm (18/24 in) high purchased in a batch of 1,000 plants

If availability or popularity was a gauge to price, then gorse and privet were more widely used for hedgerows and blackthorn was used less.

Do not place price above quality. Visit one or two local nurseries producing suitable transplants during the latter part of the summer (August–September) to see the stock growing. At this time of the year the plants will have made most of their growth and one will be able to judge their quality and freedom from diseases, particularly mildew on hawthorn, crab and field maple.

It is foolish to boast how cheaply plants were purchased and how quickly they were planted, if the following year the work has to be done all over again because of poor quality stock and workmanship.

To illustrate the possible time involved in planting a hedge, actual planting schemes carried out by the author and his staff are outlined, with details of soil conditions and mixture of plants used. The schemes were carried out during the winter. This ensured that the nursery's staff was kept fully and productively employed during the winter quiet spells. Most were priced according to the time involved, costed below normal contractor rates. Plants were supplied from 'in-house' sources i.e. the author's nursery, and priced at actual (production) cost, plus a percentage to provide a modest profit.

MACHINE PLANTING OF TRANSPLANTS

1988 The Croft Field, Marcham, Oxfordshire

(A light, free-draining, sandy loam soil of good depth.)

Schedule

To plant a hawthorn (only) hedge line along the west, south and eastern boundaries, a total length of 1,516 m (1,652 yd). The hedge to consist of two lines of 60/90 cm (2/3 ft) 1+1 transplants, trimmed and machine planted. The lines to be 60 cm (2 ft) apart and each staggered with the plants 45 cm (1.5 ft) apart in each line. A total of 4.33 plants/m run of hedge (4.7 plants/yd). The hedge to be planted on the edge of the field into a rotovated strip 1.5 m (5 ft) wide.

Worksheet	*Man hours*	*Tractor/machine hours*
Meet owner to discuss plan and prepare for work	1	—
Rotovate planting strip and clear stones	1½	1½
Lift, bundle and trim transplants as required from the nursery	19	1½
Machine plant hedge lines (tractor driver, planting machine operator and two others supplying plants and checking finished work)	86	20
	107½	23

A time of 86 man hours to machine plant 6,568 60/90 cm (2/3 ft) transplants is equivalent to a rate of 76 plants per man hour. This indicates the benefit of a machine for planting out larger transplants which otherwise would have been planted into individually dug holes.

1989 Peasemore Farm, near Newbury, Berkshire

(A sticky, brown, sandy clay loam with flints, overlying chalk.)

Schedule

To plant a twin line hawthorn (only) hedge on the edge of fields bordering a small country road. The two lines of staggered plants to be approximately 0.75 m (30 in) apart, with the plants 0.5 m (20 in) apart in each line. The lines to be machine planted into the existing crop of autumn-sown winter wheat. A total length of 1,259 m (1,372 yd). The hedge lines to be planted with 60/90 cm (2/3 ft) high 1+1 transplants, root and top trimmed.

Worksheet	*Man hours*	*Tractor/machine hours*
Meet owner to discuss plan and prepare for work	2	—
Lift and bundle plants from the nursery, and load for planting	21½	3
Drive to and from the site each day (includes transporting staff)	24	10
Machine plant hedge lines (tractor driver, planter operator and two others supplying plants and checking finished work)	93	39
	140½	52

The journey from the nursery to the farm took one hour each way each day. It required a tractor and trailer to take both the staff and fresh planting stock. This was a slower yet cost-effective way of doing the job; staff could have got there quicker in a van, but would then have had to wait for the tractor and trailer to arrive with the plants. The tractor with the machine planter remained on the farm for the duration of the work.

The total planting time of 93 man hours to machine plant 5,456 hawthorn 1+1 transplants, root and top trim with a guillotine, was equivalent to a rate of 59 plants per man hour. This again indicates the benefit of using a machine for planting stock which otherwise would have required individual holes to be dug to plant the well-rooted stock.

The slower planting speed was due to the sticky soil conditions. Soil stuck to the machine and clung to the boots like lumps of lead, making work very difficult in some of the damper spots. This was partially compensated by a good run on higher ground where the soil was more sandy.

1990 Peasemore Farm, near Newbury, Berkshire

(A dry, brown, sandy clay loam with flints.)

Schedule

To plant 1,467 m (1,599 yd) of twin line hedge into a growing crop of autumn-sown winter wheat, on the edge of one large field bordering a small country road (Plate 15.2). The two lines of staggered plants to be approximately 0.75 m (30 in) apart, with individual plants 0.5 m (20 in) apart along each row. The hedge to be planted with the following mixture of species: 50% hawthorn, 20% blackthorn, 10% field maple, 10% hazel, 10% ramanas rose. The hedge lines to be planted with 60/90 cm (2/3 ft) 1+1 transplants, top and root trimmed with a guillotine.

PLATE 15.2 The ideal site for a new hedge. An exposed lane on the Berkshire Downs at Peasemore Farm.

Worksheet	*Man hours*	*Tractor/machine hours*
Meet owner to discuss plan and prepare for work	1½	—
Lift, bundle and trim the plants from the nursery and load for planting	33	4
Drive to and from the site for 3 days' work (includes transporting staff)	28	8
Machine plant hedge (tractor driver, planter operator and three others supplying plants and checking work)	113	21
	175½	33

Working in the same area, on the same farm, again meant an hour's drive to and from the site each day with one tractor and trailer carrying the plants, but with a larger team than in the previous year.

The total planting time of 113 man hours to machine plant a total of 6,420 mixed species was equivalent to 57 plants per man hour. So the extra team member proved to be valuable in maintaining a good output when faced with the extra work of providing the planter's operator with the mixture of species in the agreed order, in addition to the usual work of treading up the plants and checking the quality of the completed work.

The ground conditions were better than in the previous year. The soil was drier and less sticky. Planting into clear, level ground sown to a cereal crop was ideal for the machine; fortunately the field crop had not grown too lush in the mild autumn conditions. In both years the work was undertaken in mid-January.

The layout of a mixed species hedge is a point for debate. Some conservationists favour planting those species other than hawthorn or blackthorn in groups at random intervals along the hedge. When machine planting along such a length it becomes difficult to maintain the correct proportions of each species being used if adopting anything but a fixed rotation of plants.

In the example at Peasemore Farm (1990) hawthorn was used alternately with each of the other four species being introduced in turn, with the exception that every time the fourth alternative was presented for planting, the operator then put in two blackthorn in succession after it, before returning to alternating hawthorn with each of the other three. This ensured that the target of 20% blackthorn was attained. At the end of planting, there were small discrepancies in the actual number of each species used, but the total number planted worked out at exactly four plants per yard run.

HAND PLANTING OF TRANSPLANTS

1982 Peasemore Farm, near Newbury, Berkshire

(A dark, fertile, clay loam with flints, overlaying chalk.)

Schedule

To hand plant two hedge lines, totalling 366 m (400 yd), across one field to divide it into three paddocks, the ground being fully cultivated beforehand. Each hedge to be planted as two staggered rows 1 m (3 ft 3 in) apart, with the plants spaced at 1 m (3 ft 3 in) along each row, using two-year-old transplants, with some container grown plants where necessary. The mixture of species to be as follows: 40% hawthorn, 11% blackthorn, 7% hazel, 7% common juniper, 7% holly, 7% bird cherry, 7% wayfaring tree, 7% field maple, 7% dog rose. (A total of 800 plants required.)

Worksheet	*Man hours*	*Tractor/machine hours*
Meet the owner to discuss and later amend the position of the hedges	2	–
Lift, trim, bag up plants on the nursery and load for planting	12	1
Drive to and from the site for three days' work (includes transporting staff)	18	6
Mark out hedge lines and plough out single furrows along each line. Hand dig holes in furrow, plant and level ground.	61	3
	93	10

The field was to be divided into three paddocks, the mixture of plants providing tall untrimmed screens between each paddock. The ground had been cropped regularly for many years and was stubble prior to planting.

To mark the line of the hedges, and ease the work of digging holes in a heavy clay loam, a single furrow plough was used to plough out two furrows, 1 m (3 ft 3 in) apart, with the soil thrown away from the centre line for each row. Holes were easy to dig against the furrow wall, which served as the planting line. However, there was a lot of soil to be shovelled back to level off all the open plough furrow; particularly with the plants at a wide spacing. An average planting rate of 12 plants per man hour was anticipated. 800 plants were put in within 61 hours, equalling 13 plants per man hour of actual time planting demonstrate the different growth rates of this hedge after nine years. Plates 15.3 and 15.4.

1989 Manor Preparatory School, Abingdon, Oxfordshire

(A brown loam soil with some coral rag limestone close to the surface.)

Schedule

To hand plant a two-line hedge close to the 229 m (250 yd) eastern boundary fence of the playing field. The hedge to contain a mixture of species, using 45/60 cm (18/24 in) 1+1 transplants, untrimmed and planted into individually hand-dug, staggered holes 45 cm (18 in) apart. The mixture of 500 plants to be as follows: 30% hawthorn, 10% blackthorn, 10% hazel, 10% field maple, 10% guelder rose, 10% wayfaring tree, 10% spindle, 10% common dogwood. A fixed price quotation for the scheme was submitted, based upon hand planting at a rate of 15 shrubs per man hour.

The work was carried out in dry soil conditions in late January. Digging conditions proved to be much harder than the trial hole (dug to prepare the quotation). The ground was dry, compacted turf with very shallow topsoil, meeting coral rag limestone in almost half the holes dug. Each hole was 0.3 m (12 in) square and 0.5 m (20 in) deep. A crowbar was needed to loosen the soil or limestone in the base of some holes. Only by determined hard work was the target planting rate achieved.

Worksheet	*Man hours*	*Tractor/machine hours*
Lift and bundle the required plants from the nursery	6	½
Drive to the site with a four-man team and plant the hedge in one day	32	1½
	38	2

Allowing half-an-hour travelling time to and from the site, the team was required to work hard to complete the work within one normal

PLATE 15.3 The hedge planted at Peasemore after nine years showing a wide selection of tree and shrub species, planted as two, wide-spaced rows and allowed to grow unchecked. The author points to the vigorous growth of bird cherry.

PLATE 15.4 A broader view of the same hedge showing the mature and natural appearance attained by the differing growth rates of the selected trees and shrubs.

working day, with the minimum of rest periods.

This experience highlights the need to dig several trial holes along a proposed hedge line when preparing a binding quotation. There will always be a fine dividing line between allowing an adequate profit margin which accommodates unforeseen problems, and the risk of losing the contract because of overpricing the work. Wherever possible the author prefers to do work on an actual cost basis. This restricts the profit margin, but it ensures that the contractor does not lose money in the face of unexpected problems or poor working conditions. Likewise, the customer can gain handsomely if the work progresses smoothly and swiftly, allowing the contractor to complete the work in less time than anticipated. Such a situation permits the contractor to move on to another job sooner than expected, or – in the author's case – to return to the priorities of his own nursery work.

The five worksheets described indicate a range of situations, each of which was affected by soil conditions, physical barriers to the use of planting machinery, weather conditions and the optimum size of the gang employed to complete the work within the required time.

Prices for the plants and the work done have not been shown, to protect the privacy of the customers and to prevent these examples from being used as a yardstick for contract planting.

MACHINE PLANTING OF SEEDLINGS

1987 Collins Farm, Frilford, Oxfordshire

Schedule

To plant a hawthorn (only) windbreak hedge, dividing one field into two smaller fields. The hedge to consist of three lines of seedlings 35 cm (14 in) apart with seedlings 20 cm (8 in) apart along each line. This will produce a thick hedge early in its life. The competition between the plants in each row will encourage good upward growth.

The hedge line was machine planted by the same planter that was used for lining out the farm's crop of trees and shrub seedlings, for the production of transplants. The rate of planting at such spacing was approximately 800 plants per man hour. The 200 m (218 yd) hedge was planted in 1¼ hours by the four-man team of three planters and one tractor driver.

This method of hedge planting using seedlings is simply the same as the nursery planting practices outlined in Chapter 6. It is recommended as an alternative to machine planting of transplants and for easily worked, light soils, where the equipment is available. It is most important to keep the young plants completely free of weeds and well tended during the first three years of growth to ensure that a fully mature, stockproof, 3 m (10 ft) hedge is achieved within ten years.

This example of machine planting shows the rates possible using seedling material. The ground must be well prepared, weed-free and rolled level prior to planting. The planting rates achieved by machine are better and more consistent than hand planting, with the added bonus that the quality of the work is better than hand work.

HAND PLANTING OF SEEDLINGS

1992 North Farm, Shillingford, Oxfordshire

The experience of Paul Warburton Esq., the farm's owner.

Schedule

To plant a 338 m (368 yd) curving hawthorn hedge beside a recently-planted woodland margin, for the improvement of game conservation. The mixture of plants to be 75% hawthorn, 15% alder buckthorn to provide a dense hedge, and the remaining 10% made up of dog rose, spindle, dogwood, field maple and hazel. The hedge to consist of two lines of plants 0.5 m (20 in) apart, with 30/40 cm (12/18 in) one year seedlings hand planted at 45 cm (18 in) staggered intervals along each line.

The ground was ploughed in the autumn and subsequently power harrowed to provide clean, open ground for ease of planting.

The chalky loam soil, which can be sticky in wet weather, was in a suitable condition after a good dry winter for achieving a rate of approximately 2½ plants per minute – 700 plants hand-planted in a five-hour spell.

The easiest way to plant these small seedlings was to work on one's hands and knees, making holes with a metal dibber to accept the small, straight-rooted plants. If a proprietary gardener's dibber is not available, it is possible to make one easily from a broken spade handle, by pointing up the broken shaft to a suitable length; alternatively find some tool which will make a suitable hole.

For planting young trees on the same farm into stickier chalk loam soil, the owner found that a strong garden fork was preferable to using a spade. Working into prepared land, the spade soon became unusable with the weight of sticky soil adhering to it. The garden fork proved a very acceptable alternative for such conditions, less soil sticking to it and yet capable of opening an adequate hole to put in small transplants behind the fork.

HEDGE PLANTING COSTS

The variability in working conditions and the cost of planting stock are enough to make a mockery of attempts to draw up standard costs for hedge planting. For instance the author's machine planting team, working on a sandy loam, were able to achieve a rate of 70 plants per man hour, yet could only achieve 59 plants per man hour doing the same work on a sticky clay loam. So a combination of trial and experience is necessary in preparing quotations.

Table 15.3 Hedge Planting Costs as a Percentage of the Total Costs

	Machine planting			*Hand planting*	
	1988 Marcham	*1989 Peasemore*	*1990 Peasemore*	*1982 Peasemore*	*1989 Abingdon*
Labour	27	32	35	48	63
Machinery	7	12	6	5	NIL
Plants	66	56	59	47	37
TOTAL	100	100	100	100	100

Table 15.3 shows the benefits obtained from machine planting, particularly when working in good field conditions. Many farmers employ their own staff on hedgerow and woodland planting during the quieter winter months, thus minimising labour costs. A contractor employed to plant long stretches of new hedges must utilise machinery wherever possible to reduce the cost of labour and time to a level which is acceptable to the client and to encourage more planting in future years.

Chapter 16

Hedges and the Law

My apple trees will never get across
And eat the cones under his pines, I tell him.
He only says, 'Good fences make good neighbours.'

ROBERT FROST

When the old saying, 'Good fences make good neighbours' evolved, a 'fence' was the name given to what we now call a hedge. The saying remains as relevant today as it did when first expressed.

Many unpleasant disputes between neighbours over hedges, ditches, fences and banks could be minimised if boundary agreements were drawn up clearly in *all* title deeds.

Uncertainties arise over the years as neighbours make verbal agreements to deal with problems. These are never formalised, nor are the relevant documents deposited with the two parties' solicitors. If more care was taken in the first instance, future disputes could be more easily resolved.

Where the title deeds of two adjoining neighbours cannot resolve a boundary dispute, the parties have to resort to the relevant texts of law statutes.

Extracts from laws relating to trees, hedges, hedgebanks and their related ditches are set out in the following pages. References made to highways relate to the Highways Act 1980.

The author wishes to thank Butterworths Ltd, Law Publishers of Kingsway, London, for their kind permission to publish the relevant extracts taken from *Halsbury's Laws of England* (Fourth Edition), Volume 4.

The section headings and paragraph numbers have been retained to allow the reader to refer to any particular point in the text or to quote the reference for any related research.

All the relevant acts of parliament have been 'translated' into a narrative form, to provide a more readable, yet accurate, interpretation of the original legal text.

The paragraphs chosen relate to hedges either directly or indirectly, the term 'fence' being used in its widest interpretation. Paragraph 887 has been included as a 'sting in the tail', which might encourage someone to plant a hedge to overcome the liability implied. The last paragraph (No. 888) is a further encouragement – no planning permission is required, so long as the height restrictions are observed.

The footnotes to the extracts have not been printed except those which may help the reader's understanding of the law.

BOUNDARIES FIXED BY LEGAL PRESUMPTIONS

845. Rebuttable Presumptions

An artificial boundary structure belongs to the owner of the land on which it exists, but very often it is difficult to determine precisely where the boundary lies and hence to whom the feature belongs. If, on their true construction with such extrinsic evidence as is admissible, the title deeds do not clearly fix the position of the boundary of land in relation to certain boundary features, resort may be had to well established legal presumptions which apply in relation to those features. All the presumptions recognised and obtaining in the case of boundaries are rebuttable, and not irrebuttable or conclusive presumptions; that is to say, evidence to rebut the presumptions is always admissible, but, until it is produced, the presumptions necessarily apply.

846. Presumption as to Hedges and Ditches

No man making a ditch may cut into his neighbour's soil, but usually he makes it at the very extremity of his own land, forming a bank on his own side with the soil which he excavates from the ditch, on the top of which bank a hedge is usually planted. Therefore, where two fields are separated by a hedge or bank and an artificial ditch, the boundary prima facie runs along the side of the ditch further from the hedge or bank. This being the origin of the presumption, it is only applicable when it is known that the ditch is artificial. Further, the presumption does not apply where the title deeds show what the boundary is.

Acts of ownership such as trimming and pollarding a hedge and cleaning a ditch, even though continued for many years by an adjoining owner, do not rebut the presumption that the ditch and hedge belong to the owner of the land nearer to the hedge, particularly if the acts were done without the knowledge of the presumptive owner.

An impression prevails in some districts that the owner of a bank and ditch is entitled to four feet of width for the base of the bank and four feet of width for the ditch, but, apart from any local custom, there is no rule to this effect*.

* In some places a right of 'freeboard' or 'deerleap' extending several feet beyond the hedge is claimed by local custom; see para. 877, post. Where, on a map attached to an award made under a local Act for the regulation of a common, the boundary of the common was delineated by a line drawn along the line of 'growers' in a hedge dividing the common from the land of an adjacent owner, the hedge belonging to such owner, there was no presumption that the owner was entitled to a ditch-width on the outside of the line of growers.

847. When Presumption Does Not Arise

Where two pieces of land are divided by two ditches one on each side of a hedge or bank, or by two hedges or banks one on each side of a ditch, or by an old hedge or bank without any ditches at all, then there is no presumption as to the ownership of the hedges, ditches, or banks, but it must be proved by acts of ownership exercised over them. If the adjoining owners on each side concurrently exercise acts of ownership, and it is not known what quantity of land each of the owners originally contributed towards the formation of the ditch or bank that would, prior to 1 January 1926*, have been evidence that the hedge, ditch or bank was a party fence held in tenancy in common.

If the true boundary is known, however, it will not be altered merely by concurrent acts of ownership.

* I.e. the date of commencement of the Law of Property Act 1925.

848. Hedges and Ditches Beside Highways

The same principles apply in the rare case of hedges and ditches running along the side of a public highway where the soil of the highway is not owned by the owners of the adjoining land*. The hedge and ditch are presumed to be owned by the owner of the adjoining land for he could only lawfully have dug the ditch in his own land. The presumption, however, would yield to contrary evidence, for example that the ditch was constructed by the owners of the road, in which case the ditch would remain part of the road. Moreover, a ditch running alongside a highway between the road and fence may be dedicated as part of the highway.

Where a highway of a definite width has been laid out under an Inclosure Act, there is no presumption that an adjoining ditch and hedge form part of the highway, if the highway by itself is of the definite width.

* As to the more usual presumption in the case of highways, see para. 850, post.

849. Fences

In the case of wooden fences, it is likely to be inferred that, in the absence of freeboard, the owner of land will use his land to the fullest extent so that the fence will be deemed to belong to the person on whose side the rails and posts are placed, the palings being placed on his neighbour's side*, but where there is a dispute it would be necessary to show acts of ownership; that is, an owner may establish acts of ownership by himself to show that the fence is his or acts of ownership by his neighbour to show that the fence is the latter's responsibility. Alternatively, the owners may have agreed to share responsibility. However, where a fenced close adjoins a piece of waste land, there is a presumption that the fence belongs to the owner of the close.

* If the fence was erected the reverse way, the palings would not enclose the small strips of land between the posts. For the meaning of 'freeboard', see para. 877, post.

850. Presumption in Case of Highway

Where land is bounded by a highway, or a private right of way, the boundary is, as a general rule, a line drawn along the middle of the highway, or way, for the owners of land adjoining* the highway or way are presumed, in the absence of any evidence to the contrary, to own the soil as far as the middle of the road and all above the soil subject only to the right of passage over the surface. The mere fact that a conveyance describes land as being bounded by a highway or that measurements or a plan by reference to which land is conveyed exclude any part of the highway will not rebut the presumption, for it would be absurd to suppose that the grantor retained the soil of the highway, which in nearly every case would be wholly valueless. The presumption applies under the general boundaries rule in the case of registered land, but it is not the practice of the Land Registry to show the half-width of the highway as being within the title.

The presumption obtains also where the land was formerly of copyhold tenure and in the case of leaseholders.

* Land adjoins a highway for this purpose although separated from it by a public right of way not being part of the street.

TREES ON BOUNDARIES

873. Right to Lop Overhanging Trees

Where the branches of a tree belonging to one landowner or occupier overhang the land of an adjoining owner or occupier, the latter may at any time cut off those parts which overhang, without notice to the former, provided that in so doing he does not trespass on the adjoining land. But an adjoining owner is not entitled to lop his neighbour's tree as a precautionary measure before it overgrows his land merely because he knows that in the course of time the boughs will probably overhang his land*. The right to lop is a right to abate a nuisance constituted by overhanging branches and does not carry with it a right to appropriate severed branches or fruit growing-on overhanging branches†.

Encroaching roots have been treated as falling within the same principle as overhanging branches.

* He may, however, be entitled to an injunction quia timet if substantial damage is a virtual certainty and also imminent. For rights to lop trees threatening to overhang highways, see para. 876, post.

† As to the right to claim damages if the remedy of abatement is not exercised and damage subsequently occurs, see para. 874, post. It is not clear whether a claim for damages will lie (e.g. to recover the cost of employing a contractor to lop the branches) if the remedy of abatement is exercised.

874. Liability for Damage Caused by Trees

Although an adjoining owner has the right to trim hedges and lop the branches of trees belonging to another which overhang his land, the burden of so doing, or of watching to see when such action is required, ought not to be put on him by the acts of the owner of the land on which the trees are growing. Thus an action in nuisance for an injunction and damages will lie against an owner or occupier who allows the branches of his trees to overhang his boundary and cause injury to his neighbour's property, or who allows the roots of his trees to burrow under the boundary and cause damage. If the overhanging trees or encroaching roots are not in fact causing damage, it seems that the only right of the person whose land is affected is to cut back the overhanging or encroaching portions*.

On the same principle, a person who permits the branches of poisonous trees growing near his boundary to extend over the land of an adjoining owner will be liable in nuisance, if the branches are eaten by the adjoining owner's cattle, for any consequent injury to the cattle; but since a lessee takes the property as he finds it, a tenant who takes land with the branches of yew trees overhanging it from the landlord's adjoining land so as to be within reach of cattle cannot recover from the landlord damages for injury to cattle through eating the branches†. Nor will any action lie if the branches do not extend over the boundary but the adjoining owner's cattle trespass by reaching over the boundary and so eat the foliage of poisonous trees growing there‡.

No right to have trees overhanging the land of another, or with their roots encroaching, can be acquired by prescription or under the Limitation Act 1939, since the trees grow from year to year.

* Allowing a tree to grow over the land of another is not in itself an actionable trespass.

† Whether the tenant would have a claim if the branches, at the beginning of the tenancy, either were not overhanging at all or were overhanging but out of reach is undecided.
‡ No action where clippings from poisonous trees taken on to neighbour's land by third party. An action will probably lie if poisonous leaves from trees growing on the land of one owner are blown on to the adjoining land and cause injury to cattle eating them.

875. Entry on Neighbour's Land

There is some authority for the proposition that if a man is unable to lop his trees without the boughs falling upon the land of his neighbour, he may justify the felling upon his neighbour's land, and that if a tree grows so that the fruit falls upon the land of another, the owner of the tree may enter upon the other's land for the purpose of taking possession of the fruit*.

* 'If trees grow in my hedge, hanging over another man's land, and the fruit of them falls into the other's land, I may justify my entry to gather up the fruit, if I may make no longer stay there than is convenient, nor break his hedge'; and it is stated that the same rule applies when trees are blown over by the wind.

876. Trees Adjoining Highways

Local authorities and the secretary of state are invested with statutory powers to order the lopping or pruning of trees or hedges overhanging and prejudicially affecting a highway or any other road or footpath to which the public has access*. Local authorities and the secretary of state are also empowered to order the felling of trees or hedges which are dead, diseased, damaged or insecurely rooted and therefore likely to cause danger by falling on to a highway or other road or footpath to which the public has access†.

Subject to specified exemptions, no tree or shrub may be planted in a highway or within fifteen feet from the centre of a made-up carriageway‡, but the highway authority may license the occupier or the owner of any premises adjoining the highway to plant or to retain trees in such part of the highway as may be specified in the licence.

* Highways Act 1959, s. 134. For the power of a secretary of state to order the lopping of trees and hedges interfering with airfields, see the Land Powers (Defence) Act 1958, s. 10; Defence (Transfer of Functions) (No. 1) Order 1964, S.I. 1964 No. 488; Ministry of Aviation Supply (Dissolution) Order 1971, S.I. 1971 No. 719.
† Highways (Miscellaneous Provisions) Act 1961, s. 10.
‡ Highways Act 1959, s. 123; Highways Act 1971, s. 43(9), (11).

RIGHTS AND DUTIES OF OWNERS OF FENCES

877. Definitions of Fences

Although fences are frequently used to mark the situation of boundaries, none the less they are primarily guards against intrusion, or barriers to prevent persons or animals straying out, and therefore in this sense the term includes not only hedges, banks, and walls, but also ditches. But an external or party wall forming part of a building and alongside or on the boundary of land is not usually regarded as a fence.

For the purposes of the Animals Act 1971, 'fencing' includes the construction of any obstacle designed to prevent animals from straying*.

A fence has been held not to be a 'building or erection' within the meaning of a local Act prohibiting the making of a building or erection within ten feet of the head of a wharf.

The term 'freeboard' or 'freebord' land is commonly applied to a strip of land, varying in width according to local custom, outside and adjoining the fence of a manor park, forest, or other estate, which belongs to or of which a right of user is claimed by the owner of the land within the fence.

* Animals Act 1971, s. 11.

887. Consequences of Neglect to Fence Where There is No Duty to Fence

Even where there is no specific duty to fence, an owner or occupier of land may be liable for damage or injury sustained by others because there is no fence or it is inadequate or defective.

It may therefore be necessary to fence to fulfil adequately the duty of care owed to lawful visitors under the Occupiers' Liability Act 1957 or to prevent children trespassing on land which contains something which could injure them, particularly where the child might not appreciate the danger or be able to read warning notices.

Under the Animals Act 1971 it may be necessary to fence to keep in livestock as the owner of livestock is generally liable to any damage the animals may cause*, and it is no defence that the person who suffered the damage could have prevented it by fencing unless he, or any other person having an interest in the land, had a duty to fence† and the livestock would not have strayed but for a breach of that duty‡. There is also a duty to take care to prevent damage from animals straying on the highway so that, having regard to the nature of the animals, fencing may be required to fulfil this duty, but the Act does provide that where a person places animals on certain unfenced land and has the right to do so, he shall not be regarded as being in breach of his duty of care merely by reason of having placed them there.

* Animals Act 1971, s. 4(1).

† It is not clear whether, to negative liability, the duty to fence has to be one owed to the possessor of the livestock or whether a duty to a third party, for example a landlord or an adjoining owner, would suffice. It appears, however, that the Act has not abrogated

the rule that where a person puts his livestock into his own field and they escape into the field of an adjoining owner and thence into the field of a third party, in an action by the third party (which would now be under the Animals Act 1971, s. 4) the owner of the livestock cannot set up as a defence that the adjoining owner was in breach of a duty to fence owed to him.
‡ Animals Act 1971, s. 5(1), (6).

888. Permitted Development

In general, subject to the fulfilment of certain conditions*, development consisting of the erection or construction of gates, fences, walls or other means of inclosure not exceeding one metre in height where abutting on a highway used by vehicular traffic or two metres in height in any other case, and their maintenance, improvement or alteration is permitted and may be undertaken on land without the specific permission of the local planning authority or the secretary of state†.

* See the Town and Country Planning General Development Order 1973, S.I. 1973 No. 31, Sch. 1, Class II.
† Town and Country Planning Act 1971, s. 24, Sch. 24, para. 1(2); Town and County Planning General Development Order 1973, art. 3(1), Sch. 1, Class II.

REFERENCES AND FURTHER READING

Halsbury's Laws of England (Fourth Edition), Volume 4 (1973) *Boundaries* (Butterworths, London).

Appendix 1

British Imperial and Continental Metric Measures

OLD IMPERIAL MEASURES

Length

In AD 1101, Henry I commanded that the length of his arm should define the yard. From that date until the introduction of metric measurement, the yard remained the British unit of length.

12 inches (in)	= 1 foot (ft)
3 feet (ft)	= 1 yard (yd)
5.5 yards (yd)	= 1 pole, rod or perch (p)
40 poles or 220 yards	= 1 furlong
8 furlongs	= 1 mile

Surface area

144 square inches (sq in)	= 1 square foot (sq ft)
9 square feet (sq ft)	= 1 square yard (sq yd)
30.25 square yards (sq yd)	= 1 square pole or perch (p)
40 square poles	= 1 rood (r)
4 roods (r)	= 1 acre

Field size

On old enclosure award maps, fields are given a name or other description to define each parcel of land. Below the name or description will be written the size of the field or piece. *For example*

a	*r*	*p*
83	1	27

This piece was of a size 83 acres, 1 rood and 27 perches.
83 acres (× 4,840 sq yd)
+ 1 rood (× 1,210 sq yd, being 0.25 acre per rood)
+ 27 perches (× 30.25 sq yd per perch)

METRIC MEASURES

Length

10 millimetres (mm)	= 1 centimetre (cm)
100 centimetres (cm)	= 1 metre (m)
100 metres (m)	= 1 kilometre (km)

Surface area

100 sq metres = 1 are (109.6 sq yards)
100 ares = 1 hectare (2.47 acres)

SEEDLING AND TRANSPLANT TREE SIZES AND CONVERSIONS

English nurseries have universally adopted metric height measures to suit the old imperial categories.

10–20 cm	= 4–8 in	60–90 cm	= 2–3 ft
20–30 cm	= 8–12 in	90–120 cm	= 3–4 ft
30–45 cm	= 12–18 in	120–150 cm	= 4–5 ft
45–60 cm	= 18 in–2 ft		

Appendix 2

Grant Aid

Grants for the planting and maintenance of hedges are currently available from the following main sources, depending on where the applicant lives in the United Kingdom.

- The Ministry of Agriculture, Fisheries and Food (M.A.F.F.)
  The Welsh Office Agriculture Department (W.O.A.D.)
  The Scottish Office Agriculture and Fisheries Department (S.O.A.F.D.)
- The Countryside Commission (England)
  The Countryside Council for Wales (C.C.W.)
  Scottish Natural Heritage (S.N.H.)
- Local county and district councils throughout England, Wales and Scotland.

THE M.A.F.F./W.O.A.D./S.O.A.F.D. GRANT SCHEME

The M.A.F.F., W.O.A.D. and S.O.A.F.D. provide aid through their Farm and Conservation Grant Scheme for the planting, replacement and improvement of hedges, hedge and wall banks together with the provision of hedgerow trees and all necessary protective fencing.

The laying or coppicing of existing and maturing new hedges is eligible for grant aid as well as the provision of gates, stiles, footbridges and all related fittings. Full details of specific items and current rates of grant are fully described in M.A.F.F. and W.O.A.D. booklets F and CGS (1991) 1, F and CGS 10 and PB 0983 (1992), in S.O.A.F.D. leaflet CSI and booklets FCS(EC) 1 and FCS(N)1. The table on page 258 shows the current levels of grant aid available as a percentage of the total eligible costs incurred. A Less Favoured Area is an upland area where the climate, landscape and soil place farmers at a disadvantage compared to their lowland counterparts. This includes most of Wales and Scotland, together with upland areas in north-west, east, central and south-west England.

It is advisable to check with your regional service centre of M.A.F.F., W.O.A.D. or S.O.A.F.D. before embarking on any hedge planting scheme. They will provide full grant details related to the area and can offer specific advice, if required.

Farm and Conservation Grant Scheme 1991 Environmental and Countryside Grants

Description	*Rate of grant %* Non LFA	LFA
3 Provision, replacement or improvement of hedges, including hedgerow trees, necessary protective fencing, and associated gates, stiles, footbridges and other fittings	40	50
4 Hedge laying	40	50
5 Provision, replacement or improvement of walls and banks built of materials traditional to the locality and associated gates, stiles, footbridges and other fittings, protective fencing for banks	40	50

M.A.F.F. Regional Service Centres

Wessex
MAFF Block 3
Government Buildings
Burghill Road
Westbury-on-Trym
Bristol BS10 6NJ
Tel: 0272 591000

North Mercia
MAFF
Berkeley Towers
Crew
Cheshire CW2 6PT
Tel: 0270 69211

East Midlands
MAFF Block 7
Government Buildings
Chalfont Drive
Nottingham NG8 3SN
Tel: 0602 291191

Anglia
MAFF Block C
Government Buildings
Brooklands Avenue
Cambridge CB2 2DR
Tel: 0223 426727

South West
MAFF
Government Buildings
Alphington Road
Exeter EX2 8NQ
Tel: 0392 77951

South East
MAFF Block A
Government Buildings
Coley Park
Reading
Berkshire RG1 6DT
Tel: 0734 581222

Northern
MAFF
Eden Bridge House
Lowther Street
Carlisle CA3 8DX
Tel: 0228 23400

North East
MAFF
Government Buildings
Crosby Road
Northallerton
North Yorkshire DL6 1AD
Tel: 0609 773751

South Mercia
MAFF Block C
Government Buildings
Whittington Road
Worcester WR5 2LQ
Tel: 0905 763355

THE COUNTRYSIDE COMMISSION

The Commission has developed Countryside Stewardship to offer encouragement for the conservation, management and recreation of specific target landscapes in danger from changing farming patterns, commercial exploitation or simple neglect. The present landscape categories under threat include:

- Chalk and limestone grassland
- Lowland heath
- Waterside landscapes, including rivers, meadows, fens and lakelands
- Coastal areas
- Upland meadows and moors
- Historic landscapes, such as deer parks, irrigated water-meadows, old orchards, hedgerows, walls and banks
- Old meadows and pastures

Any landowner with landscape which falls into any of the categories outlined can apply for grant aid for hedge planting, laying or coppicing if it can be demonstrated that the proposed plan will be conserving, enhancing or restoring that landscape for the benefit of public enjoyment. Public enjoyment does not imply public access in every case. In many cases conservation will require public exclusion if its aims are to be achieved, but there are many areas of our landscape which could become more accessible to the public within the objectives of Countryside Stewardship.

Those owning or managing landscape within the scope of the scheme may apply to the Countryside Commission for grant aid, which is provided in the form of capital payments. A ten year agreement is drawn up between the Commission and the landowner to ensure that the proposals are carried out correctly. Incentive payments are made annually in arrears. The agreement and its payments are reviewed on a three year cycle.

Current capital payments include:

Hedge planting	£1.75/metre
Hedge laying	£2.00/metre
Hedge coppicing	£1.50/metre
Plus	
for coppicing or laying hedges over 1.5 m wide at base	£0.50/metre
for post and wire removed to aid coppicing or layering	£0.50/metre
Stone faced hedgebank	
Repair	£10.00/metre
Restoration	£25.00/metre
Earth bank restoration	£3.00/metre
Planting of hedgerow trees	£6.00/tree
Coppicing bankside trees	£12.50/tree

Provision of tree guards	
Rabbit guard	£0.20 each
Tube guard	£0.50 each

Hedge or hedgebank fencing payments will be available to applicants only for work that is essential to achieve good environmental management:

Post and wire fence	£0.80/metre
Sheep fencing	£1.20/metre
Rabbit or sheep netting	£0.40/metre
Deer fencing	£3.50/metre

Apply to the local regional office of the Countryside Commission for full details of the grants and conditions currently available. Completed application forms must be submitted to the local regional office between 1 May and 30 September each year.

Countryside Commission Regional Offices

Northern
Warwick House
Grantham Road
Newcastle upon Tyne
NE2 1QF
Tel: 091 232 8252
Fax: 091 222 0185

Eastern
Ortona House
110 Hills Road
Cambridge CB2 1LQ
Tel: 0223 354462
Fax: 0223 313850

South East
4th Floor
71 Kingsway
London WC2B 6ST
Tel: 071 831 3510
Fax: 071 831 1439

Midlands
Cumberland House
Broad Street
Birmingham B15 1TD
Tel: 021 632 6503
Fax: 021 633 3159

South West
Bridge House
Sion Place
Clifton Down
Bristol BS8 4AS
Tel: 0272 739966
Fax: 0272 238086

Yorkshire and Humberside
8a Otley Road
Headingley
Leeds LS6 2AD
Tel: 0532 742935/6
Fax: 0532 787618

North West
2nd Floor
184 Deansgate
Manchester M3 3WB
Tel: 061 833 0316
Fax: 061 833 3093

COUNTRYSIDE COUNCIL FOR WALES (C.C.W.)

'Tir Cymen,' which translates into English roughly as 'a well-crafted countryside', is a new scheme for the conservation of the Welsh countryside.

Initially the scheme applies only to three pilot areas—Meirionnydd, Dinefwr and Swansea—and it will offer farmers in these areas annual payments in return for the management of their land in a manner which will benefit wildlife, landscape and archaeology to provide fresh opportunities for the quiet public enjoyment of the countryside.

It will pay farmers to use their skills and resources to look after the landscape and wildlife habitats. The scheme is voluntary and will offer annual payments for successfully following agreed management guidelines, plus the standard payments toward any capital work required.

There is a basic requirement that the Tir Cymen Code should be followed on the whole farm, and there is a basic annual payment per hectare.

The Tir Cymen Code is summarised as follows:

- Keep rights of way free of obstructions.
- Avoid pollution of water courses.
- Safeguard stone walls, slate fences, hedges and earth banks.
- Safeguard archaeological and geological sites.
- Conserve traditional stone built features and farm buildings which are still weatherproof.

Farmers, land agents or landowners wishing to join the scheme will be required to enter into a ten year management agreement with C.C.W. Agreed payments will be reviewed every two years to reflect prevailing market conditions.

Applications should be made to the local Tir Cymen Office between 1 May and 30 September each year, requesting a copy of the Tir Cymen Farmers' Pack.

Annual Management Payments cover a wide range of conservation and repair activities including:

Tir Cymen Code for the whole farm	£20.00 per ha/year (minimum £500, maximum £3,000 per farm)
Arable field margins	
Rough grass margins	£280 per ha/year
Uncropped wildlife margins	£250 per ha/year
Selected traditional field boundaries	
Hedges	£0.10 per metre/year
Stone walls, slate fences and earth banks	£0.18 per metre/year

Standard Capital Payments

Stone walls, earth banks, slate fences	
Major gapping and restoration	£12.00/metre of gap
Build from new	£19.50/metre
Supplement if stone unavailable on site	£7.50/metre
Stone step stile	£30.00 each

Item	Payment
Top wiring	£0.60/metre
Jump fencing	£1.60/metre
Fencing for environmental management	
Post and wire	
Softwood	£1.00/metre
Native hardwood	£1.20/metre
Supplement for stock netting	£0.40/metre
Rabbit fencing	
Softwood	£2.00/metre
Native hardwood	£2.20/metre
Post and rail	
Softwood	£9.00/metre
Native hardwood	£11.00/metre
Hedges	
Laying	£1.50/metre
Coppicing	£1.00/metre
Planting up gaps	£2.00/metre of gap
Planting new hedges	£2.00/metre
Gates and stiles	
Field gate	
Softwood	£100.00 each
Native hardwood	£130.00 each
Bridle gate	
Softwood	£100.00 each
Native hardwood	£120.00 each
Kissing gate	
Softwood	£110.00 each
Native hardwood	£130.00 each
For disabled people	£200.00 each
Stile	£34.00 each
Trees and shrubs	
Supply and plant	£0.75 each
Spiral rabbit guards	£0.30 each
Shelters	£0.50 or £1.00 each
Parkland stock guards	£25.00 each
Orchard tree guards	£2.50 each
Employment of specialist adviser	£150.00

Consult the regional office for any subsequent changes in payments or conditions, which may be made according to prevailing market conditions.

Countryside Council for Wales 'Tir Cymen' Regional Offices

Meirionnydd District
Tir Cymen
National Park Office
Penrhyndeudraeth
Gwynedd LL48 6LS
Tel: 0766 771222

Dinefwr District
Tir Cymen
Countryside Council for Wales
Yr Hen Bost
56 Rhosmaen Street
Llandeilo
Dyfed SA19 6HA
Tel: 0558 822239

Swansea District
Tir Cymen
Countryside Council for Wales
Oxwich Reserve Centre
Swansea
West Glamorgan
SA3 1LS
Tel: 0792 390749

SCOTTISH NATURAL HERITAGE (S.N.H.)

An independent body formed in 1992 from the amalgamation of the Countryside Commission for Scotland and the Nature Conservancy Council for Scotland. As S.N.H. is a new body, it has yet to fully prepare fresh grant details and levels of payment.

Grants are available to 'anyone who has the right to undertake the proposed scheme and the right to manage it for the duration of the grant contract'.

Those wishing to plant new hedges could receive grant help for habitat creation or for the preparation of management plans for the conservation or enhancement of the natural heritage.

Scottish Natural Heritage Offices

North West
Caithness and Sutherland
Main Street, Golspie
Sutherland, KW10 6TG
Tel: 0408 633 602

Ross & Cromarty and Inverness
Anancaun, Kinlochewe
Achnasheen, Ross-shire
Tel: 044 584 244

Lochaber and Skye & Lochalsh
Mamore House, The Parade
Fort William, Inverness-shire
Tel: 0397 704716

South East
Lothian and Borders
38 Gala Park, Galashiels
TD1 1EU
Tel: 0896 566 52

Fife and Central
The Beta Centre, Innovation Park
University of Stirling, Stirling
FK9 4NF
Tel: 0786 50363

Tayside
55 York Place, Perth PH2 8EH
Tel: 0738 39746

Western Isles
17 Francis Street, Stornoway
Isle of Lewis, Western Isles
Tel: 0851 705258

Regional Headquarters
Fraser Darling House
9 Culduthel Road, Inverness
IV2 4AG
Tel: 0463 239431

North Eastern
Badenoch & Strathspey, Nairn and Moray
Achantoul, Aviemore
Inverness-shire, PH22 1QD
Tel: 0479 810477

Banff & Buchan, Gordon
Aberdeen and Kincardine & Deeside
16/17 Rubislaw Terrace
Aberdeen, AB1 1XE
Tel: 0224 642863

Orkney and Shetland
2–4 Alexandra Building, The Esplanade, Lerwick, Shetland
ZE1 0LL.
Tel: 0595 3345

Regional Headquarters
16/17 Rubislaw Terrace
Aberdeen, AB1 1XE
Tel: 0224 642863

Regional Headquarters
Research Park, Avenue 1, Riccarton
Edinburgh, EH14 4AP
Tel: 031 449 4933

South West
Strathclyde (except Argyll & Bute)
The Castle, Balloch Castle Country Park, Dunbartonshire, G83 8LX
Tel: 0389 58511

Argyll & Bute
1 Kilmory Industrial Estate, Kilmory,
Lochgilphead, Argyll, PA31 8RR
Tel: 0546 603611

Dumfries & Galloway
106 High Street, Dalbeattie
Kirkcudbrightshire, DG5 4HB
Tel: 0556 610086

Regional Headquarters
The Castle, Balloch Castle Country Park, Balloch, Dunbartonshire,
G83 8LX
Tel: 0389 58511

THE HEDGEROW INCENTIVE SCHEME

A 1990 survey by the Institute of Terrestrial Ecology found that over 20% of a number of hedges surveyed in 1978 had disappeared as a result of wrong management either by being over-trimmed or neglected. As a result the Hedgerow Incentive Scheme was introduced in July 1992 by the Countryside Commission to rescue declining hedges and restore and maintain them as an historic part of the English landscape.

Under a ten year agreement a plan will be drawn up with the farmer or landowner for the phased restoration to bring the hedges in each application back to a condition where they will fulfil the needs of the owner and provide a rich environment to sustain all the natural flora and fauna associated with the English hedgerow.

The scheme complements the M.A.F.F. Farm and Conservation Scheme and operates in conjunction with the hedgerow grants offered under the M.A.F.F. scheme. Participation in the scheme is voluntary and open to anyone owning or managing suitable hedgerows.

Each applicant is invited to identify hedgerows on his land which require restoration, submitting a proposed programme of work to rejuvenate them. The programme should normally cover all hedgerows on the farm so that the whole farm can be treated in an overall plan.

If accepted, the programme forms the basis of a ten year agreement with the objective of carrying out initial laying, coppicing or gapping-up with new hedges during the first five years to achieve healthy and vigorous hedgerows around the farm, or estate, by the tenth year.

In addition to the hedges identified under the agreed programme of restoration all other hedges on the same land holding must be managed and protected sympathetically.

Apply to the Regional Office of the Countryside Commission requesting full details and an application form (MIS1). Applications should be made between 1 April and 30 September each year.

Incentive payments available under the scheme are listed below as a 'menu', enabling farmers and landowners to choose the items suitable to their own proposed programme.

Hedgerow Incentive Scheme Menu

Item	Payment
Gapping-up	£1.75/metre
Hedge laying	£2.00/metre
Plus on hedges over 1.5 m wide	£0.50/metre
Coppicing	£1.50/metre
Plus on hedges over 1.5 m wide	£0.50/metre
Supplement for removal of old fence posts and fence wires in hedgerow to be restored	£0.50/metre
Plus a second stage payment upon satisfactory completion of initial stages of restoration (normally five years after initial restoration work)	£1.00/metre laid, coppiced or gapped-up

Ancillary works

Item	Payment
Protective fencing	
Three line wire	£0.80/metre
Woven wire fencing	£1.20/metre
Rabbit netting	£0.40/metre

Item	Payment
Individual shrub/tree guards	
Spiral	£0.20 each
Tube	£0.50 each
Pollarding	£17.50/tree
Tree surgery	£40.00/tree
Hedgebanks	
Restoration of earth banks	£3.00/metre
Minor restoration of stone-faced banks	£10.00/metre
Major restoration of stone-faced banks	£25.00/metre
Planting hedgerow trees	£0.65 each
Technical advice/plan preparation	£100

The above incentive payments will remain available until the end of 1992. Thereafter check with the Countryside Commission Regional Offices (page 260) and M.A.F.F. Regional Service Centres (page 258) for any changes.

COUNTY AND DISTRICT COUNCILS (throughout the United Kingdom)

Most local councils run their own schemes in conjunction with the Countryside Commission (England), The Countryside Council for Wales or Scottish Natural Heritage. Each council identifies conservation needs within its boundaries and draws up a grant aid programme. Thus, levels of grant aid will vary from area to area and according to local priorities. However, hedgerow planting and maintenance grants will not appear in all local council schemes because they may not be a feature of the area which attracts conservation priority status.

Contact your local district or county council for details of their current conservation grants.

GREAT HEDGE PILOT SCHEME

The Great Hedge project has been initiated by an anonymous donation, and will be managed by Plant Life (a conservation charity for the protection of wild plants).

The aim is to protect and restore old hedgerows, establish new hedgerows, and link networks of new and old hedges across the country starting with a Great Hedge running east to west, from the west coast of Wales to the east coast of England.

This Great Hedge will not be a north/south divide, like Hadrian's Wall, but a spine joining communities to each other, onto which other hedges can join, spreading out across the country, both north and south, like a great mycelium. This will encourage its spread right across the country, to link communities and society. It will join the hawthorn farm hedge to its town garden cousins, the privet, beech and coniferous hedges; all will become integrated parts of a great national hedge. The main east/west spine will pass through small towns, where possible, or skirt round heavily developed areas to continue on its way across the country in an unbroken chain. The first section will run across Gloucestershire and will be funded by donations from conservation groups, commerce and private subscription.

Farmers, school children and the general public will be asked to help plant and maintain the hedge. Their participation will encourage a continued involvement in its future development and wellbeing. As the hedge grows, its ecology will build up to enrich the communities through which it passes.

The Great Hedge project officer is currently based at the Wilderness Environment Centre in the Royal Forest of Dean, Gloucestershire, and can be contacted at the following address:

Plant Life
The Wilderness Centre
Wilderness Drive
Mickeldene, Nr. Ross
Gloucestershire GL17 0HA.

Index

Page numbers in italics indicate illustrations and tables and **in bold indicate colour pages**

A-shape, 216, *216*
Abingdon aerodrome, hedgerows removed, 12–13
Acacia, false
  hedge, 148–149, *148*
Access for entrances, 116
Aerial surveys, 10
Age of hedges, method for assessing, 1971, 10–11
Airfields, effect on hedges, 12–14
Alder
  common, suitable for hedges, 161–163, *162*
  for conservation, 42
  for windbreaks, 39
  from seed, 74
Alder buckthorn, **6**
  from seed, 74
  suitability, 30–31
Alloxydim-sodium (Clout) after planting, 186
Alpha Accord for planting, 93
Alternative and regional hedges, 133–149
Aluminium ammonium sulphate (Spere) spray, 225
'Ancient countryside', 43, *44*
Anthocorid bug, predator of red spider mite, 60
Aphids
  action against plants, 203
  attacks, 60
  in hedgerows, 59
Ash
  common
    from seed, 77
    suitable for hedges, 160, *160*, *161*
  die-back, 151
Aspen, not suitable for hedges, 163
Atrazine (Gesaprim) after planting, 183
Autumn lifting, transplants, 107–108
Avon, species choice, 126
Badger gates, 232–233
Bank formation, 50
Bed size and plant spacing, 97–99
Beech
  for approach drive, 41
  common
    from seed, 76–77
    suitability, *22*, 23–24
Beetles
  action against plants, 203
  in hedgerows, 59
Berkshire, species choice, 125
Berkshire Hops, Southmoor, Oxfordshire, tall hawthorn hedge, *219*
Billhook styles, 208, 209
Biomass production from willow osier hedges, 144–145
Bird-catching net, 56–57, *56*, *57*
Birds, value of hedges, 54–58
  feeding areas, *55*
  nesting sites, *55*
  shelter, *55*
  species, 54–55
Black Death in 1349, effect on hedgerows, 2
Black locust hedge, 148–149
Black polythene, *see* Polythene
Blackgrass, problems in field margins, 173
Blackthorn, **5**
  description and suitability, 28–29
  for coastal sites, 39
  for conservation, 40
  for control of soil erosion, 41
  for screen hedge, 41
  from seed, 74
  on soil type division, 40
Body warmer, for outdoor work, 131
Boggy sites, species preference, 45
Boiler suit, one-piece polyester/cotton, for outdoor work, 129
Bomford Turner B577L hedge trimmer, *218*

Bomford Turner mid-position flail cutter, 218, *219*
Boots for outdoor work, 129–130
Boundaries
  fixed by legal presumptions, 248–254
    presumption as to hedges and ditches, 248–249
    rebuttable presumptions, 248
  trees on, legal presumptions, 251–253
Boundary fence, 39
Box, avoid in hedge, 35
Brimstone, 61
Brome, problems in field margins, 173
Broom, avoid in hedge, 36
Brown rat, hedgerow mammal, 59
Brunel's Great Western line from London to Bristol, *7*
Brushing, 207
Buckthorn
  alder
    description and suitability, 30–31
    from seed, 74
  common (or purging), **6**
    for conservation, 42
    suitability, 29–30
Bupirimate + triforine (Nimrod-T) against mildew, 199
Butterflies and moths, 61
  encouraging, field margins, 174

Canals, effect on hedges, 6
Care of plants prior to planting, 116–117
Caterpillars
  action against plants, 203
  encouraging, 61
Cattle fence positioned too close to hedge, *229*
Census, first agricultural, 9–10
Cereal planting, and elm trees, 150–151
Chalk soils, species preference, 45
Chamfered shape, 215
Chemical selectivity, pest control, 203
Cherry
  bird
    from seed, 78
    suitable for hedges, 154, *155*, *156*
  wild
    from seed, 78
    suitable for hedges, 154, *155*
Chestnut, sweet, from seed, 76
Chloropicrin for soil sterilisation, 81
Chlorthan-dimethyl (Dacthal) after planting, 184
Choice of plants for new hedge, 38–42
Christmas holly trade, 145–146
Civil War, effects on hedges, 5
Clay soils, species preference, 46
Clothing
  for handling hawthorn, *132*
  protective, 129–132
Coastal sites, 39
Cobbett, William, method of plant pruning (1825), *117*
Cocksfoot grass, sown margin, *171*
Cokethorpe Park, newly laid hedge, *213*
Collins Farm, Frilford, Oxfordshire, machine planting of seedlings, 244–245
Conservation, advisers' recommendations, 46–51
Conservation considerations, 54–63
  birds, 54–58
  field margins, 62–63
  invertebrates, 59–62
  mammals, 58–59
  shrubs and trees recommended, *48-49*
Conservation hedge, 40
Contact weed killers, 179
Control of Substances Hazardous to Health Regulations (COSHH) 1989, 178
Coppicing, 207, 221
Corn drill, invention, 5
Corn Laws, repeal, 1846, effect on hedges, 6
Cornwall
  hedges for protection, 46
  species choice, 126
Costings, 234–246
County War Agricultural Committees (War Ags), effect on hedges, 12
Crab apple (wild crab), **4**
  description, 26–27
  for conservation, 40
  for screen hedge, 41
  from seed, 77
  suitable for hedges, 154, *154*
  transplants, *117*
Croft Field, Marcham, Oxfordshire, machine planting, 237–238
Cultivated strip for double row hand planting, 120
Cumbria, species choice, 127
Cutters, hedge, mechanical, 217–221

Damage caused by trees, liability, 251–252
Damp sites, species preference, 45
Dazomet for soil sterilisation, 82–83
Deer, protection from, 227, *228*
  fencing, 227–233

Deltamethrin, approved for forestry, 204
Denmark, seedling source, 90
Devon, species choice, 126
Devonwade hedgebank, 133–138, *134–138*
Diflubenzuron, approved for forestry, 204
Dimensions of trees and shrubs (British Standards), *111*
Diphenamid (Enide) after planting, 184
Disease control, 197–201
  and seedling planting, 100–102
Ditches, legal presumptions, 248–250
Dithiocarbonate-based repellant, 225
Dog rose, **7**
  description, 31, *32*
  for conservation, 40
  from seed, 74
Dogwood
  common, **1**
    from seed, 70–71
    transplants, *117*
  description and suitability, 19, *20*
  for control of soil erosion, 41
  on soil type division, 40
Dome shape trimming of hedge, *217*
Domesday book, 3
Driver, Edward, Frilford parish map, 1846, 10
Driver, Robert Collier, Frilford parish map, 1860, 10
Dumfries, species choice, 128
Dutch elm disease, 150

East Anglia (Norwich area), species choice, 126
Elder, common, avoid in hedge, 36, *37*
Elm
  common, avoid in hedge, 38
  not suitable for hedges, 163, *163*
Elm trees
  and cereal planting, 150–151
  extinction, 150
Enclosing of common land, 15th century, 2–3
Enclosure awards, 10
Enclosure fields, Cotswolds, *44*
Enclosures, 1865, 8–9
Entry on neighbour's land, legal factors, 252
Ermine moth caterpillar, 61
Erwinia amylovora, cause of fire blight, 197
Essex, species choice, 126
Evergreens, use, 41–42
Exposed coastal sites, species preference, 46

False acacia
  hedge, 148–149, *148*
Farming, poverty and prosperity, 5
Farming practice, effect of soil type, 43–53
Fences
  legal presumptions, 250
  owners, rights and duties, 253–254
    consequences of neglect to fence where there is no duty to fence, 253–254
    definitions of fences, 253
    permitted development, 254
Fencing, 227–233
  tools, *231*
Fertiliser and sprays, exclusion in field margins, 174
Fertilisers
  and seedling planting, 103
  encouraging weed species, 62–63
  for emerging and growing seedlings, 86
Field maple, *see* Maple
Field margin sward trials, *172*, *173*
Field margins, 62–63, 168–174, *170*
  arable, creating, 169–170
  encouraging butterflies, 174
  exclusion of fertiliser and sprays, 174
  natural regeneration, 170–171
  problem weeds, 173
  restoration, 168–169
  set-aside, MAFF grants, 170
  sown sward, 171
    timing of mowings, 172–173
Fire blight
  control, 197–198
  symptoms, 197–198
  treatment, 198
First World War, effect on hedges, 11–12
Five Hundred Points of Good Husbandry, 1557, 3
Flies in hedgerows, 59
Footpath stiles or gates, 233
Ford tractor for planting, 98
Forearm protectors, for outdoor work, 130–131
Forestry Commission seed improvement programme, 1920s, 64
Foundation damage, 116
Fungicides, 198–200
Future of Farming (1930), 12

Galloway, species choice, 128
Gamma HCH, approved for forestry, 204
Gates, footpath, 233
Gean
  from seed, 78
  suitable for hedges, 154, *155*

Gloucestershire nursery, price guide for transplants, 236
Gloucestershire, species choice, 126
Gloves for outdoor work, 130, *131*
Glyphosate (Roundup)
in ground preparation, 112
prior to planting, 181–182
Gorse
description and suitability, 33
for coastal sites, 39
Grants from Countryside Commission or MAFF, 110
Grass, wild, to encourage field margins, 171, *171*
Gravel soils, species preference, 45
Ground adjacent to hedge and wildlife, potential, 61
Ground preparation for hedge planting, 112–114
Ground preparation for seedlings, 91
Grove airfield, hedgerows removed, 13, *13*
Growth, hedge, controlling, 206–214
Guelder rose, **8**
description, 34–35
for conservation, 40
from seed, 75
Guillotine, home-made, for trimming roots and tops of seedlings, *92*

Hampshire, species choice, 126
Hand planting
into cultivated soil, 118
of seedlings, 245–246
of transplants, 241–242
Hares, protection from, 27, 228, *228*
Harpsden village, *3*
Harvest considerations, transplants, 108–109
Hat for outdoor work, 132
Hawthorn, 37, **2**
description and suitability, 21–23
for approach drive, 41
for coastal sites, 39
for conservation, 40
for control of soil erosion, 41
enclosure hedge, 18th century, *206*
for screen hedge, 41
from seed, 71
hedge, Berkshire Hops, *219*
hedge grown from seedlings
after eleven years, *89*
after three years, *89*
on soil type division, 40
Hazel, **2**
description and suitability, 19–21
for conservation, 40
for control of soil erosion, 41
for screen hedge, 41
from seed, 71
Heavy soils, species preference, 46
Hedge honeysuckle, from seed, 73
Hedgebank
Devonwade, 133–138, *134–138*
Pembroke, 139–142, *139–141*
West Country, *58*
Hedgehog, hedgerow mammal, 58
Hedgemaking, points for consideration, 17
Hedge(s), hedgerows
newly planted, Peasemore Farm, Oxfordshire, 1992, *115*
permitted development, 254
planting
18th century, 5
effect of soil type, 50–51
reasons for, 16
suitable species, 17–42
planting and preparation, 110–132
see also Planting of hedges: Preparation for hedge planting
removal in 1865, 8–9
advantages, 8–9
removal, grant-aided, 10
species suitable, 17–35
trimmer, wide-cut, hydraulic, usefulness, 47
with two faces, planting, 122–123, *123*
Herbicides for weed control, 177–180
Herefordshire, species choice, 126–127
Highways
hedges and ditches beside, 249
presumption, 250
trees adjoining, legal factors, 252
Historical background, 1–15
Holland, seedling source, 90
Holly
description and suitability, 25
for winter colour, 41
from seed, 73
hedges, 145–148
choice of varieties, 146–147
Christmas trade, 145, 146
for cuttings and Christmas decoration trade, *145*
male and female plants, 146
on soil type division, 40
Holm oak, for winter colour, 41
Hooper, Dr, on assessing ages of hedges, 1971, 10–11

Hornbeam
  description and suitability, 18–*19*, 152, *153*
  for approach drive, 41
  for control of soil erosion, 41
  from seed, 70
Horse chestnut, for conservation, 42
Horse Hoeing Husbandry, 5
Hundred Years' War, effect on hedges, 2

Industrial Revolution, effect on hedges, 8
Insect predators instead of insecticides, 60
Insecticides, effect on field margins, 62–63
Insects in hedgerows, 59
Invertebrates in hedgerows, 59–62
  beneficial insects, 60, 61
  cost of chemicals, 59–60
  effect of spraying, 59
Irrigation
  seedling planting, 103–107
    example of manual water balance sheet, 105–107
  sprinkler, *104*

Kett, Robert (1549), Norfolk farmer, and land enclosure, 5
King Henry VIII, decisions affecting hedges, 3

Laburnum, avoid in hedge, 36
Lancashire, species choice, 127
Laying, hedge, 206, 207–214
  equipment required, 208–209
  preparations, 210–214
Legal presumptions
  permitted development, 254
  trees on boundaries, 251–253
  when they do not arise, 249
Leggings for outdoor work, 131
Legislation, weed control, 178–179
Leisure uses of farmland, effect on hedges, 205
Liability for damage caused by trees, 251–252
Lift cage, safety, *67*
Light sandy loams, species preference, 45
Limb loppers, 209
Lime
  broad-leafed, not suitable for hedges, 164
  small-leafed, not suitable for hedges, 163–164
Limestone soils, species preference, 45
Lizard, hedgerow animal, 59
Loamy soils, species preference, 45

Machine planting, 123–124
  of seedlings, 93–99, 244–245
  of transplants, 237–241
Maintenance, 205–222
Maintenance tools, *209*
Malden, W.J., 7, 16
Mammals in hedgerows, 58–59
Manor Preparatory School, Oxfordshire, hand planting of transplants, 242–244
Manual water balance sheet, 105–107
Maple
  field, **1**
    description and suitability, 17–18
    for coastal sites, 39
    for control of soil erosion, 41
    from seed, 70
    on soil type division, 40
    suitable for hedges, 152, *153*
  Norway, from seed, 75
Marking out, hedge planting, 116
Mavor, William, footnotes to Tusser's book, 4
Mechanical hedge cutters, 217–221
Mechanisation, effect on hedges, 14
Metazachlor (Butisan S) after planting, 185
Metham-sodium for soil sterilisation, 81–82
Methyl bromide for soil sterilisation, 82
Mice, hedgerow mammals, 58
Mildews, 198–199
  control, 198–199
Mites in hedgerows, 59
Mixed hedge, nine years old, *243*
Mixed species hedge, 41
  A-shape, *216*
Mixed species roadside hedge, *196*
Mole, hedgerow mammal, 59
Moths and butterflies, 61
Mountain ash, suitable for hedges, 158, *158*
Mulches, organic, for weed control, 176
Myclobutanil (Systane 6) against mildew, 199
Myrobalan, suitability, 27–28

Napoleon Bonaparte, 6
Neighbour's land, entry, legal factors, 252
New hedge, protected, *228*
Newly laid hedge, Cokethorpe Park, *213*
Norman Conquest, effect on hedges, 1–2
Normandy hedgerows, 1
North Farm, Oxfordshire, hand planting of seedlings, 245–246
North Wales, species choice, 127
Norway maple, from seed, 75

Notch planting
for double row hand planting, 122
for single row hand planting, 119–120, *119*
Nurse crop, protection, 223–225, *224*
Nutrition, seedling planting, 103

Oak
English, **8**
suitable for hedges, 158–160, *159*
from seed, 79–80
Open land, low fertility, 5
Orwin, C.S., *The Future of Farming* (1930), 12
Osier production, 143
Overgrown hedge, *219*
Overhanging trees, right to lop, 251
Owners of fences, rights and duties, 253
consequences of neglect to fence where there is no duty to fence, 253–254
definitions of fences, 253
permitted development, 254
Ownership and trimming and pollarding, 248–249
Oxadiazon (Ronstar Liquid) after planting, 184–185
Oxfordshire
nursery, price guide for transplants, 235
species choice, 125

Paint, ZIRAM (AA Protect), 225
Paraquat (Gramoxone) in ground preparation, 112
Paraquat (Gramoxone or Scythe), prior to planting, 180–181
Paraquat/diquat (Parable/Farmon PDQ) prior to planting, 181
Pear, wild, **4**
from seed, 78–79
suitable for hedges, *156*, 157, *157*
Peasemore Farm, Berkshire
hand planting of transplants, 241–242
machine planting of transplants, 238–239, 239–240
Pembroke hedgebank, 139–142, *139–141*
Pendimethalin (Stomp) after planting, 186
Permitted development, 254
Pest control, 201–204
according to chemical selectivity, 203
and seedling planting, 100–102
UK Pesticide Guide, 200
Pesticides
approved for 'forestry', 204
new regulations, 178–179
Pests
common, which attack hedgerow plants, 202
spread, 201
Pirimicarb, approved for forestry, 204
Pit (or spit) planting, for double row hand planting, 120–121, *121*
'Planned' countryside, 43, *44*
Planning for hedge planting, choice and supply of material, 110–112
Plant spacing, 97–99
Planters, 92
Planting of hedges, 110–132, 164–165, *165*
1860–1940, 10
by machine, 123–124
calculator, *113*
care after planting, 128–129
care of plants prior to planting, 116–117
costs, 246
double row hand, 120–123
hedge position, 115–116
machine, transplants, 237–241
marking out, 116
planning, choice and supply of material, 110–112
planting time and conditions, 114–115
seedlings, 92
single row hand, 118–119
spacing, 124
time and conditions, 114–115
tools, *234*
willow osier, 142–145
see also Willow osier hedges
Plants
choice and requirements, 38–42
common pests, 202–203
suitable according to soil type, 43–53
soil survey, 51–53
suitable for hedges, 17–35
to avoid, 35–38
Pleachers laid and interwoven, *213*
Pleachers neatly cut and laid, *212*
Ploughed ridge, 119
Ploughed trench for double row hand planting, 120
Ploughed trench for single row hand planting, 118, *118*
Plum, wild, **5**
description and suitability, 27–28, *28*
for conservation, 40, 42
for screen hedge, 41
from seed, 73
Polythene, black
'mulch' strip for ground preparation, 114

Polythene, black (*contd.*)
sheet mulch for trees, 152
sheet mulch for weed control, trees and shrubs, 176–177
trials, 177
Poor Law of 1601, 5
Position of hedge, 115–116
Post-emergence weed control, 192–194
Potato virus, 60
Poverty and farming, 17th century, 5
Pre-emergence weed control, 187–191
Pre-germination treatments, tree and shrub seed, *68–69*
Preparation for hedge planting, 110–132
ground, 112–114
Price guide for hedgerow transplants, 235
Prices, average, for hedgerow transplants, 236
Privet, **3**
description and suitability, 26
for coastal sites, 39
for conservation, 40
for winter colour, 41
Propyzamide (Kerb) after planting, 183
Prosperity and farming, 5
Protection, 223–227
Protective clothing, 129–132
Pruning plants prior to planting, 117
Purging buckthorn, *see* Buckthorn

Rabbits
damage to hedges, 58
protection from, 228, *230*
Railway hedges, specification, 7–8
Railways, impact on hedges, 6–7
Ramanas rose, **7**
description and suitability, 31–33
for conservation, 42
from seed, 74
Rat, brown, hedgerow mammal, 59
Rebuttable presumptions for boundaries, 248
Rectangular shape, 215
Regional hedges, 133–149
differences in choice of species, 125–128
Repellant sprays, 225
Requirements of plants for new hedge, 38–42
Residual weed killers, 180
Rhododendron, avoid in hedge, 36
Ridge, ploughed, 119
Roadside hedge
badly trimmed, *222*
mixed species, *196*, *232*
Roses, *see* Dog: Guelder: Ramanas
Rounded shape, 216–217
Rowan, suitable for hedges, 158, *158*

Safety lift cage, *67*
'Salt Way', *169*
Scale insects, action against plants, 203
Screen hedge, 41
Sea buckthorn
description and suitability, 24
for coastal sites, 39
from seed, 72
Second World War, effect on hedges, 12
Seedbeds, *65*
Seedlings
emerging and growing, fertilisers for, 86
hand planting, 245–246
harvest considerations, 108–109
machine planting, 93–99, 244–245, *99*
pest and disease control, 102–103
planting, 92
bed size and plant spacing, 97–99
weed control, 100–102
production
definition of words used in, 87
small-scale, 65
source, 90–91
to transplant, 88–109
Seed(s)
cleaning, 67
collecting costs, 67
collection, 66–67
contamination, 67
raising shrubs and trees from, 64–88
sowing, 83–86
data, 84–85
Selective weed killers, 180
Set-aside field margins, MAFF grants, 170
Shade by trees, 150
Shapes, hedge, 215
Shelters for trees, 225–227, *227*
Shrews, hedgerow mammals, 58
Shropshire, species choice, 126–127
Shrubs
dimensions (British Standards), *111*
hedgerow, from seed, 70–75
for hedges, choice, 16–42
raising from seed, 64–88
choosing suitable site, 80–81
fertilisers, 86–87
seed sowing, 83–86
soil sterilisation, 81–83
seed stratification and pre-germination treatments, *68–69*

species recommended by conservation advisers, *48–49*
Sickle, 208
Siding up, 207
'Sight lines' for drivers exiting, 116
Silt soils, species preference, 45
Simazine (Gesatop) after planting, 182–183
Single row hand planting, 118–119
Slasher, 208, 209
Slit (or notch) planting
for double row hand planting, 122
for single row hand planting, 119–120, *119*
Sloe, description and suitability, 28–29
Snake, hedgerow animal, 59
Soil
colour, change, *45*
erosion, control, 41
for seedbeds, sterilisation, 81–83
map of Frilford, Oxfordshire, *52*
sterilisation injection equipment, *82*
surveys, 51–53
type
effect, 43–53
effect on farming practice, 43–53
hedge as division, 40–41
water holding capacity, 104
MAFF classification, 104
Somerset, species choice, 125
South Wales
hedges for protection, 46
species choice, 127
Sowing seed, 83–86
Species
choice, regional differences, 125–128
suitable for hedgerows, 17–35
to be avoided in any hedge, 35–38
Spider mites, action against plants, 203
Spindle, **3**
description and suitability, *22*, 23, 40, 42
for conservation, 40, 42
for control of soil erosion, 41
from seed, 72
Spiral guards, 223, *224*
Spit planting, for double row hand planting, 120–121, *121*
Sprinkler irrigation, *104*
Stanhay-Webb Ranger T50 planter, 94, *96*
Sterilisation of soil for seedbeds, 81–83
Stiles, footpath, 233
Stoat, hedgerow mammal, 59
Stock control, fencing, 232
Stockproof hedge, 38–39
Stratification and pre-germination treatments, tree and shrub seed, *68–69*
Subsoiler slot planting, double row hand planting, 121–122
Suitability of plants and trees
for conservation, 46–51
for hedgerows, 17–35, 125–128, 152–161
Suitable site for seedbeds, choice and preparation, 80–81
Sulphur (Solfa) against mildew, 200
Summer operations, seedling planting, 107
Super Prefer planting unit, 94, *95*, 97
Sussex nursery, price guide for transplants, 235–236
Sweet chestnut, from seed, 76
Sycamore, from seed, 75

Tear gas for soil sterilisation, 81
Tine or subsoiler slot planting, double row hand planting, 121–122
Tithe map, *312*
Tools
for fencing, *231*
planting, *234*
Topography, effect, 43–53
Topped A-shape, 216–217
Tractor driver and machine operator, planting, *125*
Translocated (systemic) weed killers, 179
Transplants, 88
autumn lifting, 107–108
cutting back, 114
hand planting, 241–242
hedgerow
average prices, 236
price guide, 235
machine planting, 237–241
quality important, 236–237
trimmed, *108*
well-rooted and vigorous, *108*
Trees, 150–167
and cereal growing, 150, 151
damage caused by, liability, 251–252
dimensions (British Standards), *111*
for animals, 151–152
for hedges, choice, 16–42
from seed, 75–80
new hedges, suitable, 152–161
not recommended, 163–164
on boundaries, legal presumptions, 251–253
overhanging, right to lop, 251
planting, 164–165
raising from seed, 64–88

Trees (*contd.*)
choosing suitable site, 80–81
fertilisers, 86–87
seed sowing, 83–86
soil sterilisation, 81–83
seed stratification and pre-germination treatments, *68–69*
shade, 150
shelters, 225–227, *227*
spacing, 165–166
species, recommended by conservation advisers, *48–49*
wet sites, 161–163
wood merchant timber, 151
Trench, ploughed
for double row hand planting, 120
for single row hand planting, 118, *118*
Triadimefon (Bayleton) against mildew, 199
Trifluralin (Treflan) prior to planting, 182
Triforine (Saprol) against mildew, 199–200
Trimmer, Bomford Turner B577L, *218*
Trimming, 207
hedge, 214–221, *211*
rotational, 220–221
time and cost, 220
Tull, Jethro, 5
Tusser, Thomas, 3

UK Pesticide Guide, 200

Verge width, 116
Victorian bird-catching net, *56*
Viruses, diseases caused by, 200–201
Voles, hedgerow mammals, 58

Walnut, from seed, 77
Walnut seed, *80*
War Ags (County War Agricultural Committees), effect on hedges, 12
War of the Roses, effect on hedgerows, 2–4
Water balance sheet, manual, 105–107
Water losses, 105–107
Watering after planting, 129
Wayfaring tree
description, 34
for conservation, 40
for screen hedge, 41
from seed, 75
Weasel, hedgerow mammal, 59
Weed control, 175–195, *175*
after planting, 128, 182–195
and seedling planting, 100–102
contact, 179
mulches, 176–177
new regulations, 178
post-emergence, 192–194
pre-emergence, 187–191
prior to planting, 180–182
residual, 180
selective, 180
success of herbicides, 178
translocated (systemic), 179–180
use of herbicides, 177–180
Weedkillers, effect on field margins, 62
Weeds, problems in field margins, 173
Weevils, action against plants, 203
Wellington boots for outdoor work, 130
West Country, hedges for protection, 46
West Country hedgebank, *58*
Wet sites, trees for use in hedges, 161–163
Wild crab
description, 26–27
from seed, 77
Wild oats, problems in field margins, 173
Wild pear, *see* Pear
Wild plum, *see* Plum
Wild rose, from seed, 74
William Cobbett's method of plant pruning (1825), *117*
Willow
for coastal sites, 39
for control of soil erosion, 41
Willow cuttings, *143*
Willow osier hedges, 142–145
biomass production, 144–145
colour, 143
osier production, 143
planting, 142
willow 'sets', 142
Willow stool bed, one year's growth, *144*
Wind protection, 46–47
measurement, 46
Windbreak for growing crops, 39
Winds, effect on Cornish hedgebank, *47*
Windy sites, species preference, 46
Worlidge, John, 5

Yew, avoid in hedge, 36–38
Yorkshire, species choice, 127–128

Zetor tractors for planting, 98
ZIRAM (AA Protect) paint, 225

guelder rose
haz
spindleberry
hawthorn
sea buckt
crab apple
dog
rose
hornbeam